John Wiley & Sons, Inc.
Publishers Since 1807

READ IMPORTANT LICENSE INFORMATION

Dear Professor or Other Authorized User:

John Wiley & Sons, Inc. ("Wiley") has produced the attached solutions manual or other copyrighted material (the "Supplement") solely for use by professors and other authorized users in the manner provided below. Wiley has established these use limitations in response to concerns raised by professors and other authorized users regarding the pedagogical problems stemming from unlimited distribution of Supplements.

If the attached Supplement was delivered to you by Wiley or its representatives or if you are a professor of a course that has adopted the textbook to which the Supplement relates (the "Course"), then you are an authorized user of the Supplement. As an authorized user, Wiley grants you a non-transferable license to use the Supplement subject to the following conditions. The Supplement is for your personal use only, except that you may post the Supplement (or portions thereof) on a password protected website or otherwise provide the Supplement (or portions thereof) to students of the Course so long as such students are advised that they may not copy or distribute the Supplement to any third party. The Supplement may only be used in connection with Courses for which the related textbook has been adopted. You should take reasonable steps to protect the Supplement from unauthorized use, reproduction, or distribution. Your use of the Supplement indicates your acceptance of the conditions set forth in this Agreement. If you do not accept these conditions, you must return the Supplement unused within 30 days of receipt.

All rights (including without limitation, copyrights, patents and trade secrets) in the Supplement are and will remain the sole and exclusive property of Wiley and/or its licensors. The Supplement is furnished by Wiley on an "as is" basis without any warranties, express or implied. This Agreement will be governed by and construed pursuant to the laws of the State of New York, without regard to such State's conflict of law rules.

We hope that you find the Supplement useful.

Sincerely,

JOHN WILEY & SONS, INC.

INSTRUCTOR'S RESOURCE MANUAL

Lyn Riverstone
Oregon State University

Mathematics
for Elementary Teachers

A CONTEMPORARY APPROACH

Eighth Edition

Gary L. Musser
Oregon State University

William F. Burger

Blake E. Peterson
Brigham Young University

BICENTENNIAL
1807
WILEY
2007
BICENTENNIAL

John Wiley & Sons, Inc.

Cover Image: Miao Jin, Junho Kim, and Xianfeng David Gu
Bicentennial Logo Design: Richard J. Pacifico

To order books or for customer service, please call 1-800-CALL-WILEY (225-5945).

ISBN-13 978-0-470-23302-3

Printed in the United States of America.

10 9 8 7 6 5 4 3 2 1

Printed and bound by Lightning Source.

Preface

This manual has been prepared to assist you in using our text. There are several elements in this manual.

Philosophy: In this section, rationale are provided for the selection and organization of the material. You may want to read through this section in its entirety to obtain an overview of the text before reading the rest of this manual.

Chapter Commentaries: Specific suggestions on a section-by-section basis are provided.

Chapter Expectations: A list of expectations, or objectives, is provided for each chapter. These lists might be reproduced and distributed to students at the first meeting of the term. In addition to helping the students with their studying and review, the expectations may be useful organizer as you prepare and teach for your classes.

When Will I Teach This Topic?: Often students will ask "Where will I teach this topic." This section provides the approximate grade levels where the material they are studying appears in a school mathematics series.

Exercise Maps: In this edition of the textbook, the Exercise/Problem Sets have been updated. Not only have some new exercises and problems been added, many of the problems from the seventh edition have been deleted or renumbered. The Exercise Map is provided to help you match up both the Part A and Part B Exercise/Problem Sets from the seventh and eighth editions.

Starting Point Solutions: The Starting Points at the beginning of each section are discussion/activity questions that are designed to get the students thinking about and wrestling with the ideas in the section. The solutions to these starting points will be provided in this Instructor's Resource Manual.

Answers to Exercise/Problem Sets - Part B: Instead of providing answers to selected problems for all the odd problems, we make it convenient for you and your students by having answers to *all* of the part A portions in the text and *all* of part B in this manual. If you collect assignments, the part B sets can allow for some originality by the students. On the other hand, the part B answers can be removed or copied from this manual and placed in a learning center or library to allow students who want to work additional problems to have access to answers, thus freeing your office hours to work with students on diagnosed difficulties.

Answers for Guide to Problem Solving: The supplement entitled **Guide to Problem Solving** authored by the late Don Miller who taught at St. Cloud State University, artfully walks through all 21 strategies that are introduced in the text and can serve as an excellent source of problems to supplement your discussions of problem solving. Guide to Problem Solving contains answers for the odd-numbered problems whereas this section contains answers for the even-numbered problems. We make copies of these to share with our students.

Many resources and supplements for students and the instructor are available from Wiley on the web and for sale as described in the Preface of our textbook.

We would like this text and its supplements to provide the most effective resources possible for college teachers and their students. Thus, any comments that you can share with us will be appreciated and will permit us to adjust future editions to be as complete and error-free as possible. Please send your suggestions to Gary or Blake at the following addresses:

Gary L. Musser
Department of Mathematics
Oregon State University   or
Corvallis, OR 97331-4605
musser@math.orst.edu

1100 Emerald Tint Ct.
Las Vegas, NV 89144
glmusser@cox.net
FAX: 702-233-0181

Blake E. Peterson
Department of Mathematics Education
Brigham Young University
Provo, UT 84602-6563
peterson@mathed.byu.edu
FAX: 801-422-0511   E-mail or faxes are also welcome.

TABLE OF CONTENTS

Preface   *v*

Philosophy   1

Chapter Commentaries   13

Chapter Expectations   33

When Will I Teach This?   57

Exercise/Problem Sets Map for Eighth Edition   59

Starting Point Solutions   73

Answers to Exercise/Problem Sets - Part B   85

Answers for the Even Numbered Problems
   in Guide to Problem Solving   243

Philosophy

In writing this text we had two important commitments to balance, one to mathematics and one to elementary/middle school teachers. As experienced mathematicians can appreciate, this is a delicate task. After you see why we took the paths that we did, it may be easier for you to follow our development in its entirety. Also, making our rationale apparent may make it easier for you to adapt the material to fit your particular approach.

Because of research findings and our own experience over many years, we decided to let abstract mathematics naturally evolve from the physical world when introducing new topics. Many students who enter our courses are not operating effectively with abstractions, and these students find our concrete-pictorial-abstract approach particularly valuable. In addition to this dimension, we also like to emphasize the distinction between routine exercises and more challenging problem solving experiences. Thus, we adopted a taxonomy comprised of five cognitive levels. Finally, to help our students better conceptualize what we were trying to accomplish, we organized our content, representational levels, and cognitive taxonomy into a 3-dimensional Mathematics Learning Cube.

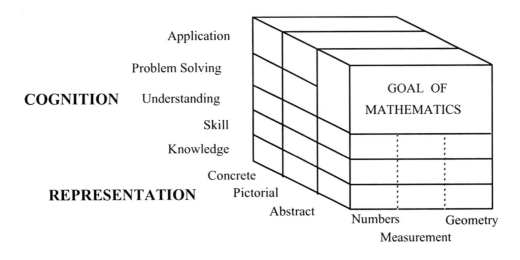

CONTENT

It is our hope that our students will carry this model with them after they study from this text and use this, or a similar model, when they teach. We reinforce the cognitive dimension of our cube in two ways. First, our exercise/problem sets separate practice exercises from problems that require a creative step.

Unfortunately, it is impossible to make a perfect dichotomy to fit all students since problems to some students may be exercises to others; conversely, some students may find some exercises to be problems. However, we believe that it is important to try to make such a distinction to keep students attentive to incorporating more problem solving in their own future classrooms. Second, we have included many problems that promote writing and discussing. These problems are found at the end of each section and in the chapter reviews. Third, we have organized the chapter tests into four cognitive levels to help model testing designed to insure coverage of these various levels of sophistication.

We believe that our mathematical development has integrity throughout. Since Gary had taught more formal courses during the "new math" era of the sixties, we were convinced that the pendulum had swung too far to formalism and a "theorem-proof" approach. [Interestingly a member of the Mathematics Association of America's Committee on Undergraduate Preparation (CUPM) of that era confided that panelists were disappointed when they saw the way that textbook authors had interpreted their recommendations - far more formally than the panel had intended.] On the other hand, we believe that it is imperative that our students see the significant logical connections inherent in a sound, mathematical approach. Thus, to balance the demands of intuition and relevance on one hand and the importance of mathematical structure on the other, our approach is to introduce nearly all topics in a concrete, informal fashion (especially early in the text). Then, we gently guide students to abstract mathematical concepts so that they will be able to appreciate how the elementary/ middle school curriculum fits together into a meaningful whole rather than simply being a collection of disparate facts.

In the remainder of this section we discuss our development chapter-by-chapter. In the next section, we have additional chapter commentaries that provide more ideas for the classroom.

Chapter 1 - Introduction to Problem Solving

Problem solving is recognized as one the most important goals of mathematics. We have found Polya's four-step process to be helpful to our students, *especially* when a rich source of strategies (heuristics) is available. A valuable tool for solving a broad range of problems is algebra so we introduce variables and basic methods of solving algebraic equations in this chapter. After some basic concepts are introduced in this chapter, margin notes are included throughout the text highlighting places where algebraic thinking is used.

We cover this chapter and selected strategies throughout the text when we teach our one-year sequence for elementary teachers. Then, we have a one-quarter course "Problem Solving for Teachers" where junior/senior level students use the "Problem Solving Study Guide" supplement to have a more in-depth discussion devoted to problem solving. Some instructors may wish to augment this chapter by including an introduction to logic (see Topic 1).

Chapter 2 - Sets, Whole Numbers, and Numeration

Here we introduce the set concepts required to develop all the major ideas in the remainder of the text. An extensive survey of colleagues showed a 50-50 split on the issue of integrating of functions throughout the text. By including relations and functions in Section 2.4, those who want to refer to this concept throughout the course can cover this section. There is also a section in Chapter 9, after the real numbers are available, where functions and their graphs are studied. We like to cover bases other than ten in this chapter so that we can use them to illustrate algorithms in Chapter 4.

Chapter 3 - Whole Numbers - Operations and Properties

Operations and their properties are covered in this chapter and techniques of computation are covered in Chapter 4. We separate these topics into two chapters rather than integrating them for three reasons. First, the separation allows us to have chapter 3 focus on the underlying conceptual meanings of the operations before moving on to the derived algorithms. Second, this dichotomy helps to clarify the fact that algorithms are separate from (although based on) the algebraic structure of the whole number system. Third, this separation allows for the broadening of the discussion of algorithms to three modes of computation - mental, electronic (calculators or computers), and written (our common algorithms and alternatives).

In this chapter our emphasis is on the algebraic structure of the whole numbers and the conceptual meaning of the operations with an eye towards how properties are useful in performing calculations. The thinking strategies approach to learning the basic facts is one important use of properties. Research has confirmed that this approach is effective with slow learners and we have had similar success working with individual students of all abilities.

Chapter 4 - Whole Number Computations - Mental, Electronic, and Written

As the chapter title suggests, we believe that students should consider performing computations mentally first (either exactly in simple cases or using estimations in more complex cases), using a calculator second (facility with a computer is also desirable), and using traditional paper-and-pencil algorithms last. Although we develop all the standard algorithms, we do not ask our students to "multiply two seven digit numbers" or "divide a seven digit number by a three digit number." Our reason for including so many nontraditional algorithms in the text and problem sets is that students find them fascinating and, through these algorithms, they can see more vividly that operations and algorithms are not synonymous. Thus, for example, since addition is *not* the addition *algorithm*, it *is* okay to adopt a combination of mental methods together with calculator techniques as an acceptable mode of calculation. Also, showing our students more algorithms helps them to support the various student developed algorithms. Our informal test to measure the effectiveness of an algorithm is to consider efficiency and accuracy when it is applied. In most cases, the mental method/calculator approach wins hands down against written algorithms. One final comment regarding division. Most of our students say that the last time that they used the long division algorithm was when they computed their gas mileage. But with onboard computers in many new cars, even this need is vanishing.

Chapter 5 - Number Theory

The chapter on number theory allows us to accomplish several objectives. First, we develop the content (factoring, GCF, and LCM) sufficient to make the work with fractions go smoothly. Second, the tests for divisibility give us a chance to make some simple proofs so that the tests aren't merely a collection of rules. Third, using some of the examples in our Focus On, we can share the notion of unsolved problems with our students at an understandable, relevant level. Mention is made of the 1995 proof of Fermat's Last Theorem in the Focus On.

Chapter 6 - Fractions

Deciding how to develop the real number system after the whole numbers poses an interesting dilemma. First, one could take the whole numbers - integers - rationals - reals approach. On the surface, this sequence may be appealing due to its efficiency. However, this approach deprives the students of seeing numbers grow out of the physical world, much the way *our* students will be teaching. Thus we took the whole numbers - fractions - integers - rationals - reals approach (the sequence from school mathematics), where first fractions (and hence reciprocals) are motivated via models and next integers (with opposites) are introduced. Then the rationals are generated using fractions and integers. We have found this approach to be the most effective, *relevant* direction to take with elementary teachers and we believe that our coverage is as efficient (in terms of time) as the other approach. Note that, to save time, we defer discussing fraction order relations involving addition and multiplication until rational numbers. However, we do bring them up in the chapter on integers because of the influence of negative numbers.

Chapter 7 - Decimals, Ratio, Proportion, and Percent

We like to view (repeating) decimals and percents as another numeration system for the fractions. Although our work with ratio and proportion is restricted to decimals, we state that this treatment can be used with other number systems (such as the reals which are covered later).

Chapter 8 - Integers

We introduce integers by extending whole number concepts using both a set model (black/red chips) and a measurement model (the integer number line). Our formal definitions of the operations are motivated by the models and patterns. Although there are many ways to define integer addition and multiplication, our approach is to use as definitions the rules that most people use when performing operations on positive and negative numbers mentally.

Chapter 9 - Rational Numbers and Real numbers, with Algebra

Our treatment of the rational numbers is brisk since the foundation for this material was laid in the chapters on fractions and integers. Real numbers are viewed as the set of all (repeating) decimals *and* as points of a "complete" number line. We like to cover rational exponents so that students can see that whole number and integer exponents can be usefully generalized. Because of their importance in problem solving, we extend the study of solving equations introduced in chapter 1 to include inequalities and equations with real numbers. Since more and more students are coming to class with graphics calculators, section 9.3, together with the Graphics Calculator webmodule on the website: www.wiley.com/college/musser, can be used to help students see the power of these devices.

Chapter 10 - Statistics

This chapter precedes the chapter on probability because of the topic's high priority in school mathematics and its importance in the everyday world of students and teachers. This also allows for early coverage in shorter courses, as soon as real numbers are developed. In section 10.1 we introduce various ways of organizing and representing data through the use of examples relevant to preservice teachers.

In section 10.2, the most commonly used measures of central tendency and dispersion are discussed, again from a teacher's point of view. We find this particularly useful for students who have not had a course on tests and measurement. The discussion of distributions is geometrical, illustrating the generalization of histograms, rather than delving into probability density functions. Section 10.3 focuses on potential misuses of statistics either in graphs or in sampling bias.

Chapter 11 - Probability

Probability is perhaps the most difficult and misunderstood topic in school mathematics. We suspect that this is due to its abstract nature, particularly the elusiveness of concrete interpretations of probability itself (not just experiments) and its reliance on set theory, ratio concepts, and counting techniques.

Because of this, we have developed the major concepts and results about probability assuming no prior background.

Section 11.1 discusses experimental probability and the need for well chosen, albeit arbitrary, theoretical probability. We discuss the case of equally likely outcomes and use simple experiments to motivate the properties of probability. We deliberately avoid any discussion of probability axioms per se; such a treatment is far too abstract for the elementary or middle school classroom. We apply some of the set theory from Chapter 2 as a means of defining the concepts of experiment, sample space, outcome, event, and so on. Examples are chosen to illustrate the central ideas, but not to involve complicated counting techniques.

In section 11.2, we discuss methods for computing probabilities in experiments whose sample spaces may be cumbersome to list. For example, Pascal's triangle is used to enumerate outcomes in binomial experiments. Tree diagrams are introduced as a means of representing the outcomes of experiments involving several stages. Then, probability tree diagrams provide a method for assigning probabilities to the outcomes of such experiments and for computing probabilities of compound events in such experiments.

In section 11.3, we present more sophisticated counting techniques, that is, those using permutations and combinations explicitly. We find the fundamental counting property sufficient for our needs. Again, our main interest is in developing a fundamental understanding of probability and its applications and not in developing skills in counting. Thus, section 11.3 uses these counting techniques to determine the size of a sample space or the number of desired outcomes without having to list the entire set.

Section 11.4 addresses four probability concepts which may be included as time permits. First, the power of simulation is discussed as a simple means of approximating probabilities in highly complex experiments. Expected value is presented to give a glimpse of how probability is applied in establishing payoffs, admission fees, insurance premiums, service contract fees, and so on. Odds are presented as an application of ratios and as an alternate method of representing probability. Finally, conditional probability is introduced to show a generalization of probability, since probabilities in real life situations are conditional probabilities. For example, insurance rates are set based on carefully researched conditional probabilities. (Some people claim that this is a form of discrimination, which, of course, it is, by definition!)

Chapter 12 - Geometric Shapes

For several reasons, we have chosen to organize the geometry material based on the van Hiele model of development. First, we find it pedagogically advantageous to start with visual experiences and move towards more formal results as we have done with number concepts. Our students have a wide variety of background experiences in geometry (including none), so we need to provide basic conceptual foundations. Second, many students have had unpleasant experiences with geometry in high school which can be summarized as "too much formalism too soon." As a result, many of our students are apprehensive about studying geometry. By discussing the van Hiele model, we are able to identify the source of many of the difficulties that our students have had. This understanding leads to a sort of healing process and a revived sense of self-esteem. Finally, our students become sensitized to the challenges that elementary and middle school students face when studying geometry and realize that the solution is *not* to delay geometry until high school. Rather, a careful development of geometric concepts throughout the elementary and middle school years is called for - again, much as is done with number concepts.

In section 12.1, we describe the van Hiele levels and incorporate an introduction to basic two-dimensional shapes. In analyzing shapes, we use investigations with paper folding, tracing, and on a square lattice. We are able to establish properties of shapes based on plausible observations, which we verify more formally in later chapters. (The plausible observations are, of course, postulates at this point, but we purposely avoid any formal discussion about the role of postulates in geometry. This directly parallels our approach with number systems and their properties.) In section 12.2, we analyze shapes using symmetry, perpendicularity, parallelism, and convexity. In section 12.3 we approach two-dimensional geometry at the level of relationships. We give more precise definitions of geometric shapes, list our basic assumptions, and establish several fundamental results. In section 12.4 we include a discussion about tessellations as an application and for esthetic reasons. In section 12.5, we describe three dimensional shapes and their properties, delaying measure of volume and surface area until Chapter 13.

Chapter 13 - Measurement

The organization of this chapter was also inspired by the van Hiele model, although we don't refer to it explicitly here. Informal measurement, using natural units, is discussed initially to illustrate holistic thinking in measurement. Once the system of natural units is standardized to the English system, the properties of the system can be discussed, culminating in the properties of an (abstract) ideal system. It is interesting to note that Thomas Jefferson had designed a system of measurement units of weights and measures with all the advantages of an ideal system. Jefferson's system was not adopted and now the metric system flourishes nearly everywhere instead.

In section 13.1, we have provided separate discussions of length, area, volume, weight (English), mass (metric), and temperature in the two systems of units since many of our students do not have a good intuitive understanding of all of these concepts. Yet, they likely will teach them. We include a discussion of dimensional analysis as a problem-solving tool in applied problems and as a procedure for converting among various units.

In sections 13.2, we study measurement as a deductive mathematical process, based on arbitrary units of length and area. (Tessellations of the plane and space are the basis of area and volume measurement.) We derive area formulas for various polygons and circles, based on the area of a rectangle. We give a proof of the Pythagorean theorem based on the areas of squares and right triangles. President Garfield's proof, using the area of a trapezoid, appears in the problem set. (Also, a transformational proof appears in Chapter 16 as a Mathematical Morsel.) In section 13.3 we derive surface area formulas based on previous results. We rely on the connections observed by Archimedes to find the surface area of a sphere. In section 13.4 we derive volume formulas for prisms, cylinders, pyramids, and cones. The formula for the volume of a sphere is done first using the 'Archimedes connection', then more formally using Cavalieri's principle.

Chapter 14 - Geometry Using Triangle Congruence and Similarity

This is the first of three chapters (Chapters 14, 15, and 16), each presenting a specific approach to problem solving in geometry. The three chapters are independent of each other, except that sections 14.1 and 14.2 are prerequisite for sections 16.2 and 16.3.

Thus, any or all of the three approaches may be covered. The last section of each of these three chapters may be omitted with no loss of continuity. On the other hand, each provides a nice capstone to its chapter if you can't cover all chapters. If there is time to cover these sections in their entirety, an alternate coverage scheme would be to cover these final sections at the end of your course *after* all three approaches have been introduced to the students.

In section 14.1, the triangle congruence properties are developed and used to justify several classical geometric constructions. In so doing, we are reasoning at van Hiele level two; that is, from the congruence conditions, we can deductively verify the construction procedures. We find this mode of reasoning to be a challenge to many of our students, particularly to those who prefer to reason holistically, that is, on the basis of the construction diagram alone. In order to build our students' skill in using deductive reasoning, we have tried to keep to verifications of only a few major steps at first. In the remainder of section 14.1, we investigate the construction of regular polygons and the consequences of Gauss's theorem.

In section 14.2, we investigate triangle similarity properties and several applications of them. Geometric constructions are covered in sections 14.3 and 14.4. In section 14.5, we apply the triangle congruence and similarity properties in solving geometric problems. In so doing, we verify, at van Hiele level two and three, several results about quadrilaterals that we observed at level one in Chapter 12.

Chapter 15 - Geometry Using Coordinates

We introduce coordinates as a powerful problem solving tool in geometry. In section 15.1 we discuss slope and distance in the coordinate plane, then in section 15.2 we discuss equations of lines and circles, and the geometry of simultaneous linear equations. Finally, in section 15.3, we solve several problems using coordinates. Some students who have experienced difficulties with triangle congruence and similarity prefer a computational approach using coordinates much like some high school students prefer algebra to geometry. Our intention is to show the value of knowing several approaches to solving problems in geometry. Our students, who are expected to have taken three years of college preparatory math, tend to do very well in this chapter.

Chapter 16 - Geometry Using Transformations

In this chapter we present an approach to Euclidean geometry via isometries and similitudes. Our purpose is two-fold: (1) to present an alternative to "synthetic" Euclidean geometry via the triangle congruence and similarity conditions of Chapter 14 and (2) to present an *additional* approach to that of Chapter 14 or 15 that can be applied when advantageous.

In section 16.1, transformations as rigid motions (translation, rotation, reflection, glide-reflection) and similitudes are defined informally. (Note the special notation of directed line segment and directed angle.) Symmetry in the plane is analyzed using transformations, as are Escher-type tessellations. Our goal is to give an overview of transformation geometry, particularly for shorter courses that may not have time for all of the problem solving in section 16.3. Section 16.1 can be done anytime after sections 12.1 and 12.2.

Congruence and similarity of polygons are treated more formally in Section 16.2. We apply several results of sections 14.1 and 14.2 to verify that translations, rotations, reflections, and glide-reflections are isometries. We give a plausible argument that there are no other isometries in the plane. Thus, we can characterize all isometries in the plane and characterize congruence of shapes in general. We also verify properties of size transformations and similitudes, and characterize similarity of shapes in general by means of similitudes. This reasoning borders on level three reasoning since we are investigating the structure of geometry itself; thus, the material must be approached with care and patience. Alternatively, it could be saved for a separate geometry course for preservice teachers.

In section 16.3 we use a transformation approach to problem solving in geometry. For example, we verify the midsegment theorem in a triangle (Example 16.16) by means of size transformations. This result is verified in each of Chapters 14, 15, and 16, using the approach of that particular chapter.

Epilogue - An Eclectic Approach to Geometry

Since we have used this approach so successively in our classes. we decided to formalize it in the book. Talking about using a variety of approaches to geometry is one thing, but providing students with examples and mixed problems is powerful. Students freely express how much they enjoy seeing geometry in this light.

Chapter Commentaries

Chapter 1 - Introduction to Problem Solving

Polya's Four Steps: We find that a careful discussion of Polya's Four Steps is helpful initially. Then we reinforce each step throughout the chapter as we introduce new strategies through problems.

Problem Solving Strategies: Most of our students are initially weak in problem solving, mainly due to lack of practice and knowing where to start. In a survey of research studies, it was concluded that strategies are helpful in problem solving; we find that a toolbox of problem solving strategies gives many students a place to start. Unfortunately, even knowing a list of *strategies* is still not sufficient to produce excellent problem solvers. To take this idea one step further, we have included *clues* to assist students in selecting an appropriate strategy. In the main, these clues were generated by students solving problems from our First Edition. As a further aid for the students, hints and additional hints and written out solutions for all part A problems are provided in the *Hints and Solutions Manual for Part A Problems*. This combination of problems, Polya's four steps, strategies, clues, hints, and solutions is a powerful resource to help students develop their problem solving abilities.

Introduction to Algebra: One of the strategies introduced in this chapter is "Use a Variable". When using this strategy, it is important for students to understand what variables are. Since variables are most often used in some form of an equation, strategies for solving equations containing variables are also discussed. In this chapter, the introduction of algebra is done a basic level and then further developed in chapter 9 after all of the number systems have been introduced.

Chapter 2 - Sets, Whole Numbers, and Numeration

Sets and Operations on Sets: We cover set theory briskly so that we can devote more time to the many other key concepts in the elementary curriculum.

Numbers and Numerals: It is instructive for students to observe the various ways that we use "numbers": "cardinal" numbers to represent how many, "ordinal" numbers to represent an ordering, and "identification" numbers to serve as names.

Numeration Systems: Our emphasis is on the various attributes of numeration systems such as grouping, additivity, multiplicativity, place value, and so on. Also, the Roman and the Mayan systems show how numeration systems evolve; in the case of the Roman system, they extended their additive system to include the subtractive and the multiplicative attributes, and the Mayans changed from a base twenty system to one based on 18´20 due to their calendar. The Babylonian system provides an early example of a place value system as well as an introduction to the notion of a place holder. Our students enjoy a discussion on naming Hindu-Arabic numerals since, although the names are familiar to us, they can be confusing for children. In particular, our students like to rename the numbers 11,12,..., 19 to be "onety-one, onety-two,..., onety-nine" to conform to the way we name 21, 22, 23, and so on.

Ordering Whole Numbers: Although we acknowledge the counting chant and number line as a way children may order numbers (in an ordinal sense), we emphasize the set method for understanding ordering whole numbers (in the cardinal sense). Ordering whole numbers using addition is covered in Chapter 3.

Physical Representations of Whole Numbers: We like our students to be familiar with a variety of representations such as multibase pieces and a chip abacus so that they will carry the philosophy of introducing mathematics at the concrete level to their students. Low cost representations can easily be made or can be found in the materials cards in our Student Activity Manual.

Nondecimal Numeration Systems: We cover this topic so that we may introduce various algorithms in Chapter 4 in an unfamiliar setting for our students, namely using a nondecimal base. This approach gives our students much more insight into how one might better teach algorithms in base ten. Although this section and the coverage of other bases is optional, we recommend its coverage keeping in mind that its usefulness is in providing students with a different point of view when studying various other number concepts in the text.

Chapter 3 - Whole Numbers - Operations and Properties

Addition: Addition is introduced using physical models and then properties are drawn out of the models. Algorithms are studied in the next chapter to make clear the separation between operations and properties, and algorithms. On the other hand, we want to emphasize as much mental mathematics as possible. Thus, we include the thinking strategies approach for learning the basic facts in this chapter. The thinking strategies lead nicely into mental math techniques that are introduced in Chapter 4.

Subtraction: We believe that students should see subtraction in various forms - take-away, missing addend, and comparison. Also, it is critical to show students how to use addition to get subtraction facts by combining the addition facts with the missing addend approach.

Multiplication: As with addition and subtraction, we introduce multiplication through models and properties evolve from viewing appropriate models.

Division: With division, as well as with all four operations, it is important that the focus be on the underlying meaning of the operation, which is why the ideas of partitive and measurement division are introduced. The development of multiplication and division closely parallels that of addition and subtraction with division being defined using the missing factor approach in place of the missing addend approach. Students appreciate the diagram in Figure 3.33, which shows the interrelationships among the four operations.

Ordering Whole Numbers using Addition: With addition now available, we can define the most mathematically useful form of order, namely, $a < b$ if and only if $a + n = b$ for some nonzero n. Then one can discuss theorems such as "If $a < b$, then $a + c < b + c$" time permitting.

Exponents: Exponents and resulting "rules" are introduced as shortcuts for multiplication. Note that the definition of exponent must be restated in the case $a^1 = a$ if one does not permit a "factor" to appear alone. After exponents are introduced, the order of operations is discussed along with the pneumonic device "**P**lease

Excuse **M**e **D**ear **A**unt **S**ally". (Order of operations is also mentioned in the calculator section in the next chapter.)

Chapter 4 - Whole Number Computation- Mental, Electronic, Written

Mental Math: Because of the need to move away from excessive work with written algorithms towards more emphasis on mental math and calculators for calculations, we begin this chapter on computation with a thorough treatment of mental math. Techniques developed in this subsection arise from properties of whole numbers and were the techniques that were observed in children who were effective mental calculators.

Computational Estimation: The techniques introduced in this subsection, which are commonly used in K-8 mathematics text series, were observed by researchers in children who were good estimators. The notion of rounding to compatible numbers is an especially powerful estimation technique.

Using a Calculator: We have found that although many students use calculators, they are not aware of many of the functions available on a scientific calculator. This subsection contains an introduction to several calculator keys. Uses of other specialized keys, such as fractions, change-of-sign, and so on, are introduced when their corresponding mathematical concepts are developed. We encourage students to get *fraction* scientific calculators (if not graphics calculators).

Written Algorithms for Whole Number Addition: We have several objectives in this chapter. First and foremost, we want students to realize that algorithms are step-by-step procedures to obtain answers. Second, since our customary algorithms will likely continue to be taught (but probably used less) for many years to come, they can be presented more effectively to students by using concrete models before moving to symbolic place value representations. Third, there are (have been) many algorithms for the four basic operations and that we are using one of each *among many*. Fourth, it is appropriate for students to use any correct algorithm. Our students like the "left-to-right" mental addition method since it allows them to focus on *understanding* the process rather that having to always follow the *rule* "always add starting on the right." Left-to-right mental methods lead quite naturally into left-to-right written algorithms.

Written Algorithms for Whole Number Subtraction: One of our favorite subtraction algorithms is the "subtract-from-the-base" method, which is easily motivated using multibase pieces. It is much like the standard "borrowing" method except that the exchanges are not made; thus, one only needs to know how to subtract from the base rather than know all the usual subtraction facts. For example, to find 35 - 17, we view this problem as (25 + 10) - (10 + 7), or (20 - 10) + (10 - 7 + 5) instead of the usual (20 + 15) - (10 + 7) = (20 - 10) + (15 - 7). Students see the value of this alternative algorithm when we actually have a race in class *in different bases* by having volunteers use this method against the rest of the class using the standard algorithm. Invariably, students find this algorithm easier since they only need to know how to subtract from the base and add.

Written Algorithms for Whole Number Multiplication: Students find the transition from the intermediate algorithms to the standard algorithms very helpful. Although the expanded multiplication technique involving more digits than available on a typical calculator display may not be used often, it does illustrate how to use mental math, a calculator, and understanding of mathematics to extend even what a calculator can do.

Written Algorithms for Whole Number Division: Here, again, a succession of intermediate algorithms, in addition to a concrete example with base-ten blocks, helps students better understand the long division algorithm and to appreciate just how difficult teaching this algorithm will be.

Algorithms in Base Five: This section affords students an opportunity to test various algorithms in unfamiliar situations. Students find many nontraditional algorithms more to their liking when doing computations in other bases. This gives us another chance to discuss the role and evaluation of algorithms. Notice that students will find that trying a long division problem in another base can be a humbling experience since they cannot perform the necessary prerequisite mental computations nor estimate in other bases.

Chapter 5 - Number Theory

Primes and Composites: The definitions of prime and composite numbers using numbers of factors provide a nice partition of the counting numbers, namely, 1 (one factor), primes (exactly two factors), and composites (more than two factors).

Tests for Divisibility: The proofs of the tests for divisibility are accessible to students; moreover, the students appreciate understanding why the various tests work in the ways that they do. Also, these proofs provide a convenient place to discuss logical terms such as biconditional and converse (at least informally).

Counting Factors: This is a nice technique that is usually overlooked. One of its applications is to serve as a check to see if one has found *all* the factors of a number. The table provides a nice visual proof of why this technique works.

Greatest Common Factor: In most instances, the prime factorization method is preferred by students. Our focus is on the GCF as a concept to be used in simplifying fractions. Also, we have included the Euclidean algorithm which, when combined with a calculator, can be used to find the GCFs of larger numbers more easily.

Least Common Multiple: Here, again, students prefer the prime factorization approach because of its efficiency. Also, finding the LCM by first finding the GCF and using the relationship $GCF(a,b)LCM(a,b) = ab$ is nice. Students will likely have a difficult time with the infinitude of primes proof the first time through. But, after applying it to several other primes, such as 3, 5, 7, and so on, and to one composite, say 4, they catch on and appreciate the proof.

Chapter 6 - Fractions

The Concept of Fraction: This was one of the toughest parts of the text to compose since there are two distinct notions that we need to get across (numeral and number), yet we didn't want to carry around the excess baggage of two names (fraction and fractional number) or equivalence classes of ordered pairs of whole numbers. We hope that your students will understand the many facets of the concept of a fraction as a numeral/number after working through this section. We decided to try to hit this issue head on instead of glossing over it as is done so often. Our definition of fraction equality is the usual cross multiplication definition, which naturally flows from models.

Ordering Fractions: Fractions are ordered using common denominators first since students find this approach to be a natural extension of whole number ordering. Then, the usual cross multiplication test for inequality is then derived. Density is introduced via the interesting theorem "if $\frac{a}{b} < \frac{c}{d}$, then $\frac{a}{b} < \frac{a+c}{b+d} < \frac{c}{d}$." This result surprises students and provides an opportunity to reinforce the fact that $\frac{a}{b} + \frac{c}{d} \neq \frac{a+c}{b+d}$ in general.

Addition and its Properties: Here, again, the definitions of addition and subtraction flow from work with models. Then we try to emphasize how properties of fraction addition are consequences of similar whole number properties.

Subtraction: Subtraction is motivated from models similar to addition.

Multiplication and its Properties: The definition of fraction multiplication evolves first as an extension of whole number multiplication; finally, a model is used to motivate the general definition.

Division: Our introduction of fraction division is novel, though not from a long-term historical perspective as can be seen in the Focus On. We try to enlighten students who have no *feeling* for fraction division, only a *rule* to invert and multiply. (How can such students possibly motivate this concept to children - in fact, most teachers don't, they just teach it as a rule much as stories are passed on from generation to generation?) Once, just after we had completed this unit, an excellent, mature, returning student confided that he was relieved to know that the operation of fraction division *existed*; he had always thought that there were only *three* fraction operations (no one ever used division since it was always changed to multiplication). Although many of our students may leave us with the "invert and multiply" rule still their predominant way of viewing fraction division, they do know that division is a legitimate operation and that it is multifaceted.

Mental Math and Estimation: Techniques introduced in Chapter 4 are extended to fractions. This approach reinforces the earlier work with whole numbers.

Chapter 7 - Decimals, Ratio, Proportion, and Percent

Decimals: Decimals are introduced as a natural extension of whole numbers using the number line and a hundreds square. Also, the fractions with terminating decimals are characterized.

Mental Math and Estimation: The techniques developed in Chapter 4 are extended to decimals. In addition, a new technique, using fraction equivalents, is introduced. Research found that skilled mental estimators would often convert decimals to convenient fractions and compatible numbers to estimate products.

Algorithms for Operations with Decimals: The key idea in this section is that computations involving decimals can be done by temporarily suppressing the decimal points *mentally*, performing the corresponding whole number algorithm, and then correctly inserting a decimal point in the answer. Multiplying decimals is a good place to apply rounding techniques and to do approximate calculations.

Classifying Repeating Decimals: This subsection allows us to completely describe the fractions in terms of their decimal representations.

Ratio: The work in ratios parallels the work with fractions *except* that numerators and denominators aren't restricted to whole numbers. Notice that ratios may have zero "denominators" (e.g. the ratio of men to women on an NFL football team). However, we restrict our study to ratios that have nonzero 'denominators'.

Proportion: Paying close attention to respective units is a key to success in solving proportions. The mental technique of scaling up/down is included to encourage mental math when solving proportions.

Converting Percents: Developing skill in converting among fractions, decimals, and percents is a prerequisite to solving percent problems mentally.

Mental Math and Estimation: The powerful mental technique of using fraction equivalents is introduced. This allows students to estimate answers as they do more formal percent calculations, perhaps using calculators.

Solving Percent Problems: Applied problems involving percent are solved using both the proportion and the equation methods. Work with calculators is especially relevant here, although one needs to watch for the different ways that various calculators handle percent.

Chapter 8 - Integers

Integers and the Integer Number Line: The set of integers and their opposites are introduced using both a black/red chip model and the integer number line. Note that the term opposite will be synonymous with additive inverse once that concept has been introduced.

Addition and its Properties: We have observed that students find the black/red chip model to be very helpful when learning integer operations. Addition is viewed as a natural extension of whole number addition when using colored chips.

Subtraction: Subtraction is demystified when using the chip model since the take-away approach naturally leads to the adding the opposite approach. Again, in the spirit of extending number systems, subtraction is shown to have an equivalent missing addend version. The two methods of whole number subtraction are extended to integer subtraction. In addition, the add-the-opposite approach is developed using models. Students profit from seeing that these three approaches to subtraction are equivalent. The mathematical morsel at the end of this section can be generalized to any finite collection of integers.

Multiplication and Its Properties: We motivate the definition of multiplication using patterns. However, one could use the chip model for this purpose as illustrated in exercises 4 and 5 of Exercise/Problem Set 8.2 - Part A. The results that $(-a)b = -ab$ and $(-a)(-b) = ab$ deserve special attention since most students view them simply as statements about the product of a negative and a positive, and the product of two negatives respectively. However, these are more general statements involving *additive inverses.*

Division: Just as with whole number division, integer division is viewed using the missing factor approach. We omit division with remainder due to its lack of application.

Negative Integers and Scientific Notation: Since decimals and the set of integers with its operations have been introduced, this is a natural place to study integer exponents and scientific notation.

Ordering Integers: Ordering integers is introduced as an extension of whole number ordering. Care must be taken to distinguish integer ordering, though, when multiplying both sides of an inequality by a negative (integer).

Chapter 9 - Rational Numbers and Real Numbers, with Algebra

Rational Numbers - An Extension of Fractions and Integers: Here we take a more formal approach than in earlier chapters. For example, our definition of equality is the familiar cross-multiplication definition (which extends a similar property in the fractions chapter). Also, our definition of addition is the general case involving unlike denominators. Since the rational numbers extend both the fractions and integers, this section can be covered at a brisk pace. The major "new" result is - $\dfrac{a}{b} = \dfrac{-a}{b} = \dfrac{a}{-b}$.

Ordering Rational Numbers: The material in this subsection ties together similar ideas in the fractions and integers.

Real Numbers- An Extension of Rational Numbers: There are several proofs to show that there is no rational number whose square is two - the one we selected can be easily generalized thus displaying the power of abstraction in mathematical reasoning. Figure 9.7, which shows the subset relationships among the number systems through the reals, is useful in helping students see the big picture.

Rational Exponents: Our students appreciate seeing how the definitions of fraction and rational exponents unfold. Although we did not include an extensive discussion of properties of radicals, they are developed in the problem set.

Algebra: In chapter 1, we had students solve equations using intuitive or "natural" methods such as guess and test, cover-up, and work backward. In this chapter, we use balance scale models to illustrate how to solve equations using the various properties of equality. Rules for solving inequalities are then developed abstractly by reasoning from the corresponding order properties. The equations and inequalities use rational numbers further extending what was introduced in chapter 1.

Functions and their Graphs: A variety of functions and their graphs are presented. This is a great place to bring a graphics calculator to class to show how useful these powerful calculators are (*and* at an affordable price).

Chapter 10 - Statistics

Organizing Information: We find that our students are especially interested in educational examples. Charts and graphs from *USA_Today* or similar news publications provide a variety of examples. *The Statistical Abstract of the United States* and various almanacs are excellent sources` of data for graphs and tables.

Measuring Central Tendency: Notice how box and whisker plots incorporate central tendency *and* dispersion.

Measuring Dispersion: Interpreting the variance and standard deviation of a collection of data can be a challenge. For large, roughly normally distributed collections, the standard deviation is about one-fourth of the range. Also, if $\bar{x}$ is the mean and s is the standard deviation, then for such collections, the intervals $\bar{x} \pm s$ and $\bar{x} \pm 2s$ capture about 68% and 95% of the data, respectively.

The fact that the mean and the standard deviation are the two parameters determining the shape of a normal distribution helps our students appreciate their prominence in statistics. The use of z-scores and percentiles allows for direct comparison of performances on several exams or other measurements. That is, z-scores and percentiles indicate relative positions within distributions (in standard deviation units.)

Deceptive Statistics: Since statistical information continues to be an influential factor in society, we used the last section to focus on the potential misuses of statistics. An understanding of these misuses should help your students and their future students become better consumers and citizens.

Chapter 11 - Probability

Simple Experiments: We find that a careful discussion of events using set theory is very useful before any assignment of probabilities.

Computing Probabilities in Simple Experiments: We have found that an informal treatment of the meaning of probability, say using relative frequency, is essential at the start. Examples from games, sports, medicine, and science are very useful.

Tree Diagrams and Counting Techniques: The relationship between outcomes in binomial experiments and Pascal's triangle can be explained using diagrams such as in Figures 11.20, 11.21, and 11.22. We have found that representing multistep experiments with probability tree diagrams is a very effective way of computing probabilities.

Probability Tree Diagrams: The additive property of probability tree diagrams is a direct application of the probability of a union of disjoint events. The multiplicative property of probability tree diagrams follows from multiplication of fractions. These two properties can be applied to equally likely and unequally likely outcomes, and to multistage experiments.

Extended Counting Techniques and Computing Probabilities: Since listing a large sample space can be unreasonable, advanced counting techniques are introduced to be used to determine the number of elements in a sample space or event. These numbers are then used to compute a probability.

Simulation: With the widespread availability of computers (and scientific calculators with random number generators), simulation of experiments provides a powerful approach to approximating probabilities. Simulations using numbered chips, dice, or random digit tables are alternatives to computer simulations.

Expected Value: In experiments with numerical sample spaces, expected value can be used to describe the most likely value, or the "weighted average." This couples nicely with simulation of complex experiments.

Odds: Odds are most naturally explained in the case of equally likely outcomes, but can easily be generalized.

Conditional Probability: An initial discussion of sample spaces "reduced" to reflect a given condition (with corresponding adjustments in probabilities) can be generalized to conditional probability as a ratio.

Chapter 12 Geometric Shapes

The van Hiele Theory: We find that our students are intrigued by the hierarchy of reasoning processes described by the van Hieles. We include a discussion of children's misconceptions about geometric shapes in part to help clear up some of our students' misconceptions. We are careful to point out that our approach to geometry will be at the lowest three levels, and not at the levels of formal deduction or axiomatics. However, we do employ informal deduction often.

Recognizing Geometric Shapes: We find that our students are generally weak in visualization skills and are challenged by the exercises and problems requiring them.

Analyzing Geometric Shapes: We gradually build up a vocabulary for describing components of shapes and, consequently, various types of shapes.

Symmetry: We discuss only reflection and rotation symmetry here, leaving a discussion of more general transformations for Chapter 16. The tests for parallel and perpendicular line segments can be interpreted in Chapter 16, using reflections. Table 12.1 provides descriptions of basic geometric shapes as well as examples of the corresponding shapes found in the world around us. Relationships among classes of quadrilaterals are shown in Figure 12.10.

Regular n-gons: We introduce these early to illustrate general families of shapes with interesting properties.

Circle: Circles are compared to regular n-gons, an approach that we exploit in computing the area of a circle and the volumes and surface areas of cones and cylinders in Chapter 13.

Points and Lines in a Plane: We find that our students better understand the abstract nature of points, lines, and planes if we use an analogy to numbers; that is, we can represent the concepts with pictures (as with numbers and numerals), but the objects themselves exist only in our imaginations. The "protractor" device here is actually a fan of rays used to measure angles.

Angles: Several consequences of the parallel postulate (property 3 of points and lines) are developed and illustrated reasoning deductively.

Regular Polygons: From the angle sum in a triangle property, we are able to derive the measures of angles in regular n-gons.

Tessellations: Tessellations with triangles and quadrilaterals illustrate several major results (see the exercise/problem sets).

Tessellations with Regular Polygons: We are able to classify all of the regular tessellations based on our previous results about angle measures. (In the problem set, the semiregular tessellations are characterized.)

Planes, Skew lines, and Dihedral Angles: We purposely avoid defining dihedral angles formed by half planes since the applications of interest to us involve polyhedra. The relationships between lines and planes are important when discussing polyhedra, also.

Polyhedra: Analogies between regular polyhedra and regular tessellations (semiregular polyhedra/tessellations) are useful.

Curved Shapes in Three Dimensions: We include a general definition of cylinder and cone, and determine their volumes in Chapter 13. Three-dimensional symmetry is investigated in the problems.

Chapter 13 - Measurement

Nonstandard Units: Many students (and teachers) seem to confuse measurement and geometry, or think of measurement as linear measurement only. Thus, we discuss the *process* of measurement and bring in systems of units in a historical way.

Standard Units - The English and Metric Systems: We emphasize common metric prefixes (e.g. kilo-, centi-, milli-) and show the usefulness of "metric converters" such as in Figure 13.11. We find that the three "metric cubes" in Figure 13.22 are useful in illustrating the interrelatedness of metric units of length, volume, and mass. We like to distinguish between volume and capacity. A flat circular disk of clay has volume, but no capacity (it doesn't hold any water poured on it). However, if the clay is formed into a dish, its volume is the same and it now has capacity. Notice that there are different (though connected) units for volume and capacity in the English system; for example, cubic units and quarts.

Dimensional Analysis: Our students need practice in estimation and approximation. Dimensional analysis gives us the opportunity to estimate first, then convert/compute. It also simplifies conversions within the English system, and, when necessary, between English and metric units.

Length: We include a brief discussion of distance on a line in part to show the relationship between order properties of the real numbers and betweenness.

Area: Our discussion of area occurs at van Hiele level two since we deduce area formulas from the area of a rectangle. It is important to point out that the area of a triangle is the product of the length of a base and its *corresponding* height, since there are *three* such pairs from which to choose.

The Pythagorean Theorem: Results about construction of irrational lengths follow immediately from the Pythagorean theorem. We can also illustrate algebraic results, such as $\sqrt{ab} = \sqrt{a} \cdot \sqrt{b}$, say on a square lattice, if one of a or b is a perfect square. The triangle inequality is useful in deciding whether three arbitrary lengths determine a triangle.

Surface Area and Volume: Our students benefit greatly from concrete experiences such as those in the Student Activity Manual. Students need practice in visualizing 'unfolded' shapes as well as the relationship between the area of the base of a right prism/cylinder and its volume. This has been one of the most difficult geometry units for our students, in part, we think, due to a lack of concrete background experiences. We urge a careful intuitive approach at first. Table 13.11 shows analogies in the volumes and surface areas of prisms/cylinders and pyramids/cones.

Chapter 14 - Geometry Using Triangle Congruence and Similarity

Congruence: We have found that many students prefer to think of triangle congruence informally ("same size and shape") rather than as a relationship (literally an equivalence relation) between triangles whose vertices are made to correspond in a suitable way. Thus, we encourage our students to extend their reasoning beyond holistic thinking. We motivate the triangle congruence properties through analytical reasoning in specific cases. (For more concrete approaches, see the Student Activity Manual.) Then we apply the congruence conditions to short verifications of properties of polygons.

Similarity: We find that students need some review of ratio and proportion in order to understand the proportionality of the sides in similar triangles.

Geometric Constructions: We have deliberately separated the construction procedures from their justifications in order to emphasize the deductive verifications using triangle congruence. We find that students benefit from practice in simply learning the procedures. You may wish to discuss only a few of the justifications, as time permits.

Constructing Regular n-gons: Our students are intrigued by the interplay between Gauss's classification of constructible regular *n*-gons and the unsolved problem of the existence of more Fermat primes. In our courses, we discuss some consequences about the constructibility of certain angles, e.g. as central angles or vertex angles in regular *n*-gons.

Geometric Problem Solving Using Triangle Congruence and Similarity: Several classical results, illustrated in Chapter 12, are verified here. Example 14.15, the converse of the Pythagorean theorem, actually uses the Pythagorean theorem! Many of the results of this section can be investigated inductively using exploration software before searching for deductive verifications.

Chapter 15 - Geometry Using Coordinates

Coordinates: If coordinates were not studied in section 9.3, the first few pages of that section could be covered here.

Distance: The midpoint formula can also be verified using triangle congruence (or similarity) if you prefer.

Slope: An analogy to the grade of a road or the pitch of a roof is helpful in understanding slope as a ratio. We have purposely kept the derivations of slope properties independent of Chapter 14. If you've discussed Chapter 14, you may wish to use triangle congruence or similarity properties in verifying the slopes of parallel lines property. We establish only the slope-intercept form of the equation of a nonvertical line to keep our treatment as lean as possible (others are found in the problem set, though). As enrichment, you may wish to discuss the geometry of other forms of a line.

Simultaneous Equations: We will apply results of this section in section 15.3 when establishing the concurrence of the medians and of the altitudes in a triangle.

Equations of Circles: We develop equations of circles to show that curves other than lines have analytical characterizations. You may wish to discuss other curves, such as the remaining conic sections. (See the problems in 15.2B.) We also apply the equation of a circle in finding the circumscribed circle of a triangle.

Geometric Problem Solving using Coordinates: Example 15.8 is much more difficult using only triangle congruence or similarity. Results about the medians and altitudes of triangles can be motivated by constructions or exploration software.

Chapter 16 - Geometry Using Transformations

Transformations: Construction or drawing activities in addition to the use of a dynamic geometry software package are helpful for many of our students to develop an intuitive feeling for transformations. See the Student Activity Manual.

Symmetry: Tessellations, wallpaper, flooring, and clothing are sources of symmetric patterns. Miras are very useful for investigating reflection symmetry.

Making Escher-Type Patterns: There are several books available from Dale Seymour Publications and Creative Publications on tessellations and Escher-type patterns that our students enjoy.

Congruence: We present a special case of the verification that reflections preserve distance to avoid overwhelming the students with too much detail. The classification of isometries can be convincingly demonstrated with construction activities, as a more concrete approach.

Similarity: The development parallels that of congruence via isometries.

Geometric Problem Solving using Transformations: Example 16.12 is an alternative to an approach using congruence. (The latter technically involves betweenness considerations.) Several interesting applications of half-turns appear. An argument based on area of parallelograms also suffices.

Epilogue - An Eclectic Approach to Geometry

Enjoy this section - your students will too! Proving the midsegment theorem using three approaches - synthetic, coordinate, and transformation - opens students' eyes to the value of multiple approaches to geometry. Give students a chance to vote on their favorite approach and discuss the pros and cons of each method. This is a great capstone to the study of geometry.

Chapter Expectations

Chapter 1 - Introduction to Problem Solving

Expectations: You will be expected to be able to

1-1.   give a general definition of problem solving in mathematics and distinguish between exercises and problems.

1-2.   explain, illustrate, and use Polya's 4-step problem solving process:
      understand the problem
      devise a plan
      carry out the plan
      look back

1-3.   explain and illustrate the following diagram for formulating and solving mathematical problems:

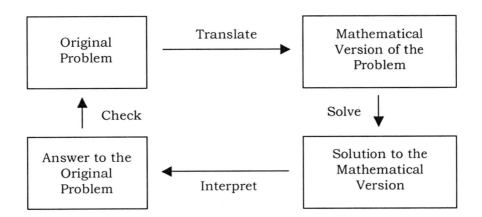

1-4.   explain, illustrate, and apply the following strategies:
      guess and test   look for a pattern
      use a variable   make a list
      draw a picture   solve a simpler problem

1-5.   use algebra and combinations of the above strategies to solve problems.

1-6.   state and apply the definitions of the following terms:
      equation   solution
      variable

Chapter 2 - Sets, Whole Numbers, and Numeration

Expectations: You will be expected to be able to

2-1.   describe the concept of set, use set notation, and define the following terms:

counting numbers	Venn diagram
whole numbers	universal set (universe)
element (member)	disjoint sets
set-builder notation	union
empty set	intersection
equivalent (matching) sets	complement
equal sets	set difference (relative complement)
1-1 correspondence	ordered pairs
Cartesian product	subset
finite set	proper subset
infinite set	

2-2.   use the concept of matching sets to formalize the meaning of whole numbers.

2-3.   explain what is meant by the number of a finite set A.

2-4.   describe and compare these concepts:

cardinal number	numeral of a whole number
ordinal number	name of a whole number numeral
identification number	place holder
whole number	

2-5.   describe the relations of less than and greater than for whole numbers using sets.

2-6.   express whole numbers using these numeration systems:
Egyptian   Roman   Babylonian   Mayan   Hindu-Arabic

2-7.   compare the attributes (additive, subtractive, multiplicative, positional, place value) of the following numeration systems:
tally   Egyptian   Roman   Babylonian   Mayan   Hindu-Arabic

2-8.   write a Hindu-Arabic numeral in any base from two to ten in its expanded form and convert from expanded form to the numeral represented.

2-9.   convert a numeral from any base to base ten and vice versa.

2-10.   state the definition and provide examples of a relation.

2-11.   identify sequences as arithmetic, geometric, or otherwise; if arithmetic(geometric), find the common difference(ratio) and the nth term.

2-12.   state the definition of a function, the domain, range, and codomain of a function.

2-13.   describe the differences and similarities between relations and functions.

2-14. describe the concept of function and represent functions in any of the following ways: arrow diagrams, tables, machines, ordered pairs, graphs, formulas, and geometric transformations.

2-15. explain, illustrate, and apply the strategy "draw a diagram."

Chapter 3 - Whole Numbers - Operations and Properties

Expectations: You will be expected to be able to

3-1.   represent addition of whole numbers using a set model and a measurement model.

3-2.   justify and apply the following properties of addition of whole numbers: closure, commutativity, associativity, identity.

3-3.   explain, illustrate, and use the following thinking strategies for learning basic addition facts:

commutativity	doubles
adding zero	adding 10
counting on by 1 and 2	associativity
combinations to 10	doubles +/- 1 and +/- 2

3-4.   represent subtraction of whole numbers using the take-away and missing addend approaches.

3-5.   explain how to obtain basic subtraction facts from addition facts using the missing addend approach.

3-6.   construct the addition facts table for any base from two through ten and read it "backwards" to find subtraction facts.

3-7.   explain and illustrate the comparison model of subtraction.

3-8.   give examples to show that subtraction of whole numbers has none of these properties: closure, commutativity, associativity, identity.

3-9.   represent addition and subtraction problems using multibase pieces, bundling sticks, and Cuisinaire rods (or centimeter strips.)

3-10.   give examples of "real world" addition and subtraction problems involving set and measurement models.

3-11.   describe multiplication of whole numbers using repeated addition and rectangular array approaches, using a set model and a measurement model.

3-12.   justify and apply the following properties for multiplication of whole numbers: closure, commutativity, associativity, identity.

3-13.   justify and apply the distributive property of multiplication over addition (and subtraction).

3-14.   explain, illustrate, and use the following thinking strategies for learning basic multiplication facts:

commutativity	multiplication by 5
multiplication by zero	multiplication by 9
multiplication by 1	associativity
multiplication by 2	distributivity

3-15. represent division of whole numbers using the missing factor approach and the repeated subtraction approach.

3-16. explain the conceptual difference between partitive and measurement division.

3-17. explain how to obtain basic division facts from multiplication facts, using the missing factor approach.

3-18. explain division problems involving zero using the missing factor approach.

3-19. construct the multiplication facts table for any base from two through ten and read it "backwards" to find division facts.

3-20. state the division algorithm and illustrate it using examples on the number line.

3-21. give examples to show that division of whole numbers has none of these properties: closure, commutativity, associativity, identity.

3-22. describe less than and greater than with whole numbers using the operation of addition.

3-23. justify and apply the following properties of less than:
(a) transitivity
(b) property of less than and addition
(c) property of less than and multiplication

3-24. state the definition of whole number exponents using repeated multiplication.

3-25. justify and apply the following properties of exponents for whole numbers a, b, and nonzero m and n:

(a) $a^m \cdot a^n = a^{m+n}$ (b) $a^m \cdot b^m = (ab)^m$

(c) $(a^m)^n = a^{mn}$ (d) $a^m \div a^n = a^{m-n}$ if $m \geq n$

3-26. motivate the definition $a^0 = 1$ for all nonzero whole numbers a and explain why 0^0 is undefined.

3-27. explain and use the order of operations to simplify arithmetic expressions.

3-28. explain, illustrate, and apply the strategy "use direct reasoning."

Chapter 4 - Whole Number Computations - Mental, Electronic, Written

Expectations: You will be expected to be able to

4-1.   give examples of and contrast mental, electronic, and written algorithms.

4-2.   identify and apply the following mental math techniques:
   using properties   the equal additions method
   using compatible numbers   using left-to-right methods
   using additive compensation   multiplying by powers of 10
   using multiplicative compensation   multiplying by special factors

4-3.   identify and apply the following estimation techniques:
   range estimation   round a five up place
   one (two)- column front-end estimation   round to a compatible number
   front-end with adjustment   round to a given
   round up/down

4-4.   distinguish between arithmetic and algebraic logic on calculators by listing the mathematical convention for order of operations.

4-5.   use the following keys on a calculator (in addition to the usual number keys):
   parentheses keys   exponent keys
   constant function keys   memory keys

4-6.   describe scientific notation as it appears on scientific calculators.

4-7.   justify the standard addition algorithm using (a) concrete models (e.g., multibase pieces and a chip abacus) and (b) place value and properties of addition.

4-8.   explain, illustrate, and use (a) intermediate algorithms for addition that lead to the standard algorithm and (b) the lattice method for addition.

4-9.   justify the standard subtraction algorithm using (a) concrete models (e.g., multibase pieces and a chip abacus) and (b) place value and properties of subtraction.

4-10.   explain, illustrate, and use nontraditional algorithms for subtraction.

4-11.   justify the standard multiplication algorithm using place value and properties of multiplication.

4-12.   explain, illustrate, and use (a) intermediate algorithms that lead to the standard multiplication algorithm and (b) the lattice method for multiplication.

4-13.   explain, illustrate, and use long division algorithms (including the scaffold method) that lead to the standard algorithm.

4-14.   justify the standard long division algorithm using multibase pieces or place value and properties of division.

4-15.   use mental procedures to approximate quotients.

4-16.   perform division with remainders on a calculator.

4-17. add, subtract, multiply, and divide in bases 2 through 12.

4-18. explain, illustrate, and apply the strategy "use indirect reasoning."

Chapter 5 - Number Theory

Expectations: You will be expected to be able to

  5-1.   state and apply the definitions of the following terms:

  prime   is divisible by
  composite   common factor (divisor)
  divides   common multiple
  factor (divisor)   greatest common factor (GCF)
  factor tree   least common multiple (LCM)
  multiple

  5-2.   use the sieve of Eratosthenes to find prime numbers.

  5-3.   state and apply the fundamental theorem of arithmetic.

  5-4.   state and apply tests for divisibility by 2, 3, 4, 5, 6, 8, 9, 10, 11, and 12.

  5-5.   find the prime factorization of a given composite number.

  5-6.   use the prime factorization of a number to find all its factors.

  5-7.   use the exponents in the prime factorization of a number to count its factors.

  5-8.   find the GCF of a given pair of numbers using
          (a) the set intersection method ,
          (b) the prime factorization method, and
          (c) the Euclidean algorithm.

  5-9.   find the LCM of a given pair of numbers using
          (a) the set intersection method ,
          (b) the prime factorization method,
          (c) the build-up method.

  5-10.   relate the GCF and LCM of any two numbers to the product of the numbers.

  5-11.   explain, illustrate, and apply the strategy "use properties of numbers."

Chapter 6 - Fractions

Expectations: You will be expected to be able to

6-1.   state the definition of a fraction as a numeral that represents part of a whole and sketch pictures which illustrate given fractions.

6-2.   state the definition of a fraction as a number that represents relative amounts and sketch pictures all of which represent the same relative amounts and, hence, are represented by the same fraction (as a number).

6-3.   state definitions of the following terms:
numerator   improper fraction
denominator   mixed number
simplest form   complex fraction
cross product

6-4.   state the definition of equality of fractions.

6-5.   express a fraction in its simplest form.

6-6.   state the definition of less than and greater than for fractions.

6-7.   show how to compare fractions using common denominators.

6-8.   state and apply the cross multiplication property of inequality.

6-9.   state the definition of density and apply it to any given pair of fractions.

6-10.   show how to motivate the definition of addition, subtraction, multiplication, and division using concrete models.

6-11.   compute sums, products, differences, and quotients of given pairs of fractions and provide rationale for your computations.

6-12.   describe the three equivalent ways to find the quotient of two fractions.

6-13.   state the definitions of multiplicative inverse and reciprocal.

6-14.   determine which of the following properties of addition and multiplication hold for fractions:
closure   distributivity
commutativity   identity
associativity   inverse

6-15.   use the following mental math/estimation techniques for fractions:
properties   range estimation
compatible numbers   front-end with adjustment
compensation   rounding

6-16.   explain, illustrate, and apply the strategy "solve an equivalent problem."

Chapter 7 - Decimals, Ratio, Proportion, and Percent

Expectations: You will be expected to be able to

7-1.   show how to motivate and represent decimals using a hundreds square and number line.

7-2.   write a given decimal numeral in expanded form.

7-3.   translate decimal numerals into their word names and vice versa.

7-4.   characterize the fractions with terminating decimal representations.

7-5.   order decimals using their (a) fraction representation and (b) decimal representation.

7-6.   use the following mental math/estimation techniques for decimals:
        properties   range estimation
        compatible numbers   front-end methods
        compensation   rounding
        fraction equivalents

7-7.   justify the "moving the decimal point" when multiplying or dividing by a power of 10.

7-8.   estimate the sum, difference, product, and quotient of pairs of decimals.

7-9.   compute sums, differences, products, and quotients of numbers in decimal form (a) using the standard algorithms and (b) using a calculator.

7-10. demonstrate that terminating decimals are a numeration system for certain fractions (see 7-3) by changing these fractions to decimals and vice versa.

7-11. change any fraction to its decimal form.

7-12. convert given repeating decimals to their fraction form and characterize the fractions that have repeating, nonterminating decimal representations.

7-13. state definitions of the following:
        ratio   proportion   means   extremes

7-14. give examples of ratios as rates and represent ratios as part-to-part and part-to-whole.

7-15. apply the definition of cross multiplication of equal ratios.

7-16. solve certain proportions mentally by scaling up and scaling down.

7-17. define $n\%$ (n percent) for any fraction n and solve problems involving percents using a variety of methods: grid, proportion, equation, calculator.

7-18. convert any fraction, decimal, or percent into any of the other two forms.

7-19. use mental math/estimation techniques to solve percent problems.

7-20.   solve applied problems involving ratios, proportions, and percents.

7-21.   explain, illustrate, and apply the strategy "work backward."

Chapter 8 - Integers

Expectations: You will be expected to be able to

8-1. state the definition of the set of integers and represent integers (a) using colored chips and (b) on the integer number line.

8-2. explain how to add integers using (a) a set model and (b) a measurement model.

8-3. define addition of integers via whole numbers and opposites.

8-4. explain and apply the following properties of integer addition:
      closure   commutativity   associativity   additive identity   additive inverse

8-5. explain and apply the opposite of the opposite and additive cancellation properties.

8-6. explain how to subtract pairs of integers using each of these approaches:
      take-away   adding the opposite   missing addend

8-7. distinguish between the terms "negative", "opposite", and "minus".

8-8. explain how to represent multiplication of integers using repeated addition and patterns.

8-9. define multiplication of integers via whole numbers and opposites.

8-10. explain and apply the following properties of integer multiplication:
       closure commutativity   associativity   identity

8-11. define and apply the distributive property of integer multiplication over addition (subtraction).

8-12. explain and apply the following properties of integer multiplication:
       (a) $a(-1) = -a$ (b) $-a(b) = -(ab) = a(-b)$ (c) $(-a)(-b) = ab$

8-13. state and apply the multiplication cancellation property.

8-14. explain division of integers using the missing factor approach.

8-15. determine which of the following properties of subtraction and division hold in the integers:
       closure   commutativity   associativity   identity

8-16. determine if a given sum, difference, product, or quotient of integers is positive, negative, zero, or undefined.

8-17. state and apply the definitions of negative exponents and scientific notation.

8-18. state the definition of less than and greater than for integers using (a) the number line approach and (b) the addition approach.

8-19. state and apply the properties of less than and greater than with respect to addition, subtraction, and multiplication.

8-20. explain, illustrate, and apply the strategy "use cases."

Chapter 9 - Rational Numbers and Real Numbers, with an Introduction to Algebra

Expectations: You will be expected to be able to

9-1.   state the definition of the set of rational numbers and the definition of equality of rational numbers.

9-2.   define addition of rational numbers and explain why $-\dfrac{a}{b} = \dfrac{-a}{b} = \dfrac{a}{-b}$.

9-3.   justify and apply the following properties of addition of rational numbers:
   closure   additive inverse
   commutativity   additive cancellation
   associativity   opposite of the opposite
   identity

9-4.   state the definition of subtraction of rational numbers.

9-5.   state the definition of multiplication of rational numbers.

9-6.   explain and apply properties of multiplication of rational numbers:
   closure   multiplicative inverse
   commutativity   distributive properties of multiplication over
   associativity   addition (subtraction)
   identity

9-7.   state the definition of division of rational numbers and explain how to divide rational numbers in three different ways.

9-8.   find sums, differences, products, and quotients of two rational numbers using both written and calculator methods.

9-9.   explain the following diagram:

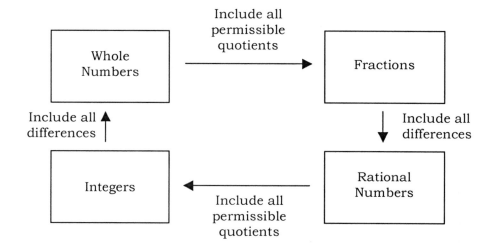

9-10.   order rational numbers using the following methods:
the number line   common positive denominators
addition   cross multiplication property of inequality

9-11.   explain and apply properties of ordering rational numbers including the density property.

9-12.   explain why the equation $x^2 = p$ has no solutions in the rational numbers for all prime numbers p.

9-13.   state the definition of the set of real numbers and explain the subset relationships among the sets of rational numbers, irrational numbers, terminating decimals, and repeating or nonrepeating infinite decimals.

9-14.   interpret the following diagram.

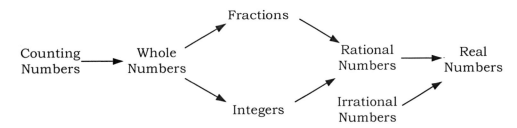

9-15.   state the definition of the square roots and principal square root of a nonnegative real number and explain how to locate square roots of whole numbers on the number line using the Pythagorean theorem.

9-16.   state the definition of and calculate nth roots.

9-17.   state the definition of rational exponent.

9-18.   state and apply properties of rational exponents.

9-19.   state and apply the definitions of inequality and solution set of an inequality.

9-20.   explain how to solve equations of the forms:
(a) $x + a = b$
(b) $ax + b = c$
(c) $ax + b = cx + d$

9-21.   apply the following properties of real number inequalities:
(a) if $a < b$ and $b < c$, then $a < c$.
(b) if $a < b$, then $a + c < b + c$.
(c) if $a < b$ and $c > 0$, then $ac < bc$.
(d) if $a < b$ and $c < 0$, then $ac > bc$.

9-22.   construct and interpret graphs of the following kinds of functions:
linear   quadratic   exponential   cubic   step

9-23.   apply the vertical line test to determine if a graph is the graph of a function.

9-24.   explain, illustrate, and apply the strategy "solve an equation."

Chapter 10 - Statistics

Expectations: You will be expected to be able to

10-1.   interpret the following types of graphs:
    line plots   histograms
    stem and leaf plots   line graphs
    pictographs   circle graphs
    bar graphs   box and whisker plots
    scatterplots

10-2.   identify clusters and gaps (if they exist) on stem and leaf plots.

10-3.   for a given collection of data, determine all types of appropriate graph(s) and construct the graphs.

10-4.   sketch a trend line on a scatterplot and explain its use.

10-5.   determine the following measures of central tendency for given data:
    mode   median   mean (arithmetic average)

10-6.   calculate the lower quartile, upper quartile, the interquartile range (IQR), and any outliers for a box and whisker plot.

10-7.   determine the following measures of dispersion for any given data using written and calculator methods:
    range   standard deviation
    variance   z-score

10-8.   interpret z-scores for given data.

10-9.   describe distributions and interpret measures of central tendency geometrically.

10-10.   describe the normal distribution and interpret the following aspects of a normal distribution geometrically:
    mean   standard deviation   z-scores

10-11.   compute the percentile rank of a value in a given set of data and explain its meaning.

10-12.   give examples of how graphs can be deceptive in the following ways:
    axes manipulation   reversing the category order
    cropping   using an inappropriate type of graph
    pictorial embellishments   three-dimensional effects
    exploding

10-13.   describe ways in which bias can be introduced in sampling.

10-14.   explain, illustrate, and apply the strategy "look for a formula."

Chapter 11 - Probability

Expectations: You will be expected to be able to

11-1. state and apply the definitions of these terms:

experiment   event

outcome   mutually exclusive events

sample space   drawing with replacement

11-2. explain what is meant by the probability of an event and distinguish between experimental and theoretical probability.

11-3. compute probabilities for events with equally likely outcomes.

11-4. explain and apply the following properties of probability:

(a) For any event A, $0 \leq P(A) \leq 1$.

(b) $P(\varnothing) = 0$

(c) $P(A) = 1$ where S is the sample space.

(d) For all events A and B , then $P(A \cup B) = P(A) + P(B) - P(A \cap B)$.

(e) If $\overline{A}$ denotes the complement of event A , then $P\left(\overline{A}\right) = 1 - P(A)$.

11-5. construct tree diagrams to represent the outcomes in a sample space.

11-6. explain and apply the fundamental counting property to determine the number of outcomes in a sample space and in an event.

11-7. apply Pascal's triangle to compute probabilities in a certain type of experiment.

11-8. construct probability tree diagrams and apply the additive property of probability tree diagrams to compute probabilities in complex experiments.

11-9. construct probability tree diagrams and apply the multiplicative property of probability tree diagrams to compute probabilities in complex experiments.

11-10. compute probabilities of events with unequally likely outcomes by using the properties in 11-8 and 11-9 above.

11-11. compute the number of permutations or combinations of n objects taken r at a time.

11-12. compute probabilities by using permutations and combinations to determine the size of the event and sample space.

11-13. explain and use simulations to estimate probabilities in complex experiments.

11-14. explain, illustrate, and apply the strategy "do a simulation."

11-15. explain and compute expected values for experiments whose outcomes are real numbers.

11-16. explain odds in favor of and odds against an event, and convert between the probability of an event and its odds.

11-17. explain and compute conditional probabilities.

Chapter 12 - Geometric Shapes

Expectations: You will be expected to be able to

12-1. explain and illustrate the first four levels of the van Hiele theory: Level 0 (Recognition), Level 1 (Analysis), Level 2 (Relationships), and Level 3 (Deduction).

12-2. give analytical descriptions of various types of triangles, quadrilaterals, and other polygons and their parts.

12-3. list several properties common to various types of triangles and quadrilaterals and explain relationships among general types.

12-4. use paper folding, dot paper, or tracing paper to demonstrate relationships in geometric figures including symmetry, perpendicularity, and parallelism.

12-5. illustrate reflection and rotation symmetry of polygons, regular *n*-gons, and other shapes, including circles.

12-6. give abstract descriptions and properties of the following:
        points   rays   lines   planes   line segments   angles

12-7. describe (a) the interior of an angle, (b) adjacent angles, and (c) how to measure an angle using a protractor.

12-8. explain and use the corresponding angles property, the alternate interior angles property, and derive the angle sum in a triangle property.

12-9. derive measures of the following types of angles in regular polygons and discuss the relationships among their measures:
        central angles   vertex angles   exterior angles

12-10. describe and analyze tessellations with polygons, particularly with regular polygons.

12-11. show how to form tessellations with arbitrary triangles and quadrilaterals and explain several results about triangles and quadrilaterals that are illustrated by tessellations.

12-12. show which regular polygons will form tessellations of the plane by themselves.

12-13. describe the following relationships among lines and planes in three dimensional space:
        parallel   intersecting   perpendicular   skew

12-14. describe how to determine the measure of a dihedral angle.

12-15. describe the following families of polyhedra:
        prisms (right and oblique)   regular polyhedra
        pyramids (right and oblique)   semiregular polyhedra

12-16. illustrate Euler's formula for polyhedra.

12-17.   describe the following curved shapes:
cones (right and oblique) cylinders (right and oblique)   spheres

12-18.   explain, illustrate, and apply the strategy "use a model."

Chapter 13 - Measurement

Expectations: You will be expected to be able to

13-1.   state the three steps of the measurement process.

13-2.   describe what is meant by informal measurement using non-standard units.

13-3.   describe the English system and perform conversions within the following groups of units:
    length: inch, foot, yard, mile
    area: in^2, ft^2, yd^2, mi^2, acre
    volume: in^3, ft^3, yd^3
    capacity: cup, pint, quart, gallon
    weight: ounce, pound, ton

13-4.   distinguish between volume and capacity.

13-5.   describe an ideal system of units.

13-6.   describe the metric system and perform conversions within the following groups of units:
    length: mm, cm, dm, m, dam, hm, km
    area: mm^2, cm^2, m^2, km^2, are, hectare
    volume: mm^3, cm^3, dm^3, m^3, km^3
    mass: g, kg, tonne

13-7.   state the definitions of and work with the following metric prefixes:
    milli-   centi-   deci-   deka-   hecto-   kilo-

13-8.   explain how the metric system is an ideal system of units and how the English system is not.

13-9.   do "rough" conversions between the metric system and the English system for length, area, volume, and weight.

13-10. do exact conversions between degrees Celsius and degrees Fahrenheit.

13-11. solve problems using dimensional analysis.

13-12. find the perimeter of a geometric figure, including polygons and circles.

13-13. show how to derive and apply area formulas to find areas of the following:
    rectangle   square   triangle
    parallelogram   trapezoid   circle

13-14. apply the Pythagorean theorem to determine lengths.

13-15. state and apply the triangle inequality.

13-16. find the surface areas of the following:
    prism   pyramid   cylinder   cone   sphere

13-17.   find the volumes of the following:

prism   pyramid   cylinder   cone   sphere

13-18.   explain, illustrate, and apply the strategy "use dimensional analysis."

Chapter 14 - Geometry Using Triangle Congruence and Similarity

Expectations: You will be expected to be able to

14-1.   establish a correspondence between two triangles to determine if they are congruent.

14-2.   state and apply the SAS, ASA, and SSS congruence properties.

14-3.   establish a correspondence between two triangles to determine if they are similar.

14-4.   state and apply the SAS, AA, and SSS similarity properties.

14-5.   use similar triangles to solve applied problems.

14-6.   perform and justify the following compass and straightedge constructions:
   (a) copy a line segment
   (b) copy an angle
   (c) construct the perpendicular bisector of a line segment
   (d) bisect an angle
   (e) construct the line perpendicular to a given line through a specified point on the line
   (f) construct the line perpendicular to a given line through a specified point not on the line
   (g) construct the line parallel to a given line through a specified point not on the line
   (h) construct the circumscribed circle of a triangle
   (i)   construct the inscribed circle of a triangle
   (j) construct an equilateral triangle given one side

14-7.   determine which regular *n*-gons can be constructed according to Gauss's theorem.

14-8.   describe the following and find them for any given triangle using a compass and straightedge:

circumcenter	centroid
incenter	orthocenter

14-9.   solve problems using congruence and similarity.

14-10.   explain, illustrate, and apply the strategy "identify subgoals."

Chapter 15 - Geometry Using Coordinates

Expectations: You will be expected to be able to

15-1. locate points in the plane using their coordinates.

15-2. find the following for any given pair of points:
the slope (if it exists) of the line segment connecting the points
the distance between the two points
the midpoint of the segment connecting the two points

15.3. determine if three points are collinear using their coordinates.

15-4. state and apply the slopes of parallel lines property and perpendicular lines property.

15-5. find the slope-intercept form of the equation of the line (a) containing a given pair of points or (b) containing a given point and having a given slope.

15-6. solve pairs of simultaneous equations and interpret geometrically.

15-7. find the equation of a circle given its center and radius and vice versa.

15-8. solve problems using coordinate geometry

15-9. explain, illustrate, and apply the strategy "use coordinates."

Chapter 16 - Geometry Using Transformations

Expectations: You will be expected to be able to

16-1.   describe the following transformation:
        translation   reflection
        rotation   glide reflection

16-2.   given points in the plane, using tracing paper, dot paper, compass and straightedge, or an algebraic description, find their images under the following transformations:
        translation   reflection
        rotation   glide reflection

16-3.   determine the following types of symmetry:
        translation   reflection
        rotation   glide reflection

16-4.   determine if two triangles are congruent by finding a distance preserving transformation that takes one triangle to the other.

16-5.   describe a size transformation.

16-6.   determine if two triangles are similar by finding a combination of a size transformation and a distance preserving transformation that takes one triangle to the other.

16-7.   state the definition of an isometry and list the four main properties of isometries.

16-8.   list the four types of isometries.

16-9.   state and apply the triangle congruence and isometries property.

16-10.   list three main properties of size transformations.

16-11.   state the definition of a similitude and list the five main properties of similitudes.

16-12.   state and apply the triangle similarity and similitudes property.

16-13.   solve geometry problems using transformations.

16-14.   explain, illustrate, and apply the strategy "use symmetry."

When Will I Teach This?

The shaded regions in the following scope and sequence chart indicate when topics in *Mathematics for Elementary Teachers - A Contemporary Approach* may be covered in the typical K-8 curriculum. Topics are introduced at the conceptual level in earlier grades. Then students develop skills and facility with problem solving and application in later grades.

Grade Level

Chapter	Topic	K	1	2	3	4	5	6	7	8
1	Problem Solving	▓	▓	▓	▓	▓	▓	▓	▓	▓
2	Whole Number Concepts	▓	▓	▓	▓	▓	▓	▓	▓	▓
	Numeration	▓	▓	▓	▓	▓	▓	▓	▓	▓
3	Whole Number Operations	▓	▓	▓	▓	▓	▓	▓	▓	▓
4	Whole Number Computation	▓	▓	▓	▓	▓	▓	▓	▓	▓
5	Number Theory				▓	▓	▓	▓	▓	▓
6	Fractions				▓	▓	▓	▓	▓	▓
7	Decimals					▓	▓	▓	▓	▓
	Ratio and Proportion					▓	▓	▓	▓	▓
	Percent						▓	▓	▓	▓
8	Integers				▓	▓	▓	▓	▓	▓
9	Rational Numbers						▓	▓		▓
	Real Numbers									▓
	Solving Equations	▓	▓	▓	▓	▓	▓	▓	▓	▓
10	Statistics	▓	▓	▓	▓	▓	▓	▓	▓	▓
11	Probability			▓	▓	▓	▓	▓	▓	▓
12	Geometric Shapes	▓	▓	▓	▓	▓	▓	▓	▓	▓
13	Measurement	▓	▓	▓	▓	▓	▓	▓	▓	▓
14	Geometry - Synthetic				▓	▓	▓	▓	▓	▓
15	Geometry - Coordinates					▓	▓	▓	▓	▓
16	Geometry - Transformations				▓	▓	▓	▓	▓	▓

Exercise/Problem Sets Map for the Eighth Edition

The following Exercise/Problem Sets Map describes changes from the seventh edition. Except where noted, problems in Part A remained Part A problems, and Part B remained Part B. Problems that were modified from seventh edition problems appear with an "m" after the problem number (such as 12m) and problems that came from the Problems for Writing and Discussion section of the seventh edition are denoted by WD.

CHAPTER 1		13	11	4	5m	17	19	11	9
Section 1.1A		14	12	5	6	18	11m	12	8m
8th ed.	7th ed.	15	14	6	7	19	20	13	11m
1	1	16	12A	7	8	20	13	14	20m
2	11	17	16	8	9	21	12	15	10m
3	2	18	17	9	10	22	New	16	18
4	3	19	18	10	11	23	New	17	19
5	4	20	19	11	12	24	14m	18	New
6	5	21	New	12	13	25	15	19	New
7	6	22	20	13	New	26	17	20	16
8	7	23	21	14	3	27	21	21	14
9	8	24	22	15	14	28	22	22	12m
10	9	25	23	16	15	29	23	23	15
11	New	27	24	17	16	30	24	24	13
12	10	27	WD 1	18	17	31	25	25	17
13	13B	**Section 1.2A**		19	18	32	26m	26	16A
14	13	1	1m	20	19	33	27	27	212
15	14	2	2m	21	20m	34	28	28	22
16	15	3	3	22	WD 2	35	29	29	23
17	16	4	4	23	WD 3	36	30	30	24
18	17	5	5	**CHAPTER 2**		37	31	31	31
19	18	6	6m	**Section 2.1A**		38	32	32	New
20	19	7	New	8th ed.	7th ed.	39	33	33	27
21	20	8	20	1	1m	40	34	34	28
22	21	9	21	2	2B	41	35	35	29
23	22	10	7	3(a)	2(a)	42	36	36	30(a)
24	23	11	8	3(b)	2(c)	43	37	37	30(b)
25	24	12	9	3(c)	2(e)	44	WD 3	38	31
26	WD 2	13	10	3(d)	2(g)	**Section 2.1B**		39	32
27	WD 3	14	11	3(e)	2(i)	1	New	40	33
Section 1.1B		15	12	4	6	2	New	41	34
1	7	16	13	5	3	3(a)	2(b) A	42	WD 1
2	15	17	14	6	New	3(b)	2(d) A	43	WD2
3	1	18	15	7	4	3(c)	2(f) A	**Section 2.2A**	
4	2	19	16	8	5	3(d)	2(h) A	1	1
5	3	20	17	9	7m	3(e)	2(j) A	2	2
6	4	21	18	10	9	4	6	3	3
7	5	22	19	11	New	5	3	4	4
8	6	23	WD 1	12	8m	6	2	5	5
9	8	**Section 1.2B**		13	New	7	4	6	4B
10	9	1	1	14	New	8	5	7	7B
11	New	2	2	15	10m	9	7m	8	8
12	10	3	4m	16	18	10	26	9	9

10	10	16	12m	2(a)	2(a)m	19	17m	14	14
11	11	17	11	2(b)	2(b)m	20	18	15	3
12	12	18	New	3(a)	2(a)B	21	19	16	14A
13	13	19	New	3(b)	2(B)B	22	20	17	15
14	New	20	13	4	3m	23	21	18	16
15	15	21	14m	5	3B m	24	22	19	17
16	16	22	16B	6	4, 5 m	25	23	20	18
17	17	23	New	7	6	26	24	21	19
18	18	24	15	8	10	27	25	22	20
19	19	25	New	9	8	28	26	23	WD 1
20	20	26	19	10	7	29	WD 1	**Section 3.2A**	
21	14	27	20	11	9	30	WD 2	1	3
22	WD 1	28	21	12	11	**CHAPTER 3**		2	New
Section 2.2B		29	22	13	12	**Section 3.1A**		3	10
1	1	30	23	14	13B	8th ed.	7th ed.	4	4B
2	2	31	WD 1	15	15	1	1	5	5
3	3	32	WD 2	16	16	2	2m	6	6
4	New	**Section 2.3B**		17	17	3(a)-(e)	3(a)-(e)	7	New
5	5	1	New	18	18	4	4	8	9
6	6	2	1m	19	19	5	New	9	New
7	9	3	New	20	20	6	5	10	11
8	8	4	New	21	21	7	5B	11	14
9	11	5	New	22	22	8	12	12	1m
10	10	6	New	23	23	9	13	13	New
11	12	7	New	24	24	10	8B	14	12
12	13	8	6	25	25	11	6	15	13
13	New	9	New	26	26	12	10	16	New
14	14	10	7A	27	13	13	13B	17	15
15	7	11	7m	28	14	14	14B	18	17B
16	15	12	8	29	New	15	14	19	16
17	16	13	12	30	WD 3	16	15	20	17
18	17	14	New	**Section 2.4B**		17	16	21	18
19	18	15	11m	1	New	18	17	22	19
20	19	16	9m	2(a)	2(c)A	19	18	23	20
21	WD 2	17	5	2(b)	2(d)A	20	19	24	21
22	WD 3	18	New	3(a)	3(a)B	21	20m	25	22
Section 2.3A		19	New	3(b)	2(d)B	22	WD 2	26	23
1	1m	20	14	4	4m	23	WD 3	27	24
2	2m	21	13m	5	5m	**Section 3.1B**		28	25
3	2B	22	New	6	4,5A	1	1	29	26
4	3B	23	15A	7	6	2	2m	30	27
5	3m	24	16A	8	10	3(a)-(e)	3(f)-(j)A	31	28
6	New	25	18	9	8	4	4	32	29m
7	4	26	19	10	7	5	New	33	WD 1
8	6	27	20	11	9	6	7m	**Section 3.2B**	
9	8m	28	21	12	11	7	7A m	1	3
10	4B	29	22	13	14	8	12	2	New
11	9	30	23	14	12	9	13	3	10
12	10	31	24	15	New	10	9	4	New
13	17	32	WD 3	16	New	11	6	5	5
14	18	**Section 2.4A**		17	15	12	10	6(a)-(d)	6(e)-(h)A
15	New	1	New	18	16m	13	13	7	New

8	7	25	WD 1	22	23	30	28	38	26
9	9	26	WD 2	23	24	31	29	39	27
10	11	**Section 3.3B**		24	New	32	30	40	28
11	14	1	1	25	11B	33	31	41	29
12	1m	2	2	26	18B	34	32	42	30
13	New	3	3	27	25	35	33	43	31
14(a)-(c)	12(d)-(f)A	4	4	28	26	36	34	44	32
15	12	5	5	29	27	37	35	45	33
16	13	6	6m	30	28	38	36	46	WD 1
17	15	7	6B	31	29	39	37	47	WD 2
`18	16	8	7B m	32	30	40	38	**Section 4.2B**	
19	18	9	8	33	31	41	39	1	New
20	8	10	9	34	32	42	WD 3	2	1m
21	19	11	New	35	33	43	14	3	2
22	20	12	New	36	34	**Section 4.2A**		4	New
23	21	13	10	37	35	1	8m	5	New
24	22	14	New	38	36	2	New	6	4
25	23	15	New	39	37	3	2	7	5
26	24	16	12	40	38	4	3m	8	6m
27	25	17	13m	41	39	5	New	9	New
28	26	18	14	42	WD 1	6	4	10	13
29	27	18	15	43	WD 2	7	5	11	14m
30	28	20	16	**Section 4.1B**		8	6	12	New
31	29	21	17	1	1	9	14	13	New
32	30	22	18	2	2	10	13	14	9
33	WD 2	23	19	3	3	11	New	15	10
34	WD3	24	New	4	4	12	8B m	16	New
Section 3.3A		25	WD 3	5	5	13	7m	17	New
1	1	**CHAPTER 4**		6	14A	14	9	18	New
2	2	**Section 4.1A**		7	16A	15	10	19	New
3	3	**7th ed.**	**8th ed.**	8	12	16	11	20	New
4	4	1	1	9	6	17	11B	21	New
5	5	2	2	10	7	18	12m	22	New
6	New	3	3	11	8	19	12B m	23	16
7	6	4	4	12	9	20	New	24	17
8	7	5	5	13	10	21	15m	25	New
9	8	6	11	14	New	22	15B m	26	New
10	New	7	15	15	13	23	16	27	New
11	New	8	12	16	17	24	17	28	New
12	11	9	6	17	New	25	18m	29	New
13	10	10	7	18	New	26	18B m	30	New
14	New	11	8	19	15	27	19	31	31A m
15	New	12	9	20	22	28	19B m	32	21m
16	New	13	10	21	21	29	New	33	22
17	12	14	16B	22	23	30	20	34	New
18	13	15	13	23	24	31	New	35	23
19	14	16	17	24	New	32	20B m	36	24
20	15	17	19	25	19	33	New	37	25
21	16	18	18	26	20	34	22	38	26
22	17	19	20	27	25	35	23	39	27
23	18	20	21	28	26	36	24	40	28
24	19	21	22	29	27	37	25	41	29

42	30	2	2	4	4	6	6	25	23
43	31	3	3	5	6	7	12	26	24
44	32	4	4	6	7	8	8	27	25
45	33	5	6	7	8	9	New	28	26
46	New	6	7	8	New	10	Mew	29	27
47	WD 3	7	8	9	New	11	10	30	28
Section 4.3A		8	12	10	9	12	3a	31	New
1	1m	9	12B	11	10	13	12	32	WD 3
2	New	10	9	12	5	14	13m	**CHAPTER 6**	
3	2m	11	10	13	11	15	13B	**Section 6.1A**	
4	3B m	12	5	14	New	16	14	**8th ed.**	**7th ed.**
5	4B m	13	11	15	13	17	15	1	1m
6	5	14	New	16	14	18	16	2	2
7	New	15	13	17	15	19	17	3	1B
8	6m	16	14	18	16	20	18	4	New
9	New	17	15	19	17	21	20	5	New
10	8	18	16	20	18	22	21	6	4
11	New	19	17	21	19	23	22	7	5B
12	9	20	18	22	20	24	23	8	6
13	10	21	19	23	21	25	24	9	7
14	11	22	20	24	22	26	25	10	8
15	12	23	21	25	23	27	26	11	9
16	13	24	22	26	24	28	27	12	10
17	14	25	23	27	25	29	28	13	New
18	15	26	24	28	26	30	29	14	11
19	16	27	25	29	27	31	WD 1	15	12
20	WD 1	28	26	30	28	32	WD 2	16	13
21	WD 2	29	27	31	29	**Section 5.2B**		17	New
Section 4.3B		30	28	32	30	1	1	18	15
1	1	31	29	33	31	2	2	19	16
2	New	32	30	34	32	3	4	20	17
3	2m	33	31	35	33	4	5	21	18
4	4A	34	32	36	34	5	9	22	19
5	New	35	33	37	35	6	6	23	20
6	5	36	34	38	36	7	7	24	21
7	New	37	35	39	37	8	New	25	22
8	6m	38	36	40	38	9	8	26	23
9	7	39	37	41	39	10	10	27	24
10	8	40	38	42	40	11	10B	28	25
11	New	41	39	43	41	12	11B	29	26
12	9	42	40	44	42	13	12	30	27
13	10	43	41	45	43	14	New	31	WD 1
14	11	44	42	46	44	15	New	32	WD 2
15	12	45	43	47	45	16	14	**Section 6.1B**	
16	13	46	44	48	46	17	15	1	1
17	14	47	45	49	WD 3	18	16	2	New
18	15	48	WD 1	**Section 5.2A**		19	17	3	New
19	16	49	WD 2	1	1	20	18	4	3A
20	WD 3	**Section 5.1B**		2	2	21	19	5	3
CHAPTER 5		1	1	3	4	22	20	6	4
Section 5.1A		2	2	4	5	23	21	7	5m
1	1	3	3	5	9	24	22	8	6

9	7	28	27	14	19	25	21	12	10
10	8	29	28	15	9	26	22	13	14m
11	9	30	29	16	15	27	23	14	12
12	10	31	WD 1	17	10m	28	24	15	15
13	New	32	WD 2	18	12	29	25	16	16
14	11	**Section 6.2B**		19	13	30	26	17	17
15	New	1	New	20	16m	31	27	18	18
16	13	2	New	21	18	32	28	19	19
17	14	3	2	22	17	33	29	20	WD 3
18	15	4	3	23	14	34	30	**Section 7.2A**	
19	16	5	5	24	20	35	31	1	1
20	17	6	6	25	21	36	32	2	2
21	18	7	4	26	22	37	33	3	3
22	19	8	7	27	23	38	34	4	4
23	20	9	15	28	24	39	11	5	5
24	21	10	8	29	25	40	WD 3	6	11 (7.1A)
25	22	11	9	30	26	**CHAPTER 7**		7	13 (7.1A)
26	23	12	10	31	27	**Section 7.1A**		8	6m
27	24	13	11	32	28	**8th ed.**	**7th ed.**	9	7m
28	25	14	12	33	29	1	1	10	8
29	26	15	14m	34	30	2	2	11	9
30	27	16	13	35	31	3	3	12	New
31	WD 3	17	16	36	32	4	4	13	10m
32	WD 4	18	17	37	33	5	9	14	11
Section 6.2A		19	18	38	New	6	5	15	12
1	1	20	19	39	WD 1	7	6	16	13
2	1B	21	20	40	WD 2	8	7(a)-(c)	17	14
3	2	22	21	**Section 6.3B**		9	8	18	15
4	3	23	22	1	New	10	New	19	16
5	5	24	23	2	1	11	New	20	17
6	6	25	24	3	2	12	10	21	18
7	4	26	25	4	3	13	14m	22	19
8	7	27	26	5	4	14	12	23	20
9	15	28	27	6	New	15	15	24	21
10	8	29	28	7	New	16	16	25	22
11	9	30	29	8	5	17	17	26	23
12	10	31	WD 3	9	New	18	18	27	24
13	11	32	WD 4	10	New	19	19	28	25
14	12	**Section 6.3A**		11	New	20	WD 1	29	26
15	14m	1	New	12	New	21	WD 2	30	27
16	13	2	1	13	8m	**Section 7.1B**		31	28
17	16	3	2	14	19	1	1	32	29
18	17	4	3	15	9m	2	2	33	30
19	18	5	4	16	15	3	3	34	31
20	19	6	16m	17	10m	4	4	35	32
21	20	7	11	18	12	5	New	36	WD 1
22	21	8	5	19	13	6	5	**Section 7.2B**	
23	22	9	6	20	New	7	6	1	1
24	23	10	7	21	18	8	New	2	2
25	24	11	6B	22	17	9	7	3	3
26	25	12	7B	23	14	10	8	4	4
27	26	13	8m	24	20	11	9	5	5

6	11 (7.1B)	21	21	3	3	9	8	14	15
7	13 (7.1B)	22	22	4	4	10	New	15	16m
8	6m	23	23	5	5	11	9	16	17
9	7m	24	24	6	6	12	10	17	18
10	8	25	25	7	New	13	11	18	6
11	9	26	26	8	7	14	12	19	19
12	13	27	27	9	8	15	13	20	20
13	New	28	28	10	9m	16	14	21	21
14	11	29	29	11	New	17	15	22	22
15	12	30	30	12	New	18	16	23	23
16	10	31	31	13	11	19	17	24	24
17	14	32	32	14	12	20	18	25	25
18	15	33	WD 1	15	13	21	19	26	26
19	16	34	WD 2	16	14	22	20	27	27
20	17	**Section 7.3B**		17	15	23	21	28	WD 1
21	18	1	1	18	16	24	22	**Section 8.1B**	
22	19	2	2	19	17	25	23	1	1
23	20	3	3	20	18	26	24	2	2
24	21	4	4	21	19	27	25	3	3
25	22	5	5	22	20	28	26	4	4
26	23	6	6	23	21	29	27	5	5
27	24	7	7	24	22	30	28	6	7
28	25	8	9	25	23	31	29	7	8
29	26	9	8	26	24	32	30	8	9
30	27	10	10	27	25	33	31	9	10
31	28	11	11	28	26	34	32	10	11
32	29	12	12	29	27	35	33	11	12
33	30	13	13	30	28	36	34	12	13
34	31	14	14	31	29	37	35	13	14
35	WD 2	15	15	32	30	38	36	14	15
36	WD 3	16	16	33	31	39	37	15	New
Section 7.3A		17	17	34	32	40	38	16	17
1	1	18	18	35	33	41	39	17	18
2	2	19	19	36	34	42	40	18	6
3	3	20	20	37	35	43	41	19	19
4	4	21	21	38	36	44	WD 3	20	20
5	5	22	22	39	37	**CHAPTER 8**		21	21
6	6	23	23	40	38	**Section 8.1A**		22	22
7	7	24	24	41	39	**8th ed.**	**7th ed.**	23	23
8	9	25	25	42	40	1	1	24	24
9	8	26	26	43	41	2	2	25	25
10	10	27	27	44	WD 1	3	3	26	26
11	11	28	28	45	WD 2	4	4	27	WD 2
12	12	29	29	**Section 7.4B**		5	5	28	WD 3
13	13	30	30	1	1	6	7	**Section 8.2A**	
14	14	31	31	2	2	7	8	1	1
15	15	32	32	3	3	8	9	2	2
16	16	33	33	4	4	9	10	3	3
17	17	34	WD 3	5	5	10	11	4	4
18	18	**Section 7.4A**		6	6	11	12	5	5
19	19	1	1	7	10A	12	13	6	8
20	20	2	2	8	7	13	14	7	New

8	9	21	20	**Section 9.1B**		18	15	28	25
9	10	22	21	1	1	19	16	29	26
10	11	23	22	2	3	20	17	30	27
11	6	24	23	3	4	21	18	31	28
12	7	25	24	4	5	22	21	32	29
13	12	26	25	5	2	23	19	33	30
14	13	27	26	6	6	24	20	34	31
15	14	28	27	7	7	25	22	35	32
16	15	29	28	8	8	26	23	36	33
17	16	30	29	9	9	27	24	37	34
18	17m	31	30	10	10	28	25	38	35
19	18	32	31	11	11m	29	26	39	36
20	19	33	32	12	21A	30	27	40	37
21	20	34	33	13	12	31	28	41	WD 2
22	21	35	34	14	13	32	28	42	WD 3
23	22	36	35	15	14	33	30	**Section 9.3A**	
24	23	37	WD 3	16	15	34	31	1	New
25	24	**CHAPTER 9**		17	16	35	32	2	2
26	25	**Section 9.1A**		18	17	36	33	3	3
27	26	**8th ed.**	**7th ed.**	19	18	37	34	4	5
28	27	1	1	20	19	38	35	5	6
29	28	2	5	21	20	39	36	6	7
30	29	3	2	22	22	40	37	7	8
31	30	4	3	23	23	41	WD 1	8	10
32	31	5	4	24	24	**Section 9.2B**		9	11
33	32	6	6	25	25	1	1	10	12
34	33	7	7	26	26	2	2	11	13
35	32	8	8	27	27	3	10	12	14
36	35	9	9	28	28	4	New	13	15
37	WD 1	10	10	29	29	5	11	14	16m
38	WD 2	11	11m	30	30	6	6	15	9
Section 8.2B		12	12	31	31	7	8	16	17
1	1	13	21B	32	32	8	New	17	18
2	2	14	13	33	WD 3	9	7	18	4
3	3	15	14	**Section 9.2A**		10	New	19	19
4	4	16	15	1	1	11	3	20	20
5	5	17	16	2	2	12	4	21	21
6	8	18	17	3	New	13	5	22	22
7	9m	19	18	4	10	14	New	23	23
8	New	20	19	5	11	15	New	24	New
9	10	21	20	6	New	16	13	25	WD 1
10	11	22	22	7	8	17	14	**Section 9.3B**	
11	6	23	23	8	6	18	15	1	1
12	7	24	24	9	7	19	16	2	2
13	12	25	25	10	New	20	17	3	3
14	13	26	26	11	3	21	18	4	5
15	14	27	27	12	4	22	21	5	6
16	15	28	28	13	5	23	19	6	7
17	16	29	29	14	12	24	20	7	8
18	17	30	30	15	12B m	25	22	8	10
19	18	31	WD 1	16	13	26	23	9	11
20	19	32	WD 2	17	14	27	24	10	12

11	13	3	3	1	1m	29	25	19	14
12	14	4	4	2	2m	30	26	20	New
13	15m	5	7	3	New	31	27	21	17m
14	16	6	8	4	6	32	WD 3	22	16
15	9	7	9m	5	7	**CHAPTER 11**		23	18
16	17	8	10	6	8	**Section 11.1A**		24	19
17	18	9	11	7	5	**8th ed.**	**7th ed.**	25	20
18	4	10	12	8	4	1	1	26	WD 3
19	19	11	5m	9	3	2	2	27	WD 4
20	20	12	6m	10	WD 3	3	3	**Section 11.2A**	
21	21	13	13	11	11	4	4	1	1
22	22	14	14	12	10	5	5	2	2
23	23	15	15	13	12	6	6	3	3m
24	24	16	16	14	13	7	7	4	4
25	WD 2	17	17	15	9	8	New	5	New
26	WD 3	18	New	16	14	9	New	6	5
CHAPTER 10		19	18m	17	15	10	New	7	New
Section 10.1A		20	19	18	16	11	New	8	6
8th ed.	**7th ed.**	21	20m	19	17	12	9	9	7
1	1	22	21	20	18	13	10	10	8
2	2	23	22	21	19	14	10B m	11	New
3	3	24	23m	22	New	15	12	12	New
4	4	25	24	23	New	16	13	13	9
5	7	26	25	**Section 10.3A**		17	14	14	10
6	8m	27	26	1	1	18	15	15	11
7	9m	28	27	2	2m	19	16m	16	12
8	10	29	WD 3	3	3	20	17	17	13
9	11	30	WD 4	4	New	21	New	18	14
10	12	**Section 10.2A**		5	4	22	18	19	15
11	5	1	1m	6	5	23	19	20	16
12	6	2	2	7	6	24	20	21	17
13	13	3	5m	8	7m	25	WD 1	22	18
14	14	4	6m	9	New	26	WD 2	23	19
15	15	5	7m	10	8	**Section 11.1B**		24	20
16	16	6	8m	11	9	1	1	25	21
17	17	7	9	12	10A	2	2	26	22
18	New	8	3	13	11	3	3	27	WD 1
19	18m	9	4	14	12,	4	4	28	WD 2
20	19m	10	WD 1	15	13m	5	5	**Section 11.2B**	
21	20m	11	11	16	14A	6	6m	1	1
22	21m	12	10	17	New	7	7	2	2
23	22m	13	12	18	New	8	New	3	New
24	23	14	13	19	17	9	11m	4	4
25	24	15	14	20	14	10	9	5	3
26	25m	16	15	21	16m	11	11m	6	5
27	26	17	16	22	18	12	New	7	New
28	27	18	17	23	19	13	9	8	6
29	WD 1	19	18	24	20	14	New	9	7
30	WD 2	20	19	25	21	15	12	10	8
Section 10.1B		21	20	26	22	16	13	11	New
1	1m	22	WD 2	27	23	17	New	12	New
2	2	**Section 10.2B**		28	24	18	14	13	9

14	10	7	New	28	25	14	1	2	New
15	11	8	5	29	26	15	2	3	3m
16	12	9	7	30	27B	16	13	4	4
17	13	10	8	31	WD 1	17	14	5	New
18	14	11	New	**Section 11.4B**		18	15	6	New
19	15	12	New	1	1	19	16	7	5
20	16	13	New	2	2	20	17	8	New
21	17	14	10	3	3	21	WD 1	9	6
22	18	15	9	4	4	**Section 12.1B**		10	7
23	19	16	4	5	New	1	New	11	8
24	20	17	11	6	5m	2	New	12	9
25	21	18	12	7	6	3	New	13	10
26	22	19	13	8	7	4	3	14	11
27	23	20	14	9	9A	5	4	15	12
28	WD 3	21	15	10	9	6	6	16	13
Section 11.3A		22	16	11	10	7	7	17	New
1	New	23	17	12	11A	8	8	18	WD 3
2	New	24	18	13	11m	9	9	**Section 12.3A**	
3	New	25	19	14	12m	10	10	1	New
4	New	26	20	15	13	11	5	2	New
5	New	27	21	16	14	12	11	3	1m
6	3	28	22	17	15	13	12	4	2
7	4	29	WD 2	18	16	14	1	5	6
8	New	30	WD 3	19	17	15	2	6	New
9	5	**Section 11.4A**		20	18	16	13	7	5
10	8	1	1	21	New	17	14	8	3
11	New	2	2	22	20	18	15	9	4
12	7	3	3	23	21	19	16	10	7
13	New	4	4	24	22	20	17	11	8
14	10	5	5	25	23	21	WD 2	12	9
15	6m	6	New	26	24m	22	WD 3	13	10
16	11	7	6	27	25	**Section 12.2A**		14	11
17	12	8	7	28	26	1	New	15	12
18	13	9	8	29	28	2	2m	16	13
19	14	10	8B	30	29	3	New	17	14
20	15	11	10	31	WD 2	4	4	18	15
21	16	12	12	32	WD 3	5	New	19	16m
22	17	13	New	**CHAPTER 12**		6	New	20	WD 1
23	18	14	New	**Section 12.1A**		7	5	21	WD 2
24	19	15	13	1	New	8	New	**Section 12.3B**	
25	20	16	14	2	New	9	6	1	New
26	21	17	15	3	New	10	7	2	1m
27	22	18	16	4	3	11	8	3	New
28	23	19	17	5	4	12	9	4	2
29	WD 1	20	18	6	6	13	10	5	6
Section 11.3B		21	19m	7	7	14	11	6	New
1	New	22	20	8	8	15	12	7	5
2	New	23	19B	9	9	16	13	8	3
3	New	24	21	10	10	17	WD 1	9	4
4	New	25	22	11	5	18	WD 2	10	7
5	3m	26	23	12	11	**Section 12.2B**		11	8
6	6	27	24	13	12	1	2m	12	9

13	10	22	19	22	18	14	10	31	29
14	11	23	20	23	19	15	15m	32	30
15	12	24	21	24	20	16	3	33	15
16	13	25	WD 1	25	21	17	16	34	WD 3
17	14	**Section 12.4B**		26	22	18	17m	**Section 13.2A**	
18	15	1	1	27	WD 1	19	18m	1	1
19	16m	2	2	28	WD 2	20	17B	2	2B
20	WD 1	3	New	**Section 12.5B**		21	19	3	3
21	WD 2	4	5	1	New	22	20	4	4B
Section 12.3B		5	6m	2	12m	23	21	5	5
1	New	6	3m	3	New	24	22	6	8B
2	1m	7	New	4	6	25	23	7	6
3	New	8	New	5	7	26	24	8	7
4	2	9	4m	6	8	27	25	9	9
5	6	10	7	7	9	28	26	10	13
6	New	11	9	8	10m	29	27	11	New
7	5	12	10	9	11	30	28	12	New
8	3	13	New	10	13	31	29	13	New
9	4	14	12	11	14	32	30	14	10
10	7	15	14A	12	New	33	WD 1	15	14
11	8	16	14	13	15	34	WD 2	16	15
12	9	17	8	14	New	**Section 13.1B**		17	New
13	10	18	15	15	1	1	New	18	16
14	11	19	16	16	2	2	1	19	12
15	12	20	17	17	3	3	2	20	17
16	13	21	18	18	4m	4	11	21	18
17	14	22	19	19	5m	5	12	22	New
18	15	23	20	20	17	6	13	23	19
19	16	24	WD 2	21	18	7	14	24	20
20	WD 3	25	WD 3	22	19	8	4	25	21
Section 12.4A		**Section 12.5A**		23	20	9	5	26	22
1	1	1	New	24	21	10	6	27	23
2	2	2	12	25	22	11	7	28	24
3	3m	3	New	26	23	12	8	29	25
4	New	4	6	27	24	13	9	30	26
5	New	5	7	28	WD 3	14	10	31	27
6	New	6	8m	**CHAPTER 13**		15	New	32	28
7	6m	7	9	**Section 13.1A**		16	3	33	29
8	4m	8	10	8th ed.	7th ed.	17	16	34	30
9	New	9	11	1	New	18	New	35	31
10	7	10	13	2	1	19	New	36	32
11	8	11	14	3	2	20	18	37	33
12	10	12	New	4	11	21	19	38	34
13	11m	13	15	5	12	22	20	39	35
14	12	14	16m	6	13	23	21	40	36
15	13	15	16B	7	14	24	22	41	37
16	13B	16	1	8	4	25	23	42	38
17	9	17	2	9	5	26	24	43	New
18	15	18	3	10	6	27	25	44	WD 1
19	16	19	4	11	7	28	26	45	WD 2
20	17	20	5	12	8	29	27	**Section 13.2B**	
21	18	21	17	13	9	30	28	1	1

2	2A	8	New	15	9	**CHAPTER 14**		8	New
3	3	9	7	16	10	**Section 14.1A**		9	5
4	4A	10	3	17	11	**8TH ed.**	**7th ed.**	10	6
5	5	11	New	18	12	1	1	11	7
6	8	12	8	19	13	2	2	12	8
7	6	13	9	20	14	3	3(a)	13	9
8	7	14	10	21	15	4	6	14	10
9	8	15	11	22	16	5	New	15	11
10	13	16	12	23	17	6	6B	16	12
11	New	17	13	24	18	7	New	17	13
12	New	18	14	25	19	8	7	18	14
13	New	19	15	26	20	9	4	19	15
14	10(ii)	20	16	27	21	10	5	20	16
15	14	21	WD 1	28	22	11	10	21	17
16	15	22	WD 2	29	23	12	8	22	18
17	New	**Section 13.3B**		30	24	13	9	23	19
18	16	1	1m	31	25	14	11	24	WD 1
19	12	2	New	32	WD 1	15	12	**Section 14.2B**	
20	17	3	6	**Section 13.4B**		16	3	1	1m
21	18	4	New	1	1m	17	14	2	2(a),(b)
22	New	5	4	2	New	18	15	3	2(c),(d)
23	19	6	New	3	New	19	New	4	4
24	20	7	New	4	New	20	WD 1	5	3
25	21	8	2m	5	3	**Section 14.1B**		6	New
26	22	9	7	6	2m	1	1	7	New
27	23	10	3	7	New	2	2	8	New
28	24	11	New	8	New	3	3(b)	9	5
29	25	12	8	9	New	4	New	10	6
30	26	13	9	10	4	5	New	11	7
31	27	14	10	11	5	6	8	12	8
32	28	15	11	12	7	7	New	13	9
33	29	16	12	13	8	8	7	14	10
34	30	17	13	14	9	9	4	15	11
35	31	18	14	15	10	10	5	16	12
36	32	19	15	16	11	11	10m	17	13
37	33	20	16	17	12	12	9	18	14
38	34	21	WD 3	18	13	13	New	19	15
39	35	**Section 13.4A**		19	14	14	11	20	16
40	36	1	1m	20	15	15	12	21	17
41	37	2	New	21	16	16	13	22	18
42	38	3	New	22	17	17	14	23	19
43	11	4	New	23	18	18	15	24	WD 2
44	New	5	3	24	19	19	WD 2	25	WD 3
45	WD 3	6	2m	25	20	20	WD 3	**Section 14.3A**	
Section 13.3A		7	New	26	21	**Section 14.2A**		1	New
1	1m	8	New	27	22	1	1m	2	New
2	5m	9	New	28	23	2	2(a),(b)	3	1m
3	6	10	4	29	24	3	2(c),(d)	4	2m
4	New	11	5	30	25	4	4	5	3
5	4	12	6	31	WD 2	5	New	6	4
6	2m	13	7	32	WD 3	6	New	7	New
7	5B m	14	8			7	New	8	5

9	6	15	12	16	New	9	New	3	3
10	New	16	13	17	New	10	New	4	4
11	New	17	14	18	13	11	7m	5	5
12	New	18	15	19	15	12	4	6	6
13	7	19	16	20	16	13	8	7	7
14	8	20	17	21	17	14	13m	8	8
15	10	21	WD 2	22	18	15	14m	9	New
16	11	22	WD 3	23	19	16	15	10	9
17	12	**CHAPTER 15**		24	20	17	16	11	10
18	13	**Section 15.1A**		25	WD 3	18	17	12	11
19	14	**7th ed.**	**8th ed.**	**Section 15.2A**		19	18	13	12
20	15	1	1	1	1m	20	19	14	13
21	16	2	2	2	New	21	20	15	14
22	17	3	3	3	New	22	22	16	15
23	WD 3	4	4	4	2m	23	10	17	116
Section 14.4A		5	5m	5	3m	24	11	18	17
1	1	6	New	6	5m	25	12	19	18
2	3	7	7	7	9	26	23	20	19
3	4m	8	6m	8	6	27	24	21	21
4	3B	9	8m	9	New	28	25	22	21
5	5	10	12	10	7m	29	26	23	WD 3
6	5B	11	9	11	New	30	27	**CHAPTER 16**	
7	9	12	New	12	4	31	21	**Section 16.1A**	
8	7	13	10	13	8	32	WD 2	**8th ed.**	**7th ed.**
9	11	14	11	14	13	33	WD 3	1	1
10	New	15	13m	15	14	**Section 15.3A**		2	2
11	12,13	16	14m	16	15	1	1	3	3
12	New	17	15	17	16	2	2	4	4
13	8	18	New	18	17	3	3	5	5
14	9B	19	16	19	18	4	4	6	6m
15	14	20	17	20	19	5	5	7	New
16	15	21	18	21	20	6	6	8	8m
17	16	22	19	22	21	7	7	9	New
18	17	23	20	23	10	8	8	10	9
19	18	24	WD 1	24	11	9	9	11	10
20	19	25	WD 2	25	12	10	10m	12	11m
21	WD 1	**Section 15.1B**		26	23	11	11	13	11B m
Section 14.4B		1	1	27	24m	12	12	14	12
1	1m	2	2	28	25	13	13m	15	13
2	New	3	3	29	26	14	14	16	14
3	New	4	4	30	27	15	15	17	15
4	2	5	New	31	22	16	16	18	16
5	6A	6	5	32	WD 1	17	17	19	17
6	New	7	7	**Section 15.2B**		18	18	20	18
7	10A m	8	6m	1	New	19	19	21	19
8	4	9	New	2	1m	20	20	22	20
9	8	10	12	3	2m	21	21	23	21
10	New	11	9	4	New	22	WD 1	24	22
11	10m	12	8m	5	3m	23	WD 2	25	23
12	New	13	10	6	New	**Section 15.3B**		26	24
13	6m	14	11	7	5	1	1	27	25
14	11m	15	New	8	6	2	2	28	26

27	25	11	11	7	4
28	26	12	12	8	New
29	27	13	13	9	8
30	28	14	14	10	9
31	New	15	15	11	10
32	WD 1	16	16	12	11
Section 16.1B		18	17	17	13
1	1m	18	18	14	13
2	2m	19	19	15	14
3	3	20	20	16	WD 1
4	4m	21	21	**Section 16.3B**	
5	5	22	22	1	1
6	6m	23	23	2	2
7	7	24	24	3	3
8	New	25	25	4	4
9	8m	26	WD 1	7	5
10	9	**Section 16.2B**		6	6
11	10	1	1	7	7
12	New	2	2	8	8
13	New	3	3	9	9
14	12	4	4	10	10
15	13	5	5	11	11
16	14	6	6	12	12
17	15	7	7	13	13
18	16	8	8	14	14
19	17	9	9	15	15
20	18m	10	10	16	WD 2
21	19	11	11m	17	WD 3
22	20	12	12		
23	21	13	13		
24	22	14	14		
25	23	15	15		
26	24	16	16		
27	25	17	17		
28	26	18	18		
29	27	19	19		
30	28	20	20		
31	29	21	21		
32	WD 2	22	22		
33	WD 3	23	23		
Section 16.2A		25	24		
1	1	25	25		
2	2	26	WD 2		
3	3	27	WD 3		
4	4	**Section 16.3A**			
5	5	1	5		
6	6	2	6		
7	7	3	7		
8	8	4	1		
9	9	5	2		
10	10	6	3		

Starting Point Solutions

Section 1.1: Starting Point
There are several possible approaches. Algebra may be the preferred approach. However, some students may use guess and test and/or make a table. The correct answer is 13 yards by 6 yards.

Section 1.2: Starting Point
One way of keeping track of the rectangles is to use one of the vertices of the set of rectangles. For example, the left upper vertex is the upper left hand corner of 12 different rectangles. Moving to the right, the various vertices have 10, 8, 6, 4, 2 rectangles. Moving down to the middle line and repeating, there are 6, 5, 4, 3, 2, 1 rectangles. In all, there are $12 + 10 + 8 + 6 + 4 + 2 + 6 + 5 + 4 + 3 + 2 + 1 = 63$ rectangles.

Section 2.1: Starting Point
The students in the shaded region will be those with curly hair that don't have brown eyes and don't have brown hair. A person whose name is not in any of the circles has none of the attributes: brown eyes, brown hair, curly hair.

Section 2.2: Starting Point
Answers will vary. Students may use various groupings like in the Egyptian and Roman systems. For example, one symbol could be a one, one a six, and the third a twelve. Then, these symbols be would written repeatedly and the absence of any symbols would represent zero.

Section 2.3: Starting Point
$68 = 2Q + 3N + 3P$, 8 coins; $39 = 1Q + 2N + 4P$, 7 coins; $83 = 3Q + 1N + 3P$, 7 coins; $97 = 3Q + 4N + 2P$, 9 coins.
The minimum number of nickels would be four since if there were 5, the student would exchange them for a quarter and then have fewer coins. The process of exchanging for a minimum number of coins is similar to the carrying process used in base 5 numbers. Any amount of money less than $1.25 can be represented with a maximum of 4 of each type of coin.

Section 2.4: Starting Point
Various relationships are possible. One relationship would associate the numbers 2, 3, 4, and 5 with any of their multiples. Another is to associate the numbers 2, 3, 4, and 5 with the numbers 12, 3, 24, and 15 because they have the same one's digits.

Section 3.1: Starting Point
To find 7 + 2, one possibility is that the student would say 7 and then count 8-9. To find 2 + 7, the student may say 2 and then count 3-4-5-6-7-8-9. To the student, there is clearly a difference in these two problems.

However, by using objects, the student will be able to see the similarity and, in this way, discover commutativity.

Section 3.2: Starting Point
In Joshua's case, he may think as follows: 12 – 3 = 9, 9 – 3 = 6, 6 – 3 = 3, 3 – 3 = 0. Thus, there are four 3s in 12. On the other hand, Emily may think about distributing the loaves to the neighbors one at a time until the twelve loaves were gone. She would find that each neighbor would end up with four loaves.

Section 3.3: Starting Point
Although counting number exponents are usually viewed as a shortcut for multiplication, 4^0 does not mean 4×0 just like 4^2 does not mean 4×2. To decide what 4^0 should be, consider the pattern $4^3 = 64$, $4^2 = 16$, $4^1 = 4$. Notice that if we divide the answer 64 by 4, we get the answer 16. Also, 16 divided by 4 is 4. So, continuing the pattern, 4 divided by 4, or 1, would suggest that $4^0 = 1$.

Section 4.1: Starting Point
Answers may vary. $32 \cdot 26 - 23 \cdot 32 = 32(26 - 23) = 32 \cdot 3 = 96$. Commutativity for multiplication and distributivity.
$(16 \times 9) \times 25 = (16 \times 25) \times 9 = 400 \times 9 = 3600$, Commutativity and associativity for multiplication.
$25 + (39 + 105) = (39 + 105) + 25 = 39 + (105 + 25) = 39 + 130 = 169$. Commutativity for addition and associativity for addition.
$49 + 27 = 50 + 26 = 76$. Associativity for addition.
$152 - 87 = 155 - 90 = 65$. Equal additions.
$46 \times 99 = 46(100 - 1) = 4600 - 46 = 4554$. Distributivity.
$252 \div 12 = (240 \div 12) + (12 \div 12) = 20 + 1 = 21$. Right distributivity of division over addition.

Section 4.2: Starting Point
Nick shows the best understanding of place value. He adds the tens, then the ones. Trevor shows the least understanding, but he is good at applying the common addition algorithm. Courtney also has a very good understanding of place value. Which one is best? All three methods are good methods. Trevor's is likely the most efficient in the long run, but the other two are likely the most meaningful for students.

Section 4.3: Starting Point
To find $34_{seven} + 65_{seven}$, think in terms of base seven blocks. Three longs plus six longs equals one flat plus two longs. Four units plus five units equals one long plus two units. Thus, we have one flat, three longs, and two units, or 132_{seven}.

Section 5.1: Starting Point

12 Squares   13 squares

More rectangles can be made with 12 squares than with 13 because 12 has more factors than 13. The dimensions of the rectangles are the various factors of the two numbers.

12: 12×1, 6×2, 4×3, shows that 12 has six factors.

13: 13×1, shows that 13 has two factors.

Section 5.2: Starting Point

The only lockers that will be open after all 1000 students entered the school are the those with perfect square numbers on them: 1, 4, 9, 16, 25, 36, ..., 961. This is because, to be open at the end, a locker must have been "changed" by an odd number of students. Thus, lockers with numbers with an odd number of factors will be open – these are the perfect squares. To see why, consider listing the factors of numbers in pairs. Since the "middle pair" of factors for a perfect square is the same number listed twice, there are odd number of factors for perfect squares. For example, 16 has factor pairs of (1, 16), (2, 8), (4, 4). When the factors of 16 are listed - 1, 2, 4, 8, 16 - it can be seen that there are an odd number of factors because 4 is only listed once.

Section 6.1: Starting Point

1. The amount shaded in the circle on the left is larger than the amount shaded in the circle on the right. Thus, the student may think that $\frac{2}{3} > \frac{3}{4}$. To compare fractions, the whole must be the same size.

2. A student may not think that the shaded regions are 'equal' since they are different shapes.

3. A student may think that the shaded region in the triangle on the right represents $\frac{1}{3}$ of the triangle since it is one of three parts. A student may misunderstand the need for having "equal" parts.

Section 6.2: Starting Point

If the two shaded regions are added, they will exceed one whole rectangle. However, $\frac{4}{6}$ is less than one rectangle. Thus, $\frac{3}{4} + \frac{1}{2}$ cannot be equal to $\frac{4}{6}$.

Section 6.3: Starting Point

a) If I have three whole pizzas and I think each person who comes for dinner will eat half of a pizza, how many people can I feed?

b) If one-third of Ricardo's birthday cake is divided evenly among four people, how much of the whole cake did each person get?

c) Chiara has $\frac{5}{8}$ of a gallon of paint and it takes one-fourth of a gallon to paint a door. How many doors can Chiara paint?

Section 7.1: Starting Point

Let the block represent one. Then, a flat is .1 of the block since 10 flats make a block. The symbol .10 represents 10 longs, which is equal to one flat. The symbol .100 represents 100 units, which is one flat. Thus, .1 = .10 = .100.

Section 7.2: Starting Point

Consider the problem 0.2 × 0.1. The result is 0.02, which is smaller than either factor. Similarly, 0.2 ÷ 0.1 = 2 and 2 is larger than either 0.2 or 0.1. The reason for the misconceptions is that the rules 'multiplication makes bigger' and 'division makes smaller' are true for all counting numbers greater than 1. It is when 1, 0, and fractions/decimals between 0 and 1 are considered that the rules are no longer valid.

Section 7.3: Starting Point

Piece A is $\frac{1}{3}$ as big as piece B: i) If A is $\frac{1}{3}$ of B and one thinks of B has having three pieces equal to A, then there are 4 equal pieces that make up the entire board so A is $\frac{1}{4}$ of the board. ii) B is three times as big as A. iii) The ratio of A to B is 1 to 3.

Piece A is $\frac{3}{4}$ as big as piece B: i) If piece A is $\frac{3}{4}$ as big as B and one thinks of B as having four pieces, then three of those pieces would be equal to A. Then the whole board would have 7 equal pieces and A would be $\frac{3}{7}$ of the board. ii) B is $\frac{4}{3}$ times as big as A. iii) The ratio of A to B is 3 to 4.

Piece A is $\frac{2}{5}$ as big as piece B: i) If piece A is $\frac{2}{5}$ as big as B and one thinks of B as having five pieces, then two of those pieces would be equal to A. Then the whole board would have 7 equal pieces and A would be $\frac{2}{7}$ of the board. ii) B is $\frac{5}{2}$ times as big as A. iii) The ratio of A to B is 2 to 5.

Section 7.4: Starting Point
Suppose the wholesale price of the jacket is $100. Then, when it is marked up 40%, the retail price is $140. When it is reduced 40% from the retail price, the sale price is $84. The reason that the sale price is less is that the 40% reduction was applied to the retail price.

Section 8.1: Starting Point
-30 + 14: I wrote a check for $30 and deposited $14. Thus, my checking account was -$16 from where I started.

-30 – 14: I wrote a check for $30 and deleted $14 that I had mistakenly written in as a deposit. Thus, my checking account was -$44 from where I started.

-30 + (-14): I wrote one check for $30 and a second check for $14. Thus, my checking account was -$44 from where it started.

Section 8.2: Starting Point
Consider $7^3 \div 7^5 = \dfrac{7^3}{7^5} = \dfrac{1}{7^2}$ but according to the previous properties of exponents, $7^3 \div 7^5 = 7^{3-5} = 7^{-2}$ so it should be the case that $7^{-2} = \dfrac{1}{7^2}$. Similarly, consider $7^2 \times 7^{-2}$. Their product should be $7^{2+(-2)} = 7^0 = 1$. Thus, $7^{-2} = \dfrac{1}{7^2}$.

Section 9.1: Starting Point
Answers may vary. Using the number line, -(2/3) can be thought of as the point two-thirds of the way from 0 to –1. The number (-2)/3 can be thought of one-third of the way from 0 to –2 on the number line which is the same point in both cases.

Section 9.2: Starting Point
Two examples are 0.1011011101111011111....
and 0.1234567891011121314151617181920212223.....

Section 9.3: Starting Point
Tanika starts going downhill and is coasting, but not quite on level ground. Marcelle began going down a steep hill, which became a more gradual downhill until she finally was going on the level.

Section 10.1: Starting Point

By simply arranging the lists in increasing order, one can see that it is likely that University B has more students that live nearer to their parents and that, perhaps, University A has more out-of-state students.

Section 10.2: Starting Point

The graph on the left is a bar graph and the one on the right is a line graph. The line graph seems to show a dramatic decrease in the number of crimes. However, this is because the vertical scale starts at 23. Mayor Marcus would use the line graph to show how crime has fallen dramatically during his reign. On the other hand, Councilwoman Claudia would display the bar graph to show that the crime rate is down very modestly since the bars are only slightly different in length.

Section 10.3: Starting Point

Once, again, arrange the two lists in increasing order. Team 1 has the tallest two players, while team 2 has the two shortest players. Both teams have the same average (mean). These factors would indicate that team 1 is taller. However, both teams have players of height 65, 66 and 67 inches and team 2 has 5 players taller than these three and team 1 has only 3 players taller than these three. This contributes to team 2 having both a taller median and mode.

Section 11.1: Starting Point

The way to determine this is to list all possible draws and to compare the number of ones that have a red with the total number of draws. All possible draws are:

RR   RW   RB
WR   WW   WB
BR   BW   BB

Of these, five have a red. Thus, the probability of having a red is $\dfrac{5}{9}$.

Section 11.2: Starting Point

This one may seem to be the same as the Starting Point for section 11.1 but the existence of two identical red cubes makes it quite different. Although the red cubes are indistinguishable, they do represent distinct outcomes. Thus all possible outcomes are:

RR   RR   RW   RB
RR   RR   RW   RB
WR   WR   WW   WB
BR   BR   BW   BB

To better see these distinct outcomes, we can label one red cube R1 and the other one R2. Then the possible outcomes would look like the following:

R1R1   R1R2   R1W   R1B

R2R1	R2R2	R2W	R2B
WR1	WR2	WW	WB
BR1	BR2	BW	BB

Since there are 16 total outcomes with 4 that consist of a Red and a Blue, the probability of a Red and a Blue is $\frac{4}{16} = \frac{1}{4}$.

Section 11.3: Starting Point

This problem can be solved by considering all different combinations of the letters R and B, or equivalently, how many different possibilities of H and T (for R and B) are there when tossing four coins. You can first break the problem into the combinations of 4 Reds, 3 Reds and 1 Blue, 2 Reds and 2 Blues, 1 Red and 3 Blues, and 4 Blues. We can the rearrange each of these combinations to form different towers for a total of 16 different towers. Pascal's Triangle can also be used to solve this problem. we can see that there are 2^4, or 16, ways.

Section 11.4: Starting Point

This problem can be solve by doing a simulation or using the ideas of expected values. One sample simulation produced an average payment of $9.30. In that case, Sterling should have accepted the $10. If a probability tree diagram is constructed, it can be determined that

$$P(\$2) = \frac{6}{21}, \quad P(\$6) = \frac{4}{21}, \quad P(\$11) = \frac{8}{21}, \quad P(\$15) = \frac{2}{21}, \quad \text{and} \quad P(\$20) = \frac{1}{21}$$

. Thus if Sterling drew from the bag 21 times, would expect to get $2 six times, $6 four times, $11 eight times, $15 two times, and $20 once for a total of $174 over 21 weeks. This would average out to be $8.29 per week. Even though he would make more than $10 over half of the time, it is still a better deal to take the $10.

Section 12.1: Starting Point

There will be a variety of methods used but it should quickly become apparent how important and useful commonly understood vocabulary can be.

Section 12.2: Starting Point

The descriptions and vocabulary will vary but the general idea is that Category 1 figures are convex. The figures in Category 1 an also be described as having the following property: For any two points in the interior of the figure, the line segment having those two points as endpoints lies in the interior of the figure. The figures in Category 2 all contain at least two points which are the endpoints of a segment that does not lie entirely inside of the figure.

Section 12.3: Starting Point

1. Three parallel lines. 2. All three lines intersect in a single point. 3. One line crosses the other two that are parallel. 4. The three lines intersect forming a triangle. 5. Impossible. The most points of intersection for three lines is three points. 6. The lines can be in space, namely, skew lines.

Section 12.4: Starting Point

One way (Option 1) to find the desired sum is to draw two diagonals from any vertex as shown. This creates three triangles whose angles combine to make up the sum of interest. Thus $a + b + c + d + e = 3 \cdot 180 = 540$.

A second approach (Option 2) would be to draw a point anywhere in the interior of the pentagon as shown below. This creates 5 triangles whose combined angles yield the desired sum plus an extra 360 around the interior point. Thus $a + b + c + d + e = 5 \cdot 180 - 360 = 540$.

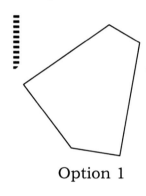
Option 1

Option 2

Section 12.5: Starting Point

There are 6 different possible block stacks that could have the three view shown. The top views of each of those six stacks is shown below with the number representing the number of blocks in each stack.

2	2	1
3	1	2

2	1	1
3	1	2

2	2	
3	1	2

2	1	
3	1	2

2		1
3	1	2

2		
3	1	2

The back view and right side view for all of these stacks are shown below. All 4 views for all 6 stacks would be the same.

Back View

Right Side

Section 13.1: Starting Point
When ordering carpeting, one orders in *square* yards, but when ordering concrete, one orders *cubic* yards.

Section 13.2: Starting Point
1. Area is the amount of a plane that is enclosed in a geometric figure.
2. The reason that squares are used is that they easily fit together along their edges (i.e. they tessellate). 3. Other possible units would be triangles or regular hexagons because they also tessellate.

Section 13.3: Starting Point
First, consider all possible boxes that could hold 24 cubic blocks and then calculate the surface area of each box.

Shape of Box	Surface Area
1 by 1 by 24	98 sq. units
1 by 2 by 12	76 sq. units
1 by 3 by 8	70 sq. units
1 by 4 by 6	68 sq. units
2 by 2 by 6	56 sq. units
2 by 3 by 4	36 sq. units

Thus, the minimum surface area is when the box is 2 by 3 by 4.

Section 13.4: Starting Point
The volume of the new box would be eight times as large as the original box. If the player doubled in height and, perhaps, in all three dimensions, one could expect him to weigh 640 pounds.

Section 14.1: Starting Point
Corey is correct since A and B have the same size and shape. Whitney is incorrect. For the triangles to be equal, they must be the same set of points. However, because they are two distinct triangles they cannot be equal.

Section 14.2: Starting Point
Objects are similar in geometry if they have the same shape but the term similar is used in the English language in a much more general sense.
   a) A volleyball and a basketball are 'similar' in that they are both spherical. However, because of the different makeup of their skins, they are technically not geometrically similar.
   b) A father and his son are not similar in a geometric sense but we may say that they look similar based on our understanding of the English language.
   c) Two squares are similar because they all have the same shape.
   d) The two soda cups are not necessarily the same shape, hence are not similar.

e) The two pieces of paper would be similar if they were the same shape. The fact that there is writing on one of them should not affect the shape.

Section 14.3: Starting Point
Properties of the diagonals of a kite:
1. One diagonal divides the kite into two congruent triangles
2. One diagonal bisects the other.
3. They are perpendicular to each other.
4. One diagonal bisects the vertex angles of the kite.

Properties of the diagonals of a rhombus:
1. They divide the rhombus into two congruent triangles.
2. They bisect each other.
3. They are perpendicular to each other.
4. They bisect the vertex angles of the rhombus.

The diagonals of a rhombus bisect the vertex angles, bisect each other, and create two congruent triangles whereas only one diagonal does this in a kite. These properties play a significant role in the various basic compass and straightedge constructions.

Section 14.4: Starting Point
Points on a perpendicular bisector of a line segment are equidistant from the endpoints of the segment. Thus, if the perpendicular bisectors are constructed to each line segment connecting pairs of cities, the intersection of the three will be equidistant from all three cities.

Section 14.5: Starting Point
Without the crosspiece A, pieces B and C form a parallelogram with two pickets of the gate. As shown with the parallelograms in the box, the gate may be unstable. However, with the crosspiece A in place, the pieces A, B and the right picket form a unique triangle because of the SSS property. Thus the triangle can have only one shape making the gate stable.

Section 15.1: Starting Point
There are three points each of which will form a parallelogram with points A, B, and C. They are (-3,4), (3,-4), (7,2)

Section 15.2: Starting Point
There are infinitely many correct answers. Namely, starting at the point (-1,4) move left 3 units and up 2 units to find the point (-4, 6). Repeat to find (-7,8) and so on. More points can also be found by moving right 3 units and down 2 units to find (2, 2) and (5, 0) and so forth.

Section 15.3: Starting Point
In addition to being perpendicular, the diagonals also bisect each other. To prove this, the midpoint of each of the diagonals can be found and

checked to see if it is the same for both diagonals. The midpoint of *XZ* is (2,1) and the midpoint of *WY* is (2, 1). Thus the diagonals bisect each other.

Section 16.1: Starting Point

ΔABC can be moved to ΔA'B'C' using a turn or a combination of a slide and a turn. ΔDEF can be moved to ΔD'E'F' using a combination of a flip.

Section 16.2: Starting Point

A rotation around the intersection of lines *m* and *l* where the angle of rotation is twice as big and the angle between *l* and *m*.

Section 16.3: Starting Point

Imagine a colored ball being reflected over one of the sides. If the cue ball is aimed at the reflected image, the path of the cue ball should line up exactly with the actual colored ball as shown below.

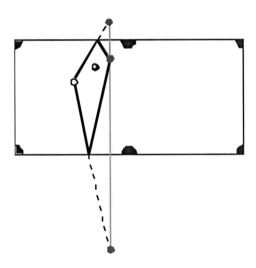

ANSWERS TO EXERCISE/PROBLEM SETS, PART B

Chapter 1

Section 1.1

1. 41,312,432

2. Same number. Let x be your num-ber. The $[([(5x + 8) \times 4 + 9] \times 5) - 105] \div 100 - 1 = [(20x + 32 + 9) \times 5 - 105] \div 100 - 1 = [(100x + 205) - 105] \div 100 - 1 = x$.

3. 15 items

4. Here 12 toothpicks form 5 squares. Remove some to solve the rest of the problem.

5. 78 and 79

6. For example, place 10 in the center. Then place numbers across from each other whose sum is 20.

7. $(6 + 6) \times 6 - 6 = 66$

8. 2520 feet

9. Product must be even since one page must have an even number on it.

10. 2 spares

11. 11 pieces

12. 3 moves

13. Pat: \$68.54, Chris: \$32.46

14. 2178 4 = 8712

15. $n + (n + 1) + (n + 2) + (n + 3) = 4n + 6$, thus the sum of four consecutive counting numbers is even since $4n + 6 = 2(2n + 3)$.

16. Bill

17. Top row: 4 10 6
    Bottom row: 11 16 5

18. Baseball - 0.35 pounds
    Football - 0.9 pounds
    Soccer ball - 1 pound

19. The answer will always be 5.
    Proof: $[(n + n + 1 + 9) \div 2] - n = [(2n + 10) \div 2] - n = n + 5 - n = 5$.

20. In the fifth row, the 3 should be 33.

21. 12 triangles

22. 18 and 22 are impossible. There are multiple possibilities for 19, 20 , and 21.

23.

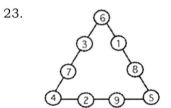

24.

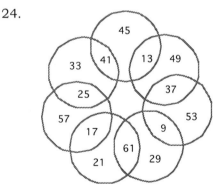

25. Solve the equation $3n - 3 = 87$ to obtain $n = 30$ or 30 dots on each side.

26. Since y is divided by 5 and then 12 is added to that quotient to obtain 23, working backward, we

should subtract 12 from 23 and then multiply that difference by 5.

27. Yes, first graders can do simple algebra. However, a symbol like a space, a box , or a question mark should be used rather than introducing them to a variable.

Problems related to the NCTM Standards and Curriculum Focal Points

1. An appropriate strategy for problem 11 of Set B is "drawing a picture" of cuts on a pizza because that is what the problem is about. Answers may vary.

2. To solve problem 24 of Set A, one might start with a hexagon with 3 dots on a side and then 4 dots on a side in order to generalize the pattern to the case where there are *n* dots on a side. Answer may vary.

3. Problem 13 of set A uses a box to represent a variable. This is one of the initial conceptions of a variable.

Section 1.2

1. (a) 26   (b) $\frac{5}{4}$

    (c) 486   (d) 2347

2. (a)

    (b)

3. (a)

Rectangular Number	Number of Dots in Shape
1	2 = 1·2
2	3 = 2·3
3	12 = 3·4
4	20 = 4·5
5	30 = 5·6
6	42 = 6·7

(b)

(c) 110 dots
(d) 19th number
(e) $n(n+1)$
(f) The *n*th rectangular number is twice the *n*th triangular number.

4. (a)

Pentagonal Number	Number of Dots in Shape
1	1
2	5
3	12
4	22
5	35

(b)

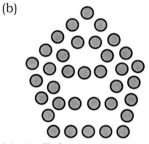

(c) 117 dots
(d) No, the 11th has 176 dots and the 12th has 210 dots.
(e) $1 + 4 + 7 + \ldots + [n + n + (n-2)]$
     $= \dfrac{n(3n-1)}{2}$

5. (a) $12 \to 5 \to 25 \to 29 \to 85 \to$
         $89 \to 145 \to 42 \to 20$
         $\to 4 \to 16 \to 37 \to 58 \to$
         $89 \to$ (a loop begins here)

13 → 10 → 1 etc.

19 → 82 → 68 → 100 → 1 → 1 → etc.

21 → 5 → 25 → (see 12 above)

127 → 54 → 41 → 17 → 50 → 25 → (see 12 above)

(b) The cycle eventually ends when you reach the number 1 or the numbers cycle and 4 is the smallest number obtained. For 13 and 19, the process ends with a 1.

(c) 111 → 3 → 9 → 81 → 65 → 61 → 37 → 58 → 89 → 145 → 42 → 20 → 4 → 16 → 37 → 58 → 89 → (a loop begins here)

6. 35

7. 1 + 49 = 50 and 25 + 25 = 50

8. 220

9. (a) 16 × 10 = 160
   (b) 10,000 × 199 = 1,990,000

10. 1 + 1 + 2 + 3 + . . . + 144 = 377 - 1 = 376

11. (a) Every third term is even, or a term is even if the number of the term is a multiple of 3.
    (b) Fibonacci numbers that are even: F_{51}, F_{150}, F_{300}
    Odd: F_{38}, F_{200}
    (c) Every fourth term is divisible by 3, or a term is divisible by 3 if the number of the term is a multiple of 4.
    (d) Fibonacci numbers that are multiples of 3: F_{48}, F_{196}, F_{1000}
    Not multiples of 3: F_{75}, F_{379}

12. 609

13. (a) 3, 7, 15
    (b) Example: To move 4 disks from the left post to the center

post, the top 3 disks must first be moved to the right post. To move those three disks to the right posts, the top two disks must first be moved to the center post. To move the top two disks to the center post, the top disk must first be moved to the right post. This general reasoning allows one to move the disks in the fewest number of moves.

(c) 63 moves

14. (a) 25 = 10 + 15
    26 = 10 + 15 + 1
    27 = 21 + 6
    28 = 28
    29 = 28 + 1
    30 = 21 + 3 + 6
    31 = 21 + 10
    32 = 21 + 10 + 1
    33 = 15 + 15 + 3
    34 = 28 + 6
    35 = 28 + 6 + 1
    (b) 74 = 36 + 28 + 10
    81 = 66 + 15
    90 = 66 + 21 + 3

15. (a) Products are both equal to 30.
    (b) Products of alternate numbers are always the same.

16. 18, 20, 22, 24, 26, 28, 30

17. (a)

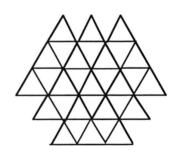

Step 5

Step 6

(b)

Step	Number of Unit Triangles
1	1
2	4
3	10
4	19
5	31
6	46

(c) 64

(d) 136, 571, 3676

18. 13

19. (a) 27   (b) 13   (c) 3^{n-1}

(d) For $n \geq 2$, $3^{n-2} + 3^{n-3} + \ldots + 1$

20. (a) 900   (b) 148   (c) 859

21. (a) 18, 29, 47
     (b) 60, 111, 189

22. A seven can be formed in six different ways, so seven is likeliest to appear.

23. The key idea here is that once the frog jumps out, it won't slip back down the two feet. It will make it out of a five-foot well in three days and out of a twenty-foot well in 18 days. This is an example of the Solve a Simpler Problem strategy.

Problems related to the NCTM Standards and Curriculum Focal Points

1. The additional problem where the strategy "Solve a Simpler Problem" is used is an example of a more sophisticated strategy. In order to solve the original problem, one must first look at simpler cases. Once the simpler cases have been solved, a pattern must be identified and used to solve the original problem. Answers may vary.

2. Answer will vary depending on the individual experiences.

3. If a table and graph are constructed, one can more readily see how the pattern grows.

Day	Pay	Day	Pay
1	1	11	1024
2	2	12	2048
3	4	13	4096
4	8	.	
5	16	.	
6	32	.	
7	64	.	
8	128	n	2^n
9	256		
10	512	31	2^{31}

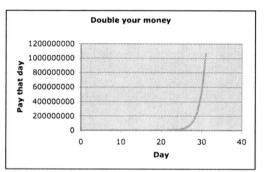

This makes it easier to see the symbolic rule.

Chapter Review

Problems for Writing/Discussion

1. Put the 7 in the middle. Put the even numbers in the four corners with 4 on the same diagonal as 10. Place the remaining odd numbers in the other spaces in such a way that all sums equal 21. Although there may appear to be many different answers, you will find they all "match" in the sense that the numbers around the outside starting with, say, 3 (going clockwise in some answers and counterclockwise in others) will be 8, 9, 4, 11, 6, 5, and 10.

2. There is more than one way. You could fill the 3 gallon container and pour it into the 5 gallon

container. Then fill the 3 gallon container again and pour it into the 5 gallon container until it was full. Then you would have 1 gallon in the 3 gallon container. Empty the 5 gallon container and pour the 1 gallon into it. Then refill the 3 gallon container and pour that into the 5 gallon container. Now there are 4 gallons in the 5 gallon container.

3. Guess and Test:
    30 + 31 + 32 = 93 - too big.
    22 + 23 + 24 = 69 - too small.
    Etc. Make a List:
    22 + 23 + 24 = 69,
    23 + 24 + 25 = 72, etc.
    Use a Variable:
    $x + (x + 1) + (x + 2) = 78$.
    Therefore, $3x + 3 = 78$, or $3x = 75$.
    Thus, the numbers are 25, 26, 27.

4. Three odd integers must add to an odd integer OR
    $x + (x + 2) + (x + 4) = 102$
    which implies $x = 32$, which is not an odd integer.

5. Using a picture, we can illustrate the problem as follows. After designating one section for the $28, the remaining part is divided into 3 equal parts. After taking out two of them for eye shadow, the part left is split into two equal parts, one of which is the lipstick, the other the $12 left.

	eye shadow	
$28	eye shadow	
	lipstick	$12

This illustrates that the lipstick is also $12, the eye shadows cost $24, and the paycheck would be $100.

6. Many possibilities.

7. The sum of the three numbers is always equal to three times the middle number.

8. You might say the sum of the four consecutive (or consecutive odd or consecutive even) numbers is equal to four times the average of the two middle numbers, or two times the sum of the largest and smallest, or four times the average of all four numbers, etc.

9. (a) Not enough information. If the problem contained a second sentence like "One number is 5 more than the other", then it would be solvable.

    (b) The first and second sentences really say the same thing. Again we need to add some additional information such as "The length is 5 more than twice the width."

10. He's out $100; that is, the $20 bill and the $80 pair of shoes that the customer left with.

Chapter 2

Section 2.1

1. (a) {9, 10, 11,...}
    (b) {1, 3, 5, 7, ..., 99}
    (c) { } or Ø

2. (a) $\{x \mid x$ is one of the 50 United States$\}$
    (b) $\{x \mid x$ is a whole number that ends in 1 or 6$\}$
    (c) $\{x \mid x$ is a letter of the alphabet$\}$
    (d) $\{x \mid x$ is an odd number less than 10$\}$

3. (a) F (b) F (c) T (d) T (e) T

4. $1 \rightarrow x$ $1 \rightarrow y$ $1 \rightarrow z$
    $2 \rightarrow y$ $2 \rightarrow z$ $2 \rightarrow w$
    $3 \rightarrow z$ $3 \rightarrow w$ $3 \rightarrow x$
    $4 \rightarrow w$ $4 \rightarrow x$ $4 \rightarrow y$
    There are many other correct correspondences.

5. For example: {1,2,3,4,5,6}

6. (a) No (b) No (c) No (d) No
    (e) No (f) No (g) No (h) Yes

7. { }, { m }, {r}, {o}, {m, r}, {m, o}, {r, o}, {m, r, o}
    All but the last one.

8. 31

9. (a) $\in$ (b) $\subseteq$ or $\subset$
    (c) $\not\subset$, ~   (d) $\in$
    (e) $\subseteq$, ~, =   (f) $\subseteq$ or $\subset$

10. (a) {1, 2, 3, ..., 19}
    (b) {1, 2, 3, ..., 14}

11. (a) Match to {4, 6, 8, ..., $n + 2$, ...}
    (b) Match to {51, 52, 53, 54, ..., $n + 1$, ...}

12. (a) F (b) T (c) F (d) T (e) T
    (f) T

13. (a) T (b) T (c) F

14. (a) True (b) False
    (c) True (d) False

15. (a)
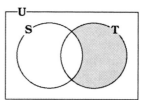

(b)
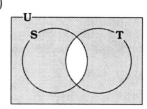

(c)
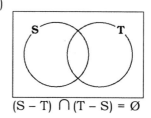

$(S - T) \cap (T - S) = \emptyset$

16. (a)
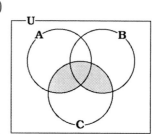

(b)
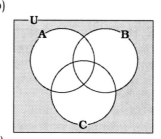

(c)
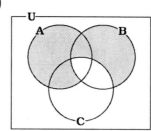

17. (a) $[A - (B \cup C)] \cup [(B \cup C) - A]$
    (b) $(B - C) \cup (A - C) \cup (B \cap C)$
    (c) $(A \cup C) - (B \cap C)$

18. (a)

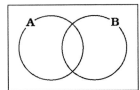

(b)

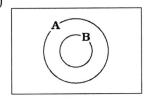

19. (a)

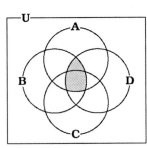

(b)

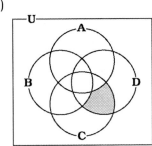

(c)

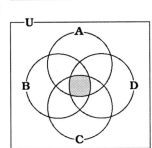

(d)

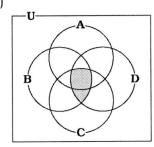

(e)

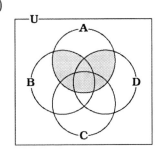

(f)

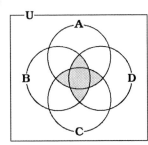

20. (a) $\{a, b, c, d, e, f, g\}$
    (b) $\{c, d, e\}$
    (c) $\{a, e, f\}$ (d) $\{a, b, c, d, e, f\}$

21. (a) Students who are either sophomores or orchestra members
    (b) Sophomores who belong to orchestra
    (c) Sophomores who do not belong to orchestra
    (d) Orchestra members who are not sophomores

22. (a) $\{h, i, j\}$ (b) $\{3,10,13\}$
    (c) {bicycles}
    (d) $\{0,2,4,6,8,10\}$

23. (a) B   (b) $\varnothing$ (c) $\varnothing$

24. (a) $\{a, b, c, d, e, f\}$ (b) $\{c\}$
    (c) $\{a, b, c, x, y, z\}$ (d) $\varnothing$
    (e) $\{c, d, e, f, x, y, z\}$ (f) $\varnothing$
    (g) $\{x, y, z\}$

25. (a) $\{50, 55, 60, 65, 70, 75, \mathbf{80}\}$
    (b) $\{60, 70, 80\}$ (c) $\{60, 70, 80\}$
    (d) $\{60, 70, 80\}$ (e) $\{50\}$ (f) $\{\mathbf{50}\}$

26. (a) Yes, because $X \cap Y \subseteq X \cup Y$
    (b) No, because x may be an element of $X - Y$ or $Y - X$.

27. (a) $\overline{A \cap B} = \overline{A} \cup \overline{B} =$
         {2, 6, 10, 12, 14}
         Yes, the sets are the same.

     (b) $\overline{A \cap B}$ and $\overline{A} \cup \overline{B}$ are both
         represented by:

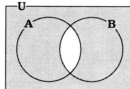

         Yes, the diagrams are the
         same.

28. (a) {(*a*, 1), (*b*, 1), (*c*, 1)}
     (b) {(1, *p*), (1, *q*), (1, *r*), (2, *p*), (2, *q*),
         (2, *r*)}
     (c) {(*p*, 1), (*p*, 2), (*q*, 1), (*q*, 2), (*r*, 1),
         (*r*, 2)}
     (d) {(*a*, 1)}

29. (a) 4   (b) 8   (c) 21

30. (a) $\{a\} \times \{b\}$ (b) $\{1, 2\}$
     (c) $\{d\} \times \{e, f, g\}$ (d) $\{3, 4\} \times \{5, 6\}$
     (e) $\{g\} \times \{v, w, x, y, z\}$
     (f) $\{1, 2\} \times \{3, 4, 5\}$
     (g) $\{512\} \times \{10, 11, 122, 205, 197,$
         $20, 21\}$
     (h) $\{ \ \} \times \{ \ \}$

31. (a) X = {*b*, *c*} , Y = {*c*}
     (b) X = {2, 5} , Y = {1, 2, 3}

32. (a) F   (b) F   (c) F   (d) T

33. (a) 2   (b) 24   (c) 720
     (d) $m (m - 1)(m - 2) \cdots (2)(1)$

34. (a) A, B not disjoint
     (b) not possible
     (c) E, F disjoint
     (d) G and K are empty sets.

35. 105

36. Rays whose endpoints are the
     center of the circle produce a 1-1
     correspondence between the circle
     and the triangle.

37. Rays whose endpoints are some
     point P in the interior of the

triangle produce a 1-1
correspondence between the circle
and the triangle.

38. $13 \times 12 \times 11 \times \cdots \times 1$

39. (a) 16   (b) 25   (c) 2

40. (a) 7 cars (b) 23 cars (c) 16 cars

41. 10 %

42. If two sets are equal, they have the
     same elements. Therefore, they
     have the same *number* of
     elements. Hence, they are
     equivalent. However, if two sets
     are equivalent, it means they have
     the same *number* of elements, not
     the *same* elements. Therefore,
     they could be, but are not
     necessarily, equal.

43. Since A is a proper subset of B, all
     its elements are elements of B.
     Since it is a *proper* subset, there
     must be at least one element of B
     which is not in A. Therefore, B
     must have at least 24 elements.

**Problems related to the NCTM
Standards and Curriculum Focal Points**

1. Young students must learn the 1-
    1 correspondence between the
    spoken words – one, two, three,
    four, ... - and the objects at which
    they are pointing. If the 1-1
    correspondence isn't maintained,
    they aren't counting objects, they
    are just reciting words.

2. Two sets are equivalent if there is
    a 1-1 correspondence between
    them. Another way to think about
    finite sets being equivalent is if
    they have the same number of
    objects. Thus, if one knows "how
    many" are in each of the two sets,
    they then know if the sets are
    equivalent.

3. Venn diagrams are used to show
    the relationships between the
    elements of sets. Thus if a

problem requires knowing what is common between two sets, the region on the Venn diagram representing the intersection can be used to solve the problem.

Section 2.2

1. Answers will vary but here are three examples.
   (a) A total of 45 students attended a meeting.
   (b) Bob was the 45th customer to enter the store.
   (c) Katy wore number 45 on her softball jersey.

2. (a) Numeral (b) Number
   (c) Numeral (d) Number

3. (a) Cannot be used because the sets do not match.
   (b) Cannot be used; the sets are equivalent but we don't begin counting elements with 0.
   (c) Should be used; it is an equivalent set using consecutive counting numbers beginning with 1.

4. Number. A numeral is a symbo; a number is an idea.

5. 9 is greater than 4.
   (i) use the counting chat: 9 comes after 4.
   (ii) use the number line: 9 is to the right of 4.
   (iii) use sets: A set with 4 elements can be matched with a proper subset of a set with 9 elements.

6. The number 5 can be represented as $n(\{a, b, c, d, e\})$. Any whole number less than 5 must be represented by a set that matches a proper subset of $\{a, b, c, d, e\}$. Such sets must have 0, 1, 2, 3, or 4 elements.

7. (a)
   (b)

8. (a) LXXIX (b) MMMLIV

9. (a)
   (b)

10. (a)   (b)

11. (a) 14,405   (b) 432
    (c) 1247   (d) 72,022

12. (a)   ▼▼▲, ﻮ∩∩, CXX

    (b) ▼▼◀◀▼▼,
        ﻮ∩∩∩∩||||, ...

    (c) ◀◀▼▼◀◀ ◀◀◀,
        CIIXXX ,

    (d) ﻮﻮﻮﻮﻮﻮﻮ∩∩||||||
        DCCXXVI,

13. Yes, Roman numerals form such a system because the position of the symbols matters but the value of the symbol is not multiplied by a place value.

14. 1989

15. (a) All 9's
    (b) 9876543210 or 98765432 (depending on size of calculator display)

16. (a) 80: 八十   19: 十九   52: 五十二

     400: 四百   603: 六百三

     6031: 六千三十

     (b) Yes. Yes. Yes.

17. (1) If A and B are in the same
         row, then B is taller than the
         rest of the row and A.
     (2) If A and B are in the same
         column, then A is shorter
         than the rest of the column
         and B.
     (3) If they are in different rows
         and columns, let C be in the
         same column as A and same
         row as B. Since A is shortest
         in its column, A < C. Since B
         is tallest in its row, C < B.
         Thus, A < C < B.

18. (a) 124,797
     (b) 8,724,640,224

19. Eiffel Tower: 984 feet
     Great Pyramid of Giza: 480 feet
     Big Ben: 316 feet
     Statue of Liberty: 305 feet
     Leaning Tower of Pisa: 179 feet

20. Impossible. There are 32 white
     squares and 30 dark squares. But
     each domino covers a white and a
     dark square.

21. No. You can write a *numeral* on
     paper, but numbers are abstract
     and exist only in the mind.

22. The Babylonian numeration
     system is a base 60 system.
     Therefore, once you have a value
     of 60 in a place, you have to
     "carry" to the next place. In our
     numeration system, when we add
     16 and 25, we can't write our
     answer as 311 or 3(11). Instead,
     the part that is more than 10
     stays in the ones place, but we
     carry one ten over to add to the
     other tens, getting an answer of

41. The correct answer to the
     problem would be

**Problems related to the NCTM
Standards and Curriculum Focal Points**

1.   Since cardinality is the number of
     elements of a set, a young child
     could look at several different sets
     of objects with three elements in it
     and notice the common
     cardinality. That common
     cardinality is the concept of
     number.

2.   Young students would need to
     understand that the numerals are
     just symbols that represent the
     idea of a number and the idea of a
     number is "how many" objects are
     in a set.

3.   Since the Mayan and Babylonian
     systems are both place value
     systems, numerals in each of
     these systems can be decomposed
     similar to the Hindu-Arabic
     system. A numeral in either
     system could be decomposed by
     multiplying the value of the
     symbols by the corresponding
     place values.

Section 2.3

1.   (a) $4 \times 100 + 0 \times 10 + 9 \times 1$
     (b) $7 \times 1000 + 0 \times 100 + 9 \times 10 + 4 \times 1$
     (c) $7 \times 100 + 4 \times 10 + 6 \times 1$
     (d) $8 \times 100,000 + 4 \times 10,000 + 1 \times 1$

2.   (a) 3075   (b) 70,600
     (c) 603,009   (d) 60,900,000

3.   (a) Thousand
     (b) Ten
     (c) One

4.   Seven, Eight, Nine, Ten

5.   (a) Thirty-two million ninety
          thousand forty seven

(b) Four hundred one billion two million, five hundred sixty thousand three hundred.

(c) Ninety eight quadrillion

6. (a) 27,069,014
   (b) 12,000,070,003,005

7. It is multiplicative because each digit is multiplied by its place value. It is additive because the various products are added together to the find the value of the number.

8. 2121_{three}

9. (a)

(b)

(c)

(d) 112_{four}, 221_{four}, 122_{four}

(e) The first digit is multiplied by the place value and in different bases the place value is different. Thus a 2 could be $2 \cdot 9$ or $2 \cdot 16$, depending on the base.

10. 1, 2, 1, 3

11. With bundles of sticks:
    (a) 3 bundles of ten, 8 units
    (b) 5 bundles of six, 2 units
    (c) 1 bundle of one hundred twenty five, 3 bundles of five, 2 units

With a chip abacus:
(a)

hundreds	tens	ones
	● ● ●	● ● ● ● ● ● ● ●

(b)

100_{six}	10_{six}	1
	● ● ● ● ●	● ●

(c)

1000_{five}	100_{five}	10_{five}	1
●		● ● ●	● ●

12. (a) 120_{eight} (b) 140_{six}
    (c) 1010_{three}

13. Base 26; 675

14. When using multibase blocks in a base-six numeration system, 6 units are exchanged for a long so only the symbols 0, 1, 2, 3, 4, and 5 are needed to describe the number of ones. Similarly, 6 longs are exchanged for a flat so 6 symbols are sufficient to describe the number of tens and so forth.

15. (a) True   (b) False
    (c) True

16. (a) 1 2 3 10 11 12 13 20 21
       22 23 30 31 32 33 100
       101 102 103 110
    (b) 127
    (c) 1 2 3 4 5 10 11 12 13 14
       15 20 21 22 23 24 25 30
       31 32 33 34 35 40 41 42
       43 44 45 50 51 52 53 54
       55 100
    (d) 1000_{nine}

17. (a) $22_{three} = 2(3) + 2(1)$
    (b) $212_{three} = 2(3^2) + 1(3) + 2(1)$
    (c) $12110_{three} = 1(3^4) + 2(3^3) + 1(3^2) + 1(3) + 0(1)$

18. (a) 111111_{two}
    (b) 1000000_{two}
       1000001_{two}
       1000010_{two}

19. $99 = 10200_{three}$
      $100 = 10201_{three}$

20.   (a) ET_{twelve} (b) 1001000_{two}
      (c) 347_{eight}

21.   (a) 97   (b) 1572   (c) 45

22.   (a) 164   (b) 16,910

23.   (a) 11_{eight} (b) 66_{eight}
      (c) 252_{eight} (d) 57_{eight}

      A shortcut is to mark off the base-two numeral in groups of three digits and then to express each group as a base eight digit.

24.   16. (a) 531   (b) 164
      (c) 7211

25.   (a) Eight   (b) Eleven   (c) Six

26.   None. Since the base number is always greater than any of the digits, if a is less than b (so that a_b makes sense), then b is greater than a (and b_a is incorrect notation).

27.   One possibility is onety-one, onety-two, onety-three, onety-nine.

28.   1234

29.   36

30.   (a) The numbers are placed on the cards according to their base 2 representations. Since 6 = 110_2 , it appears on the "4" card and "2" card.
      (b) The numbers 1-15 can be expressed in base 2 using 4 digits, so 4 cards each containing 8 numbers will suffice. The "1" card will contain the numbers 1,3,5,7,9,11,13,15, the "2" card will contain 2,3,6,7,10,11,14,15, etc.

31.   (a) In base 2, any number from 1 to 31 can be represented in terms of 1's, 2's, 4's, 8's, and 16's. For example, 13 = 1101_2, or 13 = 8 + 4 + 0 + 1
      (b) 1, 3, 9, 27 will do it.

32.   Base 2 is used in computers because the 0 and 1 can be simply represented by "off" and "on"; all numbers we type into the computer are converted to base 2, operated on in that base, then translated back into base 10 for output. Base 16 is also used in computers.

Problems related to the NCTM Standards and Curriculum Focal Points

1.   Using base-ten pieces, bundling sticks or a chip abacus all require a physical regrouping of some sort which would emphasize grouping of tens and ones.

2.   Idea 1: When you add 1 + 0 you get 1 but when you write 10 it represents the number of fingers on two hands.
      Idea 2: In some cases a 4 represents four and other cases it represents forty depending on its placement.
      Both cases show how the same digits can have very different meanings.

3.   Some physical models are base ten pieces, bundling sticks and a chip abacus. All of these provide different representations of numbers.

Section 2.4

1.   (a) {(a, t), (a, s), (i, t), (i, f), (i, s), (o, f), (o, s)}
      (b) {(a, b), (b, a), (a, c), (c, a), (b, c), (c, b)}
      (c) {(8, 7), (8, 5), (8, 4), (8, 3), (8, 2), (8, 1), (6, 7), (6, 5), (6, 4), (6, 3), (6, 2), (6, 1), (4, 7), (4, 5), (4, 3), (4, 2), (4, 1), (7, 1), (5, 1), (3, 1), (2, 1)}

(d) {(3, 6), (3, 9), (3, 12), (3, 15), (6, 12)}

2. (a)

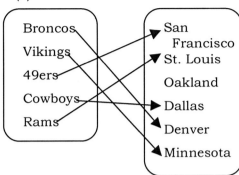

(b)

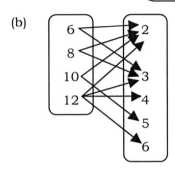

3. (a) "was the king of"
    (b) "is the square root of"

4. (a) transitive only
    (b) symmetric only
    (c) All. Equivalence relation.

5. (a) symmetric only
    (b) equivalence relation
    (c) reflexive only
    (d) symmetric only

6. (a) All. Equivalence relation. Every set in the partition has triangles of the same shape.
    (b) Reflexive and transitive
    (c) All. Equivalence relation. The partition contains 50 sets consisting of all people whose primary residence is in that state.

7. (a) Function.
    (b) Not a function. 1 has no image.
    (c) Not a function. 2 has two images.
    (d) Function.

8. (a) Function.
    (b) Not a function. Some cities have more than one zip code.
    (c) Function.
    (d) Not a function. Some pet owners have more than one pet.

9. (a) Not a function. Sue paired with both s and m.
    (b) Function.
    (c) Function.
    (d) Function.
    (e) Not a function. 2 paired with both 1 and 3; 3 paired with both 1 and 3.

10. (a) (0, 4), (1, 6), (2, 12)
        Range: {4, 6, 12}
    (b) (7, 81), (2, 16), (1, 9)
        Range: {9, 16, 81}
    (c) (2, 1), (3, 5)
        Range: {1, 5}

11. (a) 1000   (b) 18
    (c) 5   (d) 3

12. (a) $f(x) = x + 3$ for $x \in \{1, 5, 8\}$
        {(1, 4) (5, 8) (8, 11)}

x	$f(x)$
1	4
5	8
8	11

    (b) $f(x) = \dfrac{1}{x}$ for $x \in \{\frac{1}{2}, 1, 3, 4\}$

        $\{(3, \frac{1}{3}), (4, \frac{1}{4}), (1, 1), (\frac{1}{2}, 2)\}$

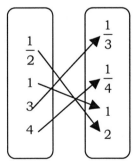

(c) $f(x) = 3x$ for $x \in \{2, 4, 7\}$

n	$T(n)$
2	6
4	12
7	21

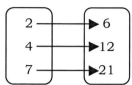

(d) $\{(2, 1) , (3, 4) , (4, 9) , (5, 16)\}$

x	$f(x)$
2	1
3	4
4	9
5	16

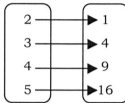

13. (a) $\{1, 7\}, \{1, 2, 3, 4, 6, 12\}$
     (b) $(4, 2), (21, 19)$
     (c) $\{7, 8, 9, 10, \ldots\}$,
          $\{951, 952, 953, \ldots\}$
     (d) $\{3, 4, 5\}, \varnothing$

14. (a) 6, 11, 26, 10
     (b) One possibility:

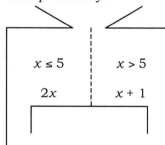

$x \le 5$ $x > 5$

$2x$ $x + 1$

15. (a) $40
     (b) $59.35
     (c) $260.95

16. $f(0) = f(2) = -3$
     $f(-1) = f(3) = 0$
     $f(-2) = f(4) = 5$
     Answers will vary. This is not
     consistent with the definition of a
     function because it is 2 x-values
     mapping to 1 y-value. It would

not be a function if there were 1 x-
value mapping to 2 y-values.

17. (a) Geometric, 10, $5(10^{199})$
     (b) Geometric, 2, $8(2^{199})$
     (c) Arithmetic, 11, $199(11) + 12 =$
          2201
     (d) Neither.

18. 5112

19. 153

20. (a) 27; 125; 1331
     (b) 4; 6; 14

21. (a) $1102.50; $1276.28; $1628.89
     (b) 15 years

22. (a) $F(x) = 125(x + 10) + 295x$
          $= 420x + 1250$
     (b) $6,080 The total cost of the
          fencing is $6,080 when the
          cost of fencing for the sides
          and back is $11.50 per foot.
     (c) $18.45 per foot for the sides
          and back, $28.45 per foot for
          the front.

23. (a) $r = 3$
     (b) 4, 12, 36, 108, 324, 972,
          2916

24. (a)

x	$f(x)$
1	12
2	19
3	26
4	33
5	40
6	47
7	54
8	61

     (b) Arithmetic, $a = 12$, $d = 7$
     (c) $T(n) = 12 + (n - 1)7 = 7n + 5$
     (d) $T(25) = 180$,
          $T(200) = 1405$
     (e) Domain: $\{1, 2, 3, 4, \ldots\}$
          Range: $\{12, 19, 26, \ldots\}$

25. (a)

Year	Increase in Population	Population of Mexico
1990	0	88,300,000
1991	2,207,500	90,507,500
1992	2,262,688	92,770,188
1993	2,319,255	95,089,443
1994	2,377,236	97,466,679
1995	2,436,667	99,903,346
1996	2,497,584	102,400,930
1997	2,560,023	104,960,953
1998	2,624,024	107,584,977
1999	2,689,624	110,274,601
2000	2,756,866	113,031,466
2001	2,825,787	115,857,253
2002	2,896,431	118,753,683

(b) Geometric, $r = 1.025$
(c) 113,031,465
     127,884,728
(d) $P(n) = 88,300,000(1.025)^n$

26. 11

27. 6,210,001,000 is the only solution.

28. Two equations are equivalent if they have the same solution set. Let E_1 and E_2 represent two equations and E_1 be related to E_2 if they have the same solution set. Then this relation is an equivalence relation.

29. One way to explain it would be to note that if the rate is 75 cents per quarter mile, then that would be 4(0.75) or $3.00 per mile.

30. Since she knew the diameter of the circle, she used the formula for circumference, $C = \pi d$; that is, circumference is a function of the length of the diameter.

Problems related to the NCTM Standards and Curriculum Focal Points

1. Example 2.18 contains 4 examples where equations are used to represent real world problems.

2. Words: The second number is the sum $1 + 2$. The third number is the sum $1 + 2 + 3$. The fourth number is the sum $1 + 2 + 3 + 4$ and so forth.
Table:

Term #	Term
1	1
2	3
3	6
4	10
5	15
6	21
7	28

Graph:

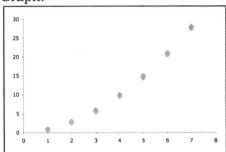

3. Any arithmetic sequence is a function with a constant rate of change and any geometric sequence is a function with a varying rate of change. A constant rate of change occurs when adding the same amount at each step. A varying rate of change occurs when adding different amounts or multiplying by the same amount at each step.

Chapter Review

Problems for Writing/Discussion

1. Tally, Roman, Egyptian, Babylonian. In the Babylonian system, which is a place value system, they left a space to represent zero. The other three systems, which did not have place value, are additive systems in which the zero would not be missed.

2. Many possible answers. For example, try 57 ´ 24 = LVII ´ XXIV.

3. Yes. The next two pairs would be (4, 11) and (5, 14). All points formed from this sequence will lie on the line $y = 3x - 1$. All arithmetic sequences are linear functions; they form straight lines.

4. No. All geometric sequences are exponential functions; they form curves, not straight lines.

5. Many possible answers.
1, 3, 9, 27, ... would be geometric.
1, 3, 4, 7, 11, 18, ... would be a Fibonacci type sequence where two previous terms are added to get the next. 1, 3, 1, 1, 3, 5, 3, 1, 1, 3, 5, 7, 5, 3, 1, ... would be a rising and falling sequence of odd numbers. 1, 3, 7, 13, ... would be a sequence of the form $x^2 - x + 1$.

6. Harvey is right. The definition of complement tells you to shade everything in the universal set that is *not* in the original set.

7. The complement of A – B is $\overline{A - B}$ which is not the same as $\overline{A} - \overline{B}$.

A – B

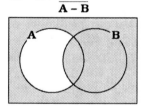

$\overline{A} - \overline{B}$

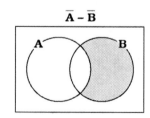

8. The picture below shows 427 (beads are only shown in the first three places).

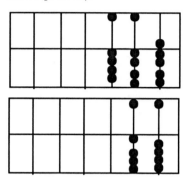

9. Each wire would need to have enough beads to count up to 19. Therefore, three 5's and four 1's would be needed.
$427 = 1 \times 360 + 3 \times 20 + 7 \times 1$

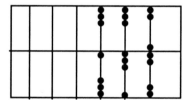

10. This problem appeared in Paulos's book *Innumeracy*. One million seconds equals 11.57 days. One billion seconds would be 1000 times as long; it equals 31.71 <u>years</u>. Many people vastly underestimate how a billion is compared to a million.

Chapter 3

Section 3.1

1. Set model:

    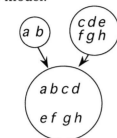

    Number line model:

    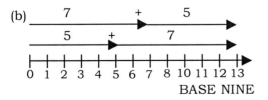

2. (b) and (c). Part (a) is false since g is common to both.

3. (a) Yes. All are multiples of 3 and the sum of two multiples of 3 is a multiple of 3.
    (b) No. $1 + 1 = 2$ and $2 \notin \{1\}$.
    (c) No. $1 + 5 = 6$ and $6 \notin \{1, 5, 9, ...\}$
    (d) Yes. All are multiples of 4 greater than 4.
    (e) No. $1 + 16 = 17$ and 17 is not greater than 17.

4. (a) 0, identity
    (b) 5, commutative
    (c) 3, associative
    (d) 6, commutative
    (e) 4, commutative
    (f) Whole, closure

5. (a)

6. By commutativity and associativity, they're equal.

7. (a) $(94 + 6) + (27 + 3) = 100 + 40 = 140$
    Associative and commutative
    (b) $(5 + 25) + (13 + 47) + 31 = 30 + 60 + 31 = 121$
    Associative and commutative

8. (a)

+	0	1	2	3	4	5
0	0	1	2	3	4	5
1	1	2	3	4	5	10
2	2	3	4	5	10	11
3	3	5	10	11	12	13
4	4	5	10	11	12	13
5	5	10	11	12	13	14

    (b) (i) $5_{six} + ? = 13_{six}; 4_{six}$
    (ii) $4_{six} + ? = 5_{six}; 1_{six}$
    (iii) $4_{six} + ? = 12_{six}; 4_{six}$
    (iv) $2_{six} + ? = 10_{six}; 4_{six}$

9. (a) $3_{six} + 2_{six} = 5_{six}$,
    $5_{six} - 3_{six} = 2_{six}$,
    $5_{six} - 2_{six} = 3_{six}$.
    (b) $5_{six} + 2_{six} = 11_{six}$,
    $2_{six} + 5_{six} = 11_{six}$,
    $11_{six} - 2_{six} = 5_{six}$.

10. (a) $x = 279 + 156$
    (b) $279 = x + 156$
    (c) $279 = x + 156$

11. (a) $7 - 3$, set model, comparison approach.
    (b) $8 - 3$, set model, missing-addend approach.
    (c) $6 - 2$, measurement model, take-away approach

12. (a) $x = 0$ (b) $x = y$
    (c) $z = 0, x \geq y$
    None are true for all.

13. (a) Set, missing addend, comparison, $200 + x = 362$

(b) Measurement, missing addend, no comparison, $114 + x = 250$

(c) Set, missing addend, no comparison, $105 + x = 1095$

14. (a) Mike needs to dig a 9-foot long trench. He's already dug 5 feet of the trench. How much more does he have left to dig?

(b) Marta and Julio are making Valentine's cards. Marta has made 9 cards and Julio has made 5 cards. How many more cards has Marta made?

(c)
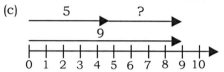
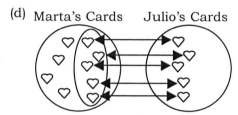

(d) Marta's Cards   Julio's Cards
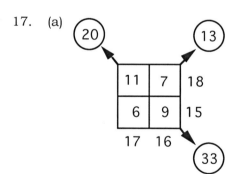

15. (a) For example, 6, 19, 12, 15, 18, 21

(b) Since 24 is the sum of eight 3's.

16. 5, 10, 15, ...

17. (a)
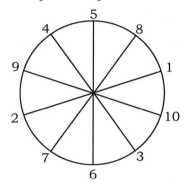

(b)
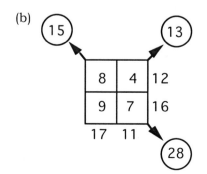

(c) Let a, b, c and d represent the entries in the four squares. Then all four sums described are equal to $a + b + c + d$.

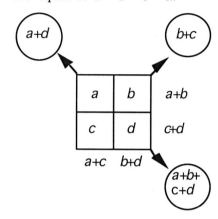

18. One possibility is shown.

19.

16	2	3	13
5	11	10	8
9	7	6	12
4	14	15	1

20.
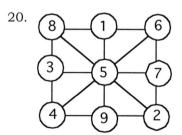

21. The sums along all lines are equal to 90. The sums of opposite triangles are equal.

22. Yes. Consider a pan balance where $a + c$ chips on one pan balance $b + c$ chips on the other pan. Remove c chips from each pan and observe that they still balance.

23. The first child is using a rounding up approach, which is a good technique. The second student is using the "doubles plus 1" approach for units place: $6 + 7 = 6 + 6 + 1$. Both students added from left to right, which is quite common and helps to solidify the idea of place value.

Problems related to the NCTM Standards and Curriculum Focal Points

1. The ideas of joining and separating sets is the beginning of the concepts of addition and subtraction.

2. Some of the understandings of subtraction are the take-away and missing-addend approaches. In conjunction with the missing addend approach students become familiar with the "four-fact families" which relate addition and subtraction facts.

3. By understanding properties such as commutative and associative, students can develop more flexible ways for doing computations mentally. For example, $(7 + 5) + 3$ is easier to solve after applying these properties.

Section 3.2

1. (a) 2×4 (b) 4×2 (c) 3×7

2. (a)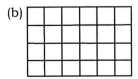

   (b)

(c)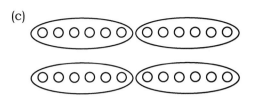

(d)

(e)

	e	f	g	h	i	j
a	(a,e)	(a,f)	(a,g)	(a,h)	(a,i)	(a,j)
b	(b,e)	(b,f)	(b,g)	(b,h)	(b,i)	(b,j)
c	(c,e)	(c,f)	(c,g)	(c,h)	(c,i)	(c,j)
d	(d,e)	(d,f)	(d,g)	(d,h)	(d,i)	(d,j)

3. (a) Cartesian product since the set of possibilities is {small, medium, large} × {cola, diet cola, lemon-lime, root beer, orange}: $x = 3 \cdot 5$

   (b) Rectangular array approach, since students form an array of 72 rows and 4 columns: $n = 72 \cdot 4$

   (c) Repeated addition, since the bill could be found by adding $70¢ + 70¢ + \dots + 70¢$ where the sum has 25 terms: $c = 25 \cdot 70$

4. (a) $39 + 39 + 39 + 39 = 156$
   (b) $231 + 231 + 231 = 693$
   (c) $172 + 172 + 172 + 172 + 172 = 860$
   (d) $843 + 843 + 843 + 843 + 843 + 843 = 5058$

5. (a) (i) No. $2 + 1 = 3$ (ii) Yes
   (b) (i) No. $4 + 3 = 7$; (ii) Yes

6. (a) Distributive over subtraction
   (b) Associative
   (c) Multiplicative by 0
   (d) Distributive over addition

7. (a) $3 \cdot 29 + 3 \cdot 30 + 3 \cdot 6$
   (b) $5x - 5(2y)$
   (c) $(3 + 6 - 4)a$
   (d) $(x + 3)(x + 2)$
   (e) $37 \cdot 60 - 37 \cdot 22$

8. (a) 14(20 - 1)   (b) 25(40 - 2)
    (c) 35(100 - 2)   (d) 27(1000 - 1)

9. (a) 463 × 16 + 463
    (b) 463 × 15 + 463 × 2
    (c) 463 × 16 + 10 × 16 + 463 + 10

10. (a) 8 × 85 = (8 × 5) 17 = 40 × 17
        = 680
    (b) 12(125) = 3 (4 × 125) = 3 × 500 = 1500

11. (a)

×	0	1	2	3	4	5	6	7
0	0	0	0	0	0	0	0	0
1	0	1	2	3	4	5	6	7
2	0	2	4	6	10	12	14	16
3	0	3	6	11	14	17	22	25
4	0	4	10	14	20	24	30	34
5	0	5	12	17	24	31	36	43
6	0	6	14	22	30	36	44	52
7	0	7	16	25	34	43	52	61

(b) (i) 61_{eight} = 7_{eight} ·?; 7_{eight}
    (ii) 17_{eight} = 3_{eight} ·?; 5_{eight}
    (iii) 30_{eight} = 6_{eight} ·?; 4_{eight}
    (iv) 16_{eight} = 2_{eight} ·?; 7_{eight}
    (v) 44_{eight} = 6_{eight} · ? 6_{eight}
    (vi) 25_{eight} = 7_{eight} ·?; 3_{eight}

12. (a) Partative. The 28 students are the groups, and the 60 cupcakes are broken into 28 groups to find out how many are in each group.
    (b) Measurement. The 2 cups is how much in each group and the solution is the number of groups you can make from 6 cups.
    (c) Partative. The 3 shirts is the number of groups and the $45 is divided among the groups. The solution is the amount of money in each group.

13. (a) Answers will vary. Kobe has 91 jelly beans and he eats 7 jelly beans every hour. How many hours until they are all gone?

(b) Answers will vary. Kobe has 91 jelly beans to give to 7 friends. How many jelly beans will each friend get?

14. (a) $24 = 12x$
    (b) $x = 27 \cdot 3$
    (c) $a = bx$

15. (a) 2, R = 1   (b) 0, R = 3
    (c) 7, R = 0   (d) 0, R = 1
    (e) 3, R = 0   (f) 0, R = 8

16. (a) 2, infinite
    (b) 1, infinite
    (c) 6, infinite
    (d) 23, infinite

17. None

18. 48

19. $21,000

20. (2,348 + 7,652) × 7,653,214 = (10,000)(7,653,214) = 76,532,140,000

21. No. Consider {0, 1}.

22. No. Since division by zero is not permitted, zero cannot be in the set. If any two nonzero numbers are in a set, then a proper fraction results, hence not closed.

23. 333,333,333; 777,777,777; 999,999,999 Associativity for multiplication.

24. $7 + 7^2 + 7^3 + 7^4 = 2800$ (2801 if you count the man.) Only 1; the speaker was going to St. Ives.

25. The number is divisible by 1001 which equals 7 × 11 × 13. (Use place value to show this.)

26. $4913 = 17^3$, $5832 = 18^3$

27. The sequence of cubes.

28. Yes. The difference of n "twos" from $2n$ "ones" will be the square of n "threes."

29. (a) Dave (b) Charlie

30. Since the sum of the ages equal to the house number does not provide a solution, there are two choices: 6,6,1 and 9,2,2. But there is an oldest child, so 9,2,2 is the answer.

31. Take a ball from the B/W box. If it's B, then the B/W box is B, the B box is W and the W is B/W. argue similarly if the ball is W.

32. *a* or *b* must be 0. If both are nonzero, the product is nonzero.

33. That seems to work in this case, but in fact the "number less than 6" is the *remainder*, not the quotient. The quotient is the number of times 6 was subtracted. For example, to divide 39 by 5, you subtract seven 5's: $39 - 5 - 5 - 5 - 5 - 5 - 5 - 5 = 4$. The quotient is 7 and the remainder is 4.

34. This is a common misuse of the distributive property. The original problem is calculated by first multiplying 7 times 3, then multiplying by 6, to obtain 126. The other problem will be 6 times as large, namely 756. Using the associative property, which is appropriate here, gives you $6(7 \times 3) = (6 \times 7) \times 3$. This equals 42 times 3, which equals 126. The distributive property distributes multiplication over *addition* (or *subtraction*), not multiplication over multiplication.

Problems related to the NCTM Standards and Curriculum Focal Points

1. Some of the key underlying concepts are the different ways that multiplication can be viewed (repeated addition, rectangular array, Cartesian product) and the different ways that division can be viewed (partitive, measurement, missing factor, repeated subtraction.)

2. One very common use of the distributive property is in factoring in algebra.

3. In a problem like 4 × 3, which means 4 groups of 3, it is assumed that all 4 groups are equal in size. For division any problem that is partitive assumed equal sharing.

Section 3.3

1. (a) 9   (b) 64

2. $29 < 44, 15 < 44, 44 > 29, 44 > 15$

3. Yes

4. (a) Yes   (b) Yes

5. (a) 4^7 (b) $3^6 \cdot 4^3$
   (c) $2x^3y^2$ (d) a^4b^4

6. $6^2 < 5^3 < 2^7 < 3^5$

7. (a) $10 \cdot a \cdot b \cdot b \cdot b \cdot b$
   (b) $2 \cdot x \cdot 2 \cdot x \cdot 2 \cdot x \cdot 2 \cdot x \cdot 2 \cdot x$
   (c) $2 \cdot x \cdot x \cdot x \cdot x \cdot x$

8. (a) x^9 (b) a^{12} (c) $(xy)^7$
   (d) 2^7 (e) 2^4 (f) 3^{23}

9. $8^5 \div 2^2$ means $(8 \cdot 8 \cdot 8 \cdot 8 \cdot 8) \div (2 \cdot 2)$ $= 32,768 \div 4 = 8,192$. We could subtract exponents to shorten the process as long as the exponents are the same. That is, $8^5 \div 2^2 = (2^3)^5 \div 2^2 = 2^{15} \div 2^2 = 2^{13} = 8,192$.

10. $7^{20} = \left(\left(7^2\right)^2\right)^5 = \left(\left(7^2\right)^5\right)^2 = \left(\left(7^5\right)^2\right)^2$

11. Sometimes true. If $b = m = 1$, then $a^n \cdot 1^1 = a^n$ and $a^{n \cdot 1} = a^n$.

12. (a) 12   (b) Any whole number
    (c) 7

13.   (a) 2,203   (b) 31,226   (c) 2,304

14.   (a) $2 \cdot 3(3 - 2) = 6$

(b) $\dfrac{2 \cdot 3^3}{15 - 6} = \dfrac{2 \cdot 3^3}{3^2} = 6$

(c) $25 - 16 + 4 = 13$

(d) $32 - 2^4 \cdot 3^4 \div \left(2^3 \cdot 3^2\right)$
$= 32 - 2 \cdot 9 = 14$

15.   By agreement and because exponents can be thought of as repeated multiplication.

16.   (a) $1 + 2 + 3 = 6$, $1^3 + 2^3 + 3^3 = 36 = 6^2$

(b) $1^3 + 2^3 + 3^3 + \ldots + n^3 = (1 + 2 + 3 + \ldots + n)^2$

(c) $1^3 + 2^3 + 3^3 + \ldots + 10^3 = (1 + 2 + 3 + \ldots + 10)^2 = 55^2 = 3,025$

17.   Correct; wrong; sometimes equal (whenever $b \times c = b^c$)

18. $\underline{4^{14}} = (2^2)^{14} = 2^{28} < 2^{30} = (2^3)^{10} = \underline{8^{10}} < \underline{9^{10}} = (3^2)^{10}$
$= 3^{20} < \underline{3^{22}}$

19.   Approximately 80,530,000 mm or 80.5 km.

20.   (a) $2^7 = 128$ (b) 21
(c) 1   (d) 7   (e) 7

21.   (a) 11   (b) 1,111
(c) 111,111   (d) 11,111,111

22.   Using variables, this problem is equivalent to showing that $10a + b$ divides evenly into $(10a)^2 - b^2$, or that $x + y$ divides into $x^2 - y^2$. But $x^2 - y^2 = (x + y)(x - y)$. Thus $x + y$ divides into $x^2 - y^2$ exactly $x - y$ times.

23.   (a) $3 < 7$ and $3 \cdot 5 = 15 < 7 \cdot 5 = 35$.

(b) $3 < 7$ and $3 \cdot 0 = 0 \not< 7 \cdot 0 = 0$

(c) Let $a < b$ and $c \neq 0$. By the Property of Less Than and Addition, $a + a + \cdots + a$ (c times) $< b + b + \cdots + b$ (c times). Thus, $ac < bc$.

(d) If $a < b$ and c is a factor of a and b, then $a \div c < b \div c$.

24. $\dfrac{\overbrace{a \cdot a \cdots a}^{n} \cdot \overbrace{a \cdot a \cdots a}^{m-n}}{\underbrace{a \cdot a \cdots a}_{n}} = a^{m-n}$

25.   Although this looks a like the associative property, the quantities on either side of the equal sign are *not* equal. If you calculate what is inside the parentheses first, $\left(3^4\right)^2$ equals 81 squared which is 6561, whereas $3^{\left(4^2\right)}$ equals 3 to the 16th power which is 43,046,721.
$\left(a^b\right)^c = a^{\left(b^c\right)}$ is true when $c = 1$.

Problems related to the NCTM Standards and Curriculum Focal Points

1.   Since the definition of ordering in Section 2.2 is based on objects in sets, it is more concrete and more appropriate for young students. The definition in section 3.3 is based on an understanding of addition which more abstract than physical objects in sets.

2.   Exponential notation like 3^4 is just a simpler and more efficient way to write $3 \times 3 \times 3 \times 3$. Exercise #5 in Set B is a similar example of how exponential notation simplifies some expressions.

3.   Since 2 inches is a positive whole number amount that will be added to a previous height, we know that the previous height is "less than" the new height. IF a students didn't grow, then no height would be added and last year's height

would not be less than this year's height.

Chapter Review

Problems for Writing/Discussion

1. Most people who make this mistake forget to "borrow." They subtract 10 - 7 = 3 and 10 - 2 = 8. A good technique to avoid making this mistake would be to change the 100 to 99, subtract 99 - 27 = 72, then add back the 1 to get 73.

2. Many possible answers. One way would be to round the $39.64 up to $40. Subtract $40 from $127.42 which equals $87.42, then add the 36¢ to get $87.78. Another way might be to do the cents then the dollars, finding the difference by adding the amounts above and below 100, say 36¢ plus 42¢ = 78¢, but we've taken 1 from the 127. So $61 + $26 = $87, plus the cents is $87.78

3. Many possible answers. The NCTM (The National Council of Teachers of Mathematics) recommends that students learn basic number facts, without excessive drill, and then be allowed to use calculators. If you think of the calculator as just another tool, saying that a student is "calculator dependent" may not be much different from saying a student requires pencil and paper to do a problem. For centuries mankind was abacus-dependent!

4. Believe it or not, only three weighings are required. Again divide the coins into three piles of 3 coins each, labeled A, B, and C. Weigh two against each other, say A and B. If they balance, then those 6 coins are genuine and C contains the counterfeit. Then take 3 of those coins and weigh them against C to determine whether the counterfeit is heavier

or lighter than the genuine coins. Then you need only one more weighing as in the example. If, on the other hand, your first weigh did <u>not</u> balance, then the coins in C are genuine and either A or B contains the counterfeit. But notice which was heavier, A or B. Then take one of the first two, say A, and weigh it against C. If A and C balance, the counterfeit is in B, and from the first weighing you know if the counterfeit is heavier or lighter. If A and C do not balance, then the counterfeit is in A, and you can tell from the first weigh whether the counterfeit is heavier or lighter than the genuine coins. Now you need only one more weighing as in the example.

5. With 24 cards, there would be 4 rectangles: 1 × 24, 2 × 12, 3 × 8, and 4 × 6. With 49 cards, there would be only 2 rectangles: 1 × 49 and 7 × 7. Both 36 and 48 would give you 5 different rectangles.

6. $9567 and $1085

7. Neither. 4 ‡ 5 ≠ 5 ‡ 4, because 3 ≠ 6. Also, (4 ‡ 5) ‡ 6 ≠ 4 ‡ (5 ‡ 6) because 3 ‡ 6 = 0 and 4 ‡ 4 = 4.

8. The operation Ω is neither commutative nor associative, which can be shown by counterexample, such as, B Ω C ≠ C Ω B. There are many possible tables; however, in any commutative operation, the table will be symmetric to its main diagonal (upper left to lower right).

9. Division by 0 is undefined. However, 0 ÷ 5 = 0 and 5 ÷ 5 = 1. Remembering that division problems can be checked by multiplication, the two problems that have answers can be checked by multiplying 5 × 0 = 0 and 5 × 1 = 5. But no matter what number a student gives as an answer for 5 ÷ 0, she can never multiply by 0 and get 5. Even worse, one can

give many answers for 0 ÷ 0 and
have them check, which really
tells us there is no answer.

10.   It is not closed under addition
      because 1 + 1 = 2, and 2 is not in
      the set. However, the set is closed
      under multiplication because
      every product is an element of the
      set. No set which contains 0 is
      closed under division, because 1 ÷
      0, for example, has no answer in
      the set.

Chapter 4

Section 4.1

1. (a) 520 (b) 3700 (c) 137
    (d) 270

2. (a) 27 (b) 46 (c) 128
    (d) 263

3. (a) 598 (b) 301 (c) 321
    (d) 104

4. (a) 955 (b) 1900 (c) 148
    (d) 3626 (e) 248

5. (a) 12,800,000
    (b) 72,000,000
    (c) 1,400,000,000
    (d) 150,000,000,000
    (e) 480,000,000,000
    (f) 115,000,000,000,000

6. (a) 52 – 35: 52 – 30 = 22, 22 – 5 = 17
    (b) 173 – 96: 173 – 90 = 83, 83 – 6 = 77
    (c) 241 – 159: 241 – 100 = 141, 141 – 50 = 91, 91 – 9 = 82
    (d) 83 – 55: 83 – 50 = 33, 33 – 5 = 28

7. (a) 16 × 21 = 8 × 42 = 4 × 84 = 2 × 168 = 336
    (b) 4 × 72 = 2 × 144 = 288
    (c) 8 × 123 = 4 × 246 = 2 × 492 = 984
    (d) 16 × 211 = 8 × 422 = 4 × 844 = 2 × 1688 = 3376

8. Overestimate. For example, if her calculations show that houses with in seven miles are at risk, she should raise her estimate to ten miles to be safe.

9. (a) (i) 12,000
        (ii) 12,000 to 14,000
        (iii) 12,700 (iv) 12,800
    (b) (i) 5,000 (ii) 5,000 to 9,000
        (iii) 6,400 (iv) 6,800
    (c) (i) 10,000
        (ii) 10,000 to 50,000
        (iii) 17,000 (iv) 19,000

10. (a) 200,000 to 600,000
    (b) 40,000 to 100,000
    (c) 35,000,000 to 48,000,000

11. (a) 84 × 50 = 4,200
    (b) 5,600 ÷ 80 = 70
    (c) 2,400 ÷ 60 = 40
    (d) 80 × 80 = 6,400
    (e) 200 × 75 = 15,000
    (f) 6,300 ÷ 90 = 70

12. (a) 250 (b) 600 (c) 590
    (d) 4,200 (e) 7,000

13. (a) 2000 (b) 810,000
    (c) 720 (d) 216,000,000

14. (a) 52 × 40 = 2080 and
        50 × 38 = 3800/2 = 1900
    (b) 20 × 70 = 1400 and
        20 × 75 = 1500
    (c) 90 × 10 = 900 and
        90 × 11 = 990
    (d) 25 × 40 = 1000 and
        25 × 44 = 4400/4 = 1100

15. (a) <u>15,000</u> to <u>24,000</u> using range estimation
    (b) <u>50,000</u> to <u>120,000</u> using range estimation
    (c) <u>8,000,000</u> to <u>27,000,000</u> using range estimation

16. (a) 9 (b) 7

17. (a) 5^5 (b) 3^8 (c) 9^3 (d) 6^6

18. a. Multiply 14 and 39 with the calculator and then multiply by 100 = 20 × 5 mentally to get 54,600.
    b. Multiply 27 and 23 with the calculator and then multiply by 1000 = 40 × 25 mentally to get 621,000.
    c. Multiply 647 and 89 with the calculator and then multiply by 10000 = 50 × 200 mentally to get 575,830,000.
    d. Multiply 91 and 173 with the calculator and then multiply by 100 = 25 × 2 × 2 mentally to get 1,574,300.

19. (a) 489 R 21 (b) 2,593 R 100
    (c) 6,928 R 998 (d) 1,091 R 134

20. (a) Yes (b) Yes (c) No (d) No

21. True

22. All are true.

23. All

24. (a) 104,506 (b) 864
    (c) 31,753 (d) 161,590

25. (a) $136 \rightarrow 1^3 + 3^3 + 63^3 = 244 \rightarrow$
    $2^3 + 43^3 + 4^3 = 136$
    (b) $160 \rightarrow 1^3 + 6^3 + 0^3 = 217 \rightarrow$
    $2^3 + 1^3 + 7^3 = 352 \rightarrow$
    $3^3 + 5^3 + 2^3 = 160$
    (c) $919 \rightarrow 9^3 + 1^3 + 9^3 = 1,459$
    $\rightarrow 1^3 + 4^3 + 5^3 + 9^3 = 919$

26. 123,456,789

27. (a) 9,801
    (b) 998,00
    (c) 99,980,001

28. Row 1: 9
    Row 2: 7 4 2
    Row 3: 6
    Row 4: 362,880

29. 36×5
    (i) Special factor: $36 \times 5 =$
    $(36 \times 10) \div 2 = 180$.
    (ii) Multiplicative compensation:
    $36 \times 5 = (18 \times 2) \times 5 =$
    $18 \times (2 \times 5) = 180$.
    In (i) 360 was divided by 2 and in
    (ii) 36 was divided by 2 .

30. 27,777,777,555,555,556

31. Find $712 \cdot 864$, then affix 6 zeros
    at the end.

32. 777,777,776,222,222,223

33. $\boxed{[(}\ 299\ \boxed{+}\ 20\ \boxed{+}\ 20\ \boxed{+}\ 2\ \boxed{+}$
    $1\ \boxed{)}\ \boxed{\times}\ \boxed{[(}\ 20\ \boxed{+}\ 20\ \boxed{+}\ 2\ \boxed{+}$
    $1\ \boxed{)]}$

34. 1,234,321
    23,454,321
    12,345,654,321

35. 132, 264, 385, 594, 682, 396,
    407, 649, 836

36. 121,932,631,112,635,269

37. (a) 1,649; 3,136; 2,604
    (b) $(10a + c)(10b + c)$ should be
    $100(ab + c) + c^2$ where $a + b$
    $= 10$.
    Proof: $(10a + c)(10b + c)$
    $= (10a + c)10b + (10a + c)c$
    $= 100ab + 10bc + 10ac + c^2$
    $= 100ab + 10c(b + a) + c^2$
    $= 100ab + 100c + c^2$
    $= 100(ab + c) + c^2$
    (since $a + b = 10$)

38. (b) 678,947,368,421,052,631,588

39. (i) Identify the digit in the
    place to which you are
    rounding.
    (ii) If the digit(s) in the place(s) to
    the right is (are) a 5 (and all
    zeros) and the number in the
    place to which you are
    rounding is even, change the
    5 to a zero. If the number in
    the place to which you are
    rounding is odd, increase it by
    1 and change the 5 to a zero.
    (iii) If the digit(s) in the place(s) to
    the right is (are) a 5 (and
    something other than all
    zeros), add 1 to the digit in
    rounding and change all digits
    to its right to zeros.
    (iv) If the digit in the place to the
    right is a 4, change the 4 and
    all digits to its right to 0.

40. (a) 4 (b) 4 (c) 9 (d) 9

41. If the answer is odd, the odd number of coins is in the left hand. If even, the even number of coins is in the left hand.

42. Dividing by 5 and multiplying by 2 are similar, but not "the same." As in problem 41, dividing by 5 would be the same as dividing by 10 and then multiplying by 2. Therefore, $70 \div 5$ would equal $7 \times 2 = 14$. 70×2 would equal 140, so the student would have to remember to divide the answer by 10.

43. The first method is correct. Some students may subtract twice rather than subtracting a larger number, then adding to compensate.

Problems related to the NCTM Standards and Curriculum Focal Points

1. An example of a problem to estimate could be 21×32. A student could do this by mentally calculating 20 and 30 to get $(2 \times 3) \times (10 \times 10) = 600$. A student could also mentally calculate 14×7 as $(10 + 4) \times 7 = 70 + 28 = 98$.

2. (a) A group of 14 friends wants to go to the movie which costs $7 each. What is the total cost?
    (b) Items costing $1.28, $3.21, $2.79, and $.95 are going to be purchased. Is $10 sufficient?
    (c) Items costing $1.28, $3.21, $2.79, and $.95 are going to be purchased. What is the exact total?
    (d) This could be the same question as part c but with no access to a calculator.

3. Once a problem is understood, a person could estimate the answer before doing the computations. When the final answer is calculated, it can be compared to this estimation as a way of looking back. If the estimation and actual calculation are not close, the problem should be reexamined.

Section 4.2

1. (a)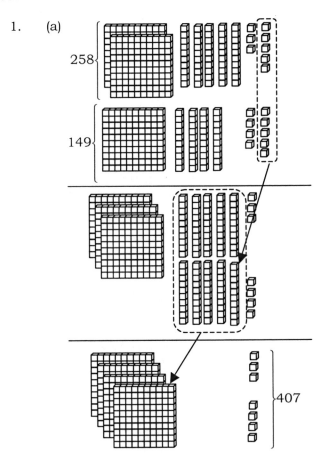

(b)

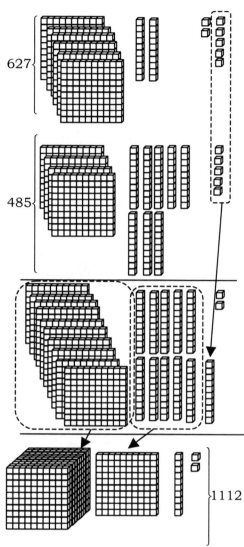

627

485

1112

2. (a) S = Stick
        B = Bundle of 10 sticks
        H = Bundle of 10 bundles
        BBBBSSSSS + BBBBBSSSSS
        = BBBBBBBBBSSSSSSSSSSS
        = BBBBBBBBBBS = HS

    (b)

100	10	1
	• • • •	• • •
	• • •	• • •

    =101

3. Expanded form, commutative and
    associative properties of addition,
    single-digit addition facts,
    expanded form, associative

property of addition, distributive
property of multiplication over
addition, associative property and
single-digit addition facts, place
value.

4. (a) $4(100) + 7(10) + 8$
           $+ 2(100) + 6(10) + 9$
           $= 6(100) + 13(10) + 17$
           $= 7(100) + 7$

    (b) $1(1000) + 9(100) + 6(10) + 5$
           $+ 0(1000) + 8(100) + 5(10) + 7$
           $= 1(1000) + 17(100) + 11(10) + 12$
           $= 2(1000) + 8(100) + 2(10) + 2$

5. (a) $+\begin{array}{r} 347 \\ 679 \\ \hline 16 \\ 11 \\ 9 \\ \hline 1026 \end{array}$ (b) $+\begin{array}{r} 3538 \\ 784 \\ \hline 12 \\ 11 \\ 12 \\ 3 \\ \hline 4322 \end{array}$

    (c) More efficient, but less
         meaningful without the zeros.

6. (a) 856   (b) 1763   (c) 535

7. (a) 1641   (b) 10,185

8. (a) Simple, requires more writing
         and crossing out numbers.
    (b) Fewer symbols, more
         complicated due to the carry.

9.   616   There are many other
        919   correct answers.
        898
        868
        686
        989

10. Estimate: The sum is greater than
    80,000.

11. (a) B A C   (b) B C A
    (c) A B C   (d) C B A

12. (a)

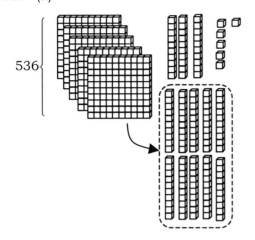

536

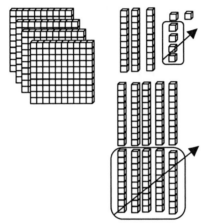

Exchange 1 flat for 10 longs.

536 take away 54 leaves 482.

(b)

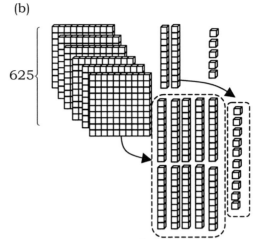

625

Exchange 1 flat for 10 longs
and 1 long for 10 units.

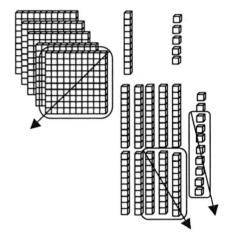

625 take away 138 leaves 487.

13. (a)

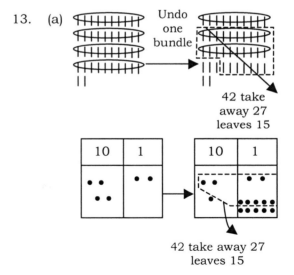

Undo
one
bundle

42 take
away 27
leaves 15

10	1		10	1

42 take away 27
leaves 15

(b)

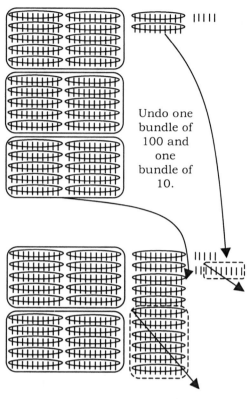

Undo one bundle of 100 and one bundle of 10.

625 take away 68 leaves 257

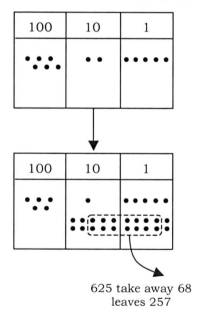

100	10	1

625 take away 68 leaves 257

14. 10, 10, 11

15. b, c, a

16. (a)
$$
\begin{array}{r}
4(100) + 5(10) + 5 \\
- 2(100) + 7(10) + 8 \\
\hline
3(100) + 14(10) + 15 \\
- 2(100) + 7(10) + 8 \\
\hline
1(100) + 7(10) + 7
\end{array}
$$

(b)
$$
\begin{array}{r}
5(100) + 0(10) + 3 \\
-1(100) + 4(10) + 7 \\
\hline
4(100) + 9(10) + 13 \\
-1(100) + 4(10) + 7 \\
\hline
3(100) + 5(10) + 6
\end{array}
$$

(c)
$$
\begin{array}{r}
3(1000) + 4(100) + 2(10) + 6 \\
- 0(1000) + 6(100) + 5(10) + 2 \\
\hline
2(1000) + 13(100) + 12(10) + 6 \\
- 0(1000) + 6(100) + 5(10) + 2 \\
\hline
2(1000) + 7(100) + 7(10) + 4
\end{array}
$$

17. (a) "29, 30, 40." Change is $12.
   (b) "34, 35, 40, 60, 80, 100."
   Change is $67.

18. (a)
$$
\begin{array}{r}
3479 \\
-2175 \\
\hline
\end{array}
\qquad
\begin{array}{r}
3479 \\
+ 7824 \\
\hline
11303 \\
+ 1 \\
\hline
1304
\end{array}
$$

(b)
$$
\begin{array}{r}
6,\ 0\ 0\ 2,\ 0\ 0\ 5 \\
-\ 4,\ 1\ 8\ 7,\ 2\ 6\ 9 \\
\hline
\\
6,\ 0\ 0\ 2,\ 0\ 0\ 5 \\
+\ 5,\ 8\ 1\ 2,\ 7\ 3\ 0 \\
\hline
1\ 1,\ 8\ 1\ 4,\ 7\ 3\ 5 \\
+\ 1 \\
\hline
1,\ 8\ 1\ 4,\ 7\ 3\ 6
\end{array}
$$

(c) The method with three-digit numbers is the same except the leading digit may be a zero. If so, the answer is the two-digit number that remains, plus 1.

19. (a)

$$\begin{array}{r} \overset{1}{3}476 \\ -\;5\,\overset{6}{\cancel{5}}8 \\ \hline 1\,8 \end{array} \longrightarrow \begin{array}{r} \overset{1}{3}\overset{1}{4}76 \\ -\;5\,\overset{6}{\cancel{5}}8 \\ \hline 2918 \end{array}$$

(b)

$$\begin{array}{r} 5\;\;{}^{1}0,\;{}^{1}0\;\;{}^{1}0\;\;{}^{1}4 \\ -\;{}^{4}3\;\;{}^{7}6,\;{}^{3}2\;\;{}^{9}8\;\;9 \\ \hline 1\;\;3,\;\;7\;\;1\;\;5 \end{array}$$

(c) Yes. Because the amount that is added to the minuend is added to the subtrahend, the difference remains the same.

20. (a)

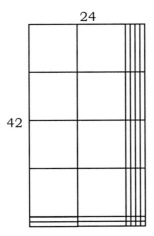

(b)

$$\begin{array}{r} 24 \\ \times\;42 \\ \hline 8 \\ 40 \\ 160 \\ \underline{800} \\ 1008 \end{array}$$

(c) The product of the ones digits, 8, is represented by the unit blocks in (a); the product of the tens and ones digits, 40 and 160, by the longs; and the product of the hundreds digits, 800, by the flats.

21.

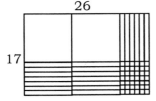

22. (a)

	20	3	
920	800	120	40
184	160	24	8
1004			

23 ⎫ 48

(b)

	30	4	
170	150	200	50
68	60	8	2
1768			

34 ⎫ 52

(c) The numbers within the grid are the same as the steps of the intermediate algorithm 1.

23. Expanded form, distributivity, expanded form, associativity of multiplication, place value, place value, addition

24. (a) 11,376　　(b) 552,832

25. (a)

$$\begin{array}{r} 276 \\ \times\;\;43 \\ \hline 1104 \\ +\;\;828 \\ \hline 11868 \end{array}$$

(b)

$$\begin{array}{r} 768 \\ \times\;891 \\ \hline 6144 \\ 6912 \\ \underline{\;\;768} \\ 684288 \end{array}$$

26. (a)

$$\begin{array}{l} \cancel{44 \times 83} \\ \cancel{22 \times 166} \\ 11 \times 332 \\ 5 \times 664 \\ \cancel{2 \times 1328} \\ 1 \times 2656 \\ \hline 3652 \end{array}$$

(b)

$$\begin{array}{l} 31 \times 54 \\ 15 \times 108 \\ 7 \times 216 \\ 3 \times 432 \\ 1 \times 864 \\ \hline 1674 \end{array}$$

27. (a) Left Hand:　　4 up, 1 down
Right Hand:　1 up, 4 down
$(4 + 1) \times 10 + (4 \times 1)$
$= 54$

(b) Left Hand:　　2 up, 3 down
Right Hand:　4 up, 1 down
$(4 + 2) \times 10 + (3 \times 1)$
$= 63$

(c)   Left Hand: 3 up, 2 down
       Right Hand: 3 up, 2 down
$$(3 + 3) \times 10 + (2 \times 2)$$
$$= 64$$

28. (a) ~~1 × 43~~
        2 × 86
        4 × 172
        <u>8 × 344</u>
        14 × 43
$$= (2 + 4 + 8) \times 43$$
$$= 86 + 172 + 344 = 602$$

 (b) 1 × 67
        ~~2 × 134~~
        4 × 268
        ~~8 × 536~~
        <u>16 × 1072</u>
        21 × 67
$$= (1 + 4 + 16) \times 67$$
$$= 67 + 268 + 1072 = 1407$$

 (c) 1 × 73
        2 × 146
        ~~4 × 292~~
        8 × 584
        ~~16 × 1168~~
        <u>32 × 2336</u>
        43 × 73
$$= (1 + 2 + 8 + 32) \times 73$$
$$= 73 + 146 + 584 + 2336 = 3139$$

 (d) Distributive property

29. (a)
$$\begin{array}{r} 22 \overline{)\,749} \\ \underline{-660} \quad 30(22) \\ 89 \\ \underline{-66} \quad 3(22) \\ 23 \\ \underline{-22} \quad 1(22) \\ 1 + 34(22) = 749 \end{array}$$

(b)
$$\begin{array}{r} 14 \overline{)\,3251} \\ \underline{-2800} \quad 200(14) \\ 451 \\ \underline{-280} \quad 20(14) \\ 171 \\ \underline{-140} \quad 10(14) \\ 31 \\ \underline{-28} \quad 2(14) \\ 3 + 232(14) = 3251 \end{array}$$

30. (a)
$$\begin{array}{r} 63 \\ \underline{-\ 9} \\ 54 \\ \underline{-\ 9} \\ 45 \\ \underline{-\ 9} \\ 36 \\ \underline{-\ 9} \\ 27 \\ \underline{-\ 9} \\ 18 \\ \underline{-\ 9} \\ 9 \\ \underline{-\ 9} \\ 0 \quad 63 \div 9 = 7 \end{array}$$

 (b) Repeated subtraction

31. (a) $39 - 3 - 3 - 3 - 3 - 3 - 3 - 3 - 3 - 3 - 3 - 3 - 3 - 3 = 0$ so $39 \div 3 = 13$.
 (b) $89 - 8 - 8 - 8 - 8 - 8 - 8 - 8 - 8 - 8 - 8 - 8 = 1$ so $89 \div 8 = 11$ r1.
 (c) $75 - 6 - 6 - 6 - 6 - 6 - 6 - 6 - 6 - 6 - 6 - 6 - 6 = 3$ so $75 \div 6 = 12$ r3.
 (d) Use the calculator to do repeated subtraction and count the number of times the divisor is subtracted.

32. (a) $18114\ \boxed{\div}\ 37\ \boxed{=}$ $\boxed{489.56757}$
     $\boxed{-}\ 489\ \boxed{=}\ \boxed{\times}\ 37\ \boxed{=}$ $\boxed{21}$

The quotient is 489 and the remainder is 21.

(b) 381271 ÷ 147 = 2593.680272

− 2593 = × 147 = 100

The quotient is 2593 and the remainder is 100.

(c) 9346870 ÷ 349 = 26781.86246

− 26781 = × 349 = 301

The quotient is 26781 and the remainder is 301.

(d) Yes, if a is divided by b, we have $a = bq + r$. This method finds $a - bq$, which is r.

33.

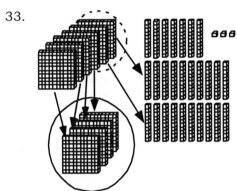

In 673, there is *one* group of 4 flats. The two remaining flats are exchanged for 20 longs.

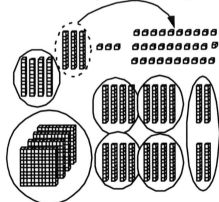

In the remaining 273, there are *six* groups of 4 longs. The three remaining longs are exchanged for 30 units.

remainder

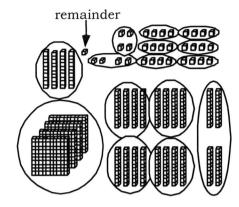

34. There is 1 flat in each of 3 groups and so there are 2 flats still to be divided (these will be grouped with the longs at the next step, making 22 longs.)

35. Peter subtracted in the wrong order in 2 places. Jeff did not borrow properly. John did not need to borrow a second time in hundreds place.

36. 2, 3, 4, 5

37. (a) 631   (b) 37

38. (a) 10652 cents   (b) 10562 cents

39. (a) 12, 123, 1234,····
    (b) 10 addends

40. The hundreds digit plus the ones digit is 9 and the middle digit is always 9.

41. Yes

42. All except 9.

43. Carol: 124   Steve: 96 Tracy: 44 r 6

44. There is no extra dollar. 30 - 5 = 25. Also 3(9) - 2 = 25.

45. $x(x+2) + 1 = (x+1)^2$

46.

The yellow region on the rectangle corresponds to the units $7 \times 3 = 21$. Similarly, 7×3 in the lattice is the product of the units. The other colors have similar correspondences.

47. This case, discussed in Robert Davis's book, *Learning Mathematics: The Cognitive Science Approach to Mathematics Education,* involved a student who believed that you could not "borrow" from a zero place. Therefore, each time she needed to borrow, she went directly to the 4 and borrowed from it without changing the zeros. She subtracted 7 from 15 and got 8, and she subtracted 3 from 10 and got 7. But both times she borrowed from the 4, which became a 3 and then a 2. The problem, as cited in the book, was that the girl was really convinced that this was the correct way to subtract, and even her teacher telling her the correct way to do the problem did not change her mind. A teacher might use Dienes blocks or some similar manipulative to show her that borrowing one from the thousands place means changing the thousand to ten hundreds, then borrowing one from the hundreds place means changing the one hundred to ten tens, etc. Whitney was borrowing 1000 when she needed 10. It might also help to have her check her answer by adding 2078 and 37 to see if she gets 4005. Since she was basically a good math student,

this might at least make her think twice about her method.

Problems related to the NCTM Standards and Curriculum Focal Points

1. When adding or subtracting multidigit numbers, the addition or subtraction of the hundreds, thousands, or millions can always be boiled down to adding or subtracting single digit numbers. Thus, having quick recall of the addition and subtraction facts allows one to focus on the principles of place value essential to understanding these multidigit operations.

2. Maintaining an understanding of the meaning of division is valuable in developing a solid understanding of the algorithm. If $21 \div 7$ is only the memorized fact of 3 and not seen as 21 broken into 7 groups or groups of size 7, then confusion in the steps of the algorithm is likely.

3. Some students naturally think of doing the operations from right to left instead of left to right. This method can be as effective if the student has a solid understanding of the expanded form of numbers as well as place value and the distributive property. For example, some students may compute 27×12 as $27 \times 10 = 270$ and $27 \times 2 = 54$ to get 324.

Section 4.3

1. (a)

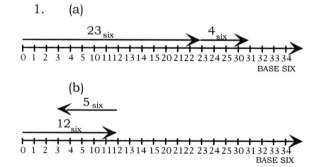

(c)

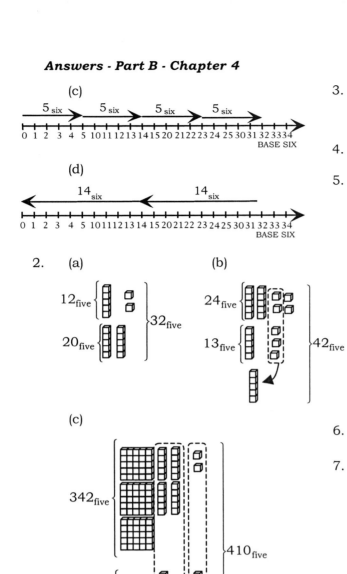

2.   (a)   (b)

(c)

(d)

3.   (a) 131_{four} (b) 131_{eight}

      (c) 842_{nine}

4.   (a) 154_{nine} (b) $1TT_{twelve}$

5.   (a)

6.   (a) 142_{twelve} (b) $18T_{eleven}$

7.   (a)

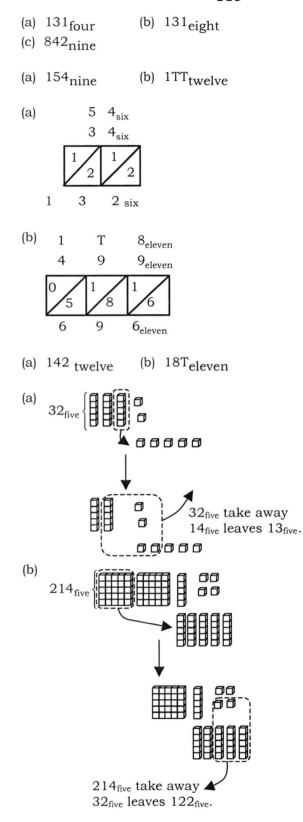

(c)

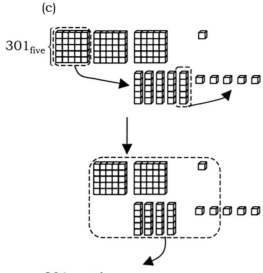

301_{five}

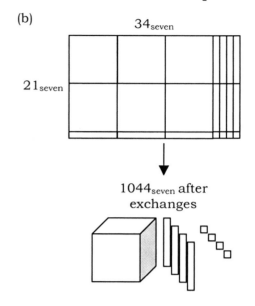

(b)

34_{seven}

21_{seven}

1044_{seven} after exchanges

301_{five} take away
243_{five} leaves 3_{five}.

8.   (a) 44_{five} (b) 155_{eight}
     (c) 11_{two}

9.   (a) 6_{seven} (b) $1E_{twelve}$
     (c) 1_{eight}

10. $1001010_{two} - 111001_{two}$
    $= 1001010_{two} + 110_{two}$
      $- 1000000_{two} + 1_{two}$
    $= 10001_{two}$

11.   (a) 13_{six}

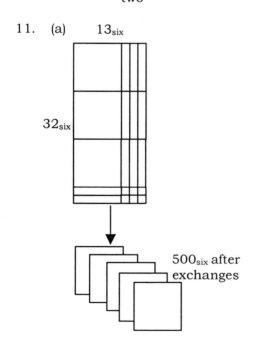

32_{six}

500_{six} after exchanges

12.   (a) 101011111_{two} (b) 969_{twelve}
     (c) 65601_{seven}

13.   (a) 3_{five} (b) 121_{six}
     (c) 143_{seven}

14.   (a) 6_{seven} (b) 8_{nine}
     (c) T_{twelve}

15.

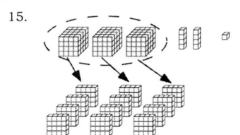

Since there is not a group of size 11_{four} cubes, the three cubes are exchanged for flats.

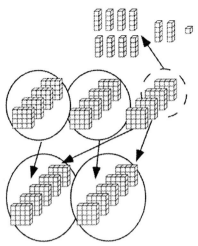

There are two groups of flats of size 11_{four}. The remaining two flats are exchanged for longs.

remainder

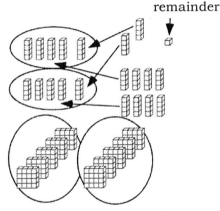

There are two groups of longs of size 11_{four} with no longs left over. There are no groups of units of size 11_{four}, but there is one unit remaining. Thus the quotient is 220_{four} with remainder 1.

16.   eight

17.   Betty has $6; Tom has $2.

18.   10

19.   Assume n is even. Then n can be expressed as $2m$ where m is a whole number. Then $n^2 =$ $(2m)^2 = 4m^2$ which is even. This contradicts the given information, so n must be odd.

20.   You may be asking students to learn division in base ten. For students learning division, doing a division problem in our number base will be at least as difficult as doing a division problem in base five is for you. To make division easier for your students, make certain that they have the necessary prerequisite skills , especially mental math and estimation skills in multiplication.

Problems related to the NCTM Standards and Curriculum Focal Points

1.   When adding in other bases like base 6, for example, you are forced to always look for groups of 6 because any group of 6 units, longs, or flats can be exchanged for 1 long, flat or cube respectively. Thus, the relationships of numbers that add to 6 become more important. The thinking required in base 6 is identical to that in base 10 so working in one base system builds on the understanding of another.

2.   When doing multidigit addition in base 7, for example, you may need to know what $5_{seven} + 5_{seven}$ is before you can make the decision whether or not to carry. By first building a table of addition facts, you can refer to the table to see that the sum is 13_{seven} and then think about how the "carrying" procedure might work. Thus, the table of addition facts in base seven is needed because you likely don't have quick recall of those facts.

3.   When finding the product 27×63, you will need to know the individual products of 7×3, 2×3, 7×6, and 2×6 before the desired product can be found. Thus having quick recall of the multiplication facts, makes it easier to focus on whether you are multiplying by a 2 or 20 and whether you should carry or not.

Thus, fluency of multidigit multiplication is enhanced.

Chapter Review

Problems for Writing/Discussion

1. Knowing that 5% of a number equals half of 10% of the same number, some people take 10%, then add half again of that amount. For example, 10% of the bill is about $4.80. Half of that is $2.40. Adding mentally, you get $7.20. In some states, the sales tax provides some help for finding 15%. For example, in a place where the sales tax is 7 1/2 %, the tip would be twice the sales tax. Of course, the tax is being figured on the amount of the meal before the tax was added (in this case, if the meal was roughly $44, the sales tax brought the bill up to $47.31), so you would be tipping 15% on $44 (which is $6.60) instead of 15% on $47.31 (which is $7.10). Another way to estimate the tip is to realize that 1/6 of the bill is $16\frac{2}{3}$%. So you could divide the bill by 6, and then round down a little. $47.31 ÷ 6 is about $7.90, which you might round down to $7.50. Or you could divide the bill before tax by 6, which would give you about $7.30.

2. Obviously this is a matter of opinion. The recommendations of NCTM lean toward letting students use a method that makes sense to them rather than making them memorize an algorithm that does not make sense to them.

3. Ten raised to any positive whole number power will be a number whose units digit is zero. Similarly, 5 raised to any whole number power will be a number which ends in 5. To find the other

two answers, you need to examine the pattern more closely.

The positive whole number powers of 2 are 2, 4, 8, 16, 32, 64, 128, 256, 512, 1024, 2048, etc. Notice that the units digits follow a pattern: 2, 4, 8, 6, 2, 4, 8, 6, etc. 2^{348} will have a units digit of 6 since 348 is a multiple of 4. Three numbers past 6 would mean the units digit of 2^{351} would be 8. Notice that the units digits are always even, but never equal to zero.

The positive whole number powers of 7 are 7, 49, 343, 2401, 16807, etc. Notice that the units digits are always odd, but never 5. The progression of four units digits 7, 9, 3, 1 is similar to that of powers of 2. So the units digit of 7^{351} would be 3.

4. The answer is found by adding $1 \times 51 + 2 \times 51 + 8 \times 51 + 16 \times 51$. By the distributive property, this equals $(1 + 2 + 8 + 16) \times 51 = 27 \times 51 = 1377$. 27, as a base-two numeral, equals 11011_{two}. In the "doubling" column, the numbers included in the sum are the ones, and the numbers crossed out are the zeros.

5. You want to put the smaller number in the "halving" column if you want the shorter route to the answer. The smaller number goes to 1 faster.

Halving	Doubling
47	375
23	750
11	1500
5	3000
2	6000
1	12000

The 2 and 6000 get crossed out. The sum of the remaining numbers in the "doubling" column is 17,625. Notice that 47 =

101111_{two} where each 1 represents a power of two multiplied times 375. The sum of those products is the answer.

6. Grace Hopper was a Navy admiral who knew that battleships were built to face the dangers of the high seas, whether in peace or wartime. To use this saying as an analogy for students is like saying, "Your brain was 'built' to reason. If you aren't facing up to the risks and challenges of learning, your brain may be 'safe,' but that's not what it was created for."

7. The smallest product is 6×6 (2 fingers up is 20, plus $4 \times 4 = 16$ from the closed fingers, equals 36); the largest is 10×10 (10 fingers up is 10 tens, plus 0 fingers closed which is 0, gives 100). There are many possible correct answers to the other questions. Some teachers are opposed to having their students count on their fingers "like babies." Nevertheless, concrete manipulatives have the endorsement of NCTM who see them as a natural stepping stone to more abstract methods of arithmetic. Abstract methods often make more sense to students if they have been preceded by concrete methods. The word "manipulatives" is from the Latin "manipulus" which means "handful." What could be more manipulative than a handful of fingers?

8. Estimating here means rounding to compatible numbers first then doing the calculation mentally. Yet the student's answer is the answer one might get by estimating. Sometimes students are more interested in getting the "right" answer than in following a particular approach. Students should be urged to put the calculator away for such problems.

9. $(x - y)(x + y) = x^2 - y^2$. So $(50 - 3)(50 + 3) = 50^2 - 3^2$ $= 2500 - 9 = 2491$. Similar problems might be: 36×44, 21×19, 65×75, etc.

10. There are no precise answers for these questions. Students should compare answers and share what reasoning went into their conclusions.

Chapter 5

Section 5.1

1. Multiples of 2 in columns 2, 4, and 6; multiples of 3 in columns 3 and 6; multiples of 5 on diagonal; multiples of 7 on diagonals

2. (a) $2^6 \times 3$

    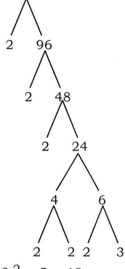

    (b) $2^2 \times 5 \times 19$

    (c) $3^3 \times 59$

    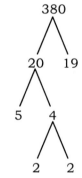

(d) $3 \times 29 \times 43$

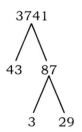

3. (a) 3×13 (b) $3 \times 13 \times 29$
    (c) 5×11 (d) $5 \times 11 \times 17$
    (e) $11 \times 13 \times 23$ (f) $3 \times 13 \times 151$

4. (a) 7   (b) 10   (c) 3×18
    (d) $2 \times 5 \times 7$
    (e) $2^3 \times 3 \times 7^3 \times 13^5$
    (f) $2^2 \times 3^9 \times 5^6 \times 17^8$
    (g) $2^{17} \times 3^{16} \times 5^{86} \times 29^{37}$
    (h) 2×11
    (i) $p^2 q^8 r^6 s^2 t^{27}$
    (j) $(5 \times 3 + 2)$

5. 1,2,3,4,6,8,12, and 24

6. (a) 114 ends in 4; $x = 57$
    (b) $3 + 3 + 6 = 12$ which is divisible by 3; $x = 112$

7. (a) 3, 4, 9
    (b) 3, 9

8. (a) $9 + 5 + 4 = 18$, $4 + 1 + 2 = 7$, $18 - 7 = 11$. Since $18 \mid 11$, $11 \mid 945, 142$.
    (b) $6 + 2 + 4 + 1 = 13$, $2 + 7 + 5 = 14$, $14 - 13 = 1$. Since $11 \nmid 1$, $11 \nmid 6, 247, 251$.
    (c) $3 + 5 + 2 = 10$, $8 + 6 + 7 = 21$, $21 - 10 = 11$. Since $11 \mid 11$, $11 \mid 385, 627$.

9. (a)   3,709,069
            -      18 $= 2 \times 9$
          370,888
            -      16 $= 2 \times 8$
           37,072
            -       4 $= 2 \times 2$
            3,703
            -       6 $= 2 \times 3$
              364
            -       8 $= 2 \times 2$
               28

    $7 \mid 28$ so $7 \mid 3,709,069$

    (b)   275,555
            -      10 $= 2 \times 5$
           27,545
            -      10 $= 2 \times 5$
            2,744
            -       8 $= 2 \times 4$
              266
            -      12 $= 2 \times 6$
               14

    $7 \mid 14$ so $7 \mid 275,555$

    (c)   39,486
            -      12 $= 2 \times 6$
            3,936
            -      12 $= 2 \times 6$
              381
            -       2 $= 2 \times 1$
               36

    $7 \nmid$ so $7 \nmid 39,486$

10. (a) F. Try 24.
     (b) F. Try 12.

11. (a) False $2 \mid 18$ and $6 \mid 18$ but
              $12 \nmid 18$
     (b) False $6 \mid 4 \cdot 15$ but $6 \nmid 4$ and
              $6 \nmid 15$

12. (a) T. $8 \mid 608$ and
              $3 \mid (3 + 2 + 5 + 6 + 8)$.
     (b) F. $9 \nmid (1 + 3 + 7 + 5)$
     (c) T. $40 \mid 800$
     (d) T. $4 \mid 16$ and
              $9 \mid (6+7+7+9+1+6)$

13. All are composite.
     (a) even
     (b) a multiple of 127
     (c) a multiple of 3

14. 2, 3, 5, 7, 11, 13, 17, 19, 23. No
     other primes need to be checked.

15. (a) Yes   (b) No

16. Let $r = a \cdot 10^3 + b \cdot 10^2 + c \cdot 10 + d$ be
     any 4 digit number.
     Rewrite:
     $r = a(999+1) + b(99+1) + c(9+1) + d$
     $= a \cdot 999 + a + b \cdot 99 + b + c \cdot 9 + c + d$
     $= (a \cdot 111 + b \cdot 11 + c)9 + (a + b + c + d)$
     Since $9 \mid 9$ it also divides
     $(a \cdot 111 + b \cdot 11 + c) \cdot 9$. Thus, if
     $9 \mid (a + b + c + d)$, it is true that
     $9 \mid r$.

17. Observe that $4 \mid 10^n$ for $n \geq 2$ and
     that $8 \mid 10^n$ for $n \geq 3$. Then make
     a proof modifying the proof for
     divisibility by 2.

18. $9! - 8! + \ldots + 1! = 326981 =$
     79×4139

19. (a) 31, 37, 41, 43, 47, 53, 59
     (b) 53, 59, 61, 67, 71 (and others)
     (c) 101, 103, 107, 109 (and
          others)

20. Yes, we have checked all primes p
     such that $p^2 \leq 211$.

21. False.   When $n = 41$, $n^2 - n + 41 =$
     $41^2 - 41 + 41 = 41^2$, a composite.

20. $2^3 - 1 = 7$, a prime;
     $2^5 - 1 = 31$, a prime;
     $2^7 - 1 = 127$, a prime;
     $2^{13} - 1 = 8191$, a prime.

23. Every number can be expressed as one of the following: $6n$, $6n + 1$, $6n + 2$, $6n + 3$, $6n - 2$, or $6n - 1$. But $6 \mid 6n$, $2 \mid (6n + 2)$, $3 \mid (6n + 3)$, and $2 \mid (6n - 2)$. Thus the only ones that could be primes are $6n + 1$ or $6n - 1$.

24. No, sum of two odd numbers is even. All evens, except 2, are composite.

25. Answers will vary.

26. 3,5,7 is the only prime triple. For suppose p, $p+ 2$, $p+ 4$ is another prime triple. Then p *is* not a multiple of 3, so (i) $p = 3k + 1$ or (ii) $p = 3k + 2$. If $p = 3k + 1$, then $p + 2 = 3k + 1 + 2 = 3k + 3$, which is a multiple of 3, hence not prime. If $p = 3k + 2$, then $p + 4 = 3k + 2 + 4 = 3k + 6$, which again is a multiple of 3. Thus p, $p + 2$, and $p + 4$ can all be prime only when $p = 3$.

27. (a) $17 - 5$
    (b) $43 - 23$
    (c) $41 - 13$
    Note: Each part has many possible answers.

28. One possible solution:
    Row 1 - 67, 1,43;
    Row 2 13,37,61;
    Row 3 - 31, 73,7

29. No - according to Fundamental Theorem of Arithmetic, there is exactly one way to write any number as a product of prime

30. 16, 25

31. $2^3 \times 3 \times 5 \times 7 = 840$

32. $2^4 \times 3^2 \times 5^2 \times 7 \times 11 \times 13 \times 17 \times 19 \times 23$

33. 5. Proof: $n + (n + 1) + (n + 2) + (n + 3) + (n + 4) = 5n + 10 = 5(n + 2)$.

34. Yes

35. (a) 9
    (b) 99
    (c) 9

36. True. This can be proved using the test for divisibility by 3.

37. $16.22 or $5.11

38. (a) 2
    (b) 24
    (c) 248

39. 428571

40. 6 and 66 years old.

41. True. Let n = any whole number. Then
    $n + (n + 1) + (n + 2) + ... + [n + (m-2)] + [n + (m - 1)] = mn + \dfrac{(m-1)m}{2} = m[n + \dfrac{(m-1)}{2}]$.

    Therefore (since m is odd, $n + m$-1 is a whole number) the m consecutive whole numbers beginning with n are divisible by m.

42. 349 at $1.73

43. (a) 9   (b) 10

44. Numbers that have a multiple of six 9s as digits.

45. 27,374,985

46. Yes

47. Let x and y be any two consecutive numbers in the Fibonacci sequence. Then, the next eight numbers are $x + y$, $x + 2y$, $2x + 3y$, $3x + 5y$, $5x + 8y$, $8x + 13y$, $13x + 21y$, and $21x + 34y$. The sum of these ten numbers is $55x + 88y$, a multiple of 11.

48. This table should be created on a spreadsheet.

n	p(n)	n	p(n)
1	43	11	173
2	47	12	197
3	53	13	223
4	61	14	251
5	71	15	281
6	83	16	313
7	97	17	347
8	113	18	383
9	131	19	421
10	151	20	461

49. This question seems to indicate some confusion with the distributive property. The second part of the statement represents a conditional which is true in one direction but not true in the other. It is true that if $a \mid b$ and $a \mid c$, then $a \mid (b - c)$. However, it is not true in general that if $a \mid (b -c)$, then $a \mid b$ and $a \mid c$ as the example "If 5 divides (32 - 22), then 5 divides 32 and 5 divides 22," shows.

Problems related to the NCTM Standards and Curriculum Focal Points

1. In order to determine whether a number is prime or composite, one must look at the number and then think through their division facts to know if it has any whole number divisors. This may also be done by thinking through the multiplication facts to see if any two numbers multiplied together are equal to the number of interest.

2. Which is bigger 3/7 or 39/91? When determining the fractions that are equivalent to 3/7, one must use the multiples of 3 and 7. To simplify a fraction like 39/91 one must determine the prime factorizations of both numerator and denominator in order to see the common factors that can be divided out. Either of these methods could be used to see that these fractions are the same.

Section 5.2

1. (a) 9   (b) 16   (c) 2016
   (d) 45

2. (a) $120 = 2 \times 2 \times 2 \times 3 \times 5$
   (b) $2, 3, 4 = 2 \times 2, 5,$
       $6 = 2 \times 3, 8 = 2 \times 2 \times 2,$
       $10 = 2 \times 5, 12 = 2 \times 2 \times 3,$
       etc.
   (c) Same factors, not used more times than in (a)
   (d) Prime factors of n are 11 and/or 13, not more than 5 factors of 11 and 3 factors of 13.

3. (a) 18   (b) 1   (c) 17

4. (a) 6   (b) 111   (c) 3   (d) 1

5. (a) 22   (b) 9   (c) 2

6. (a) 2   (b) 6   (c) 8   (d) 7
   (e) 39   (f) 169

7. (a) check 2, 4
   (b) check 13
   (c) check 3, 11

8. (a) 105   (b) 70   (c) 300
   (d) 264   (e) 910   (f) 209,920

9. (a) $1260 = 2^2 \cdot 3^2 \cdot 5 \cdot 7$
   (b) $59,400 = 2^3 \cdot 3^3 \cdot 5^2 \cdot 11$
   (c) $36,036 = 2^2 \cdot 3^2 \cdot 7 \cdot 11 \cdot 13$

10. (a) 357   (b) 1443   (c) 1125

11. (a) (i)

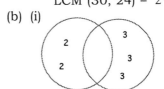

   (ii) GCF (30, 24) = $2 \cdot 3$
        LCM (30, 24) = $2 \cdot 2 \cdot 2 \cdot 3 \cdot 5$
   (b) (i)

(ii) GCF(4, 27) = 1
LCM(4, 27) = $2 \cdot 2 \cdot 3 \cdot 3 \cdot 3$

(c) (i)

(ii) GCF(18, 45) = $3 \cdot 3$
LCM(18, 45) = $2 \cdot 3 \cdot 3 \cdot 5$

12. LCM(a, b) except when $a = b$, in which case they are equal.

13. (a) abundant   (b) perfect
    (c) abundant   (d) deficient

14. (a) 1648:
    1 + 2 + 4 + 8 + 16 + 103 + 206 + 412 + 824 = 1576
    1576:
    1 + 2 + 4 + 8 + 197 + 394 + 788 = 1394
    No
    (b) 2620:
    1 + 2 + 4 + 5 + 10 + 20 + 131 + 262 + 524 + 655 + 1310 = 2924
    2924:
    1 + 2 + 4 + 17 + 34 + 43 + 68 + 86 + 172 + 731 + 1462 = 2620
    Yes
    (c) 18, 416

15. (a) 248:
    2 + 4 + 8 + 31 + 62 + 124 = 231
    231:
    3 + 7 + 11 + 21 + 33 + 77 = 152
    NO
    (b) 1050:
    2 + 3 + 5 + 7 + 10 + 14 + 15 + 21 + 25 + 30 + 35 + 42 + 50 + 70 + 75 + 105 + 150 + 210 + 350 + 525 = 1925
    1925:
    5 + 7 + 11 + 25 + 35 + 55 + 77 + 175 + 275 + 385 = 1050
    Yes
    (c) 1575:
    3 + 5 + 7 + 9 + 15 + 21 + 25 + 35 + 45 + 63 + 75 + 105 + 175 + 315 + 525 = 1648

1648:
2 + 4 + 8 + 16 + 103 + 206 + 412 + 824 = 1575
Yes

16. (a) 3:   1,3   2
    4:   1,2,4   3
    5:   1,5   2
    6:   1,2,3,6   4
    7:   1,7   2
    8:   1,2,4,8   4
    9:   1,3,9   3
    10: 1,2,5,10   4
    11: 1,11   2
    12: 1,2,3,4,6,12   6
    13: 1,13   2
    14: 1,2,7,14   4
    15: 1,3,5,15   4
    16: 1,2,4,8,16   5
    (b) prime numbers
    (c) perfect square

17. (a) p
    (b) p^2
    (c) pq or p^3
    (d) p^4
    (e) p^5 or $p^2 q$
    (f) p^{11}, $p^5 q$, $p^3 q^2$, $p^2 q r$

18. (a) b is a multiple of a
    (b) a is a multiple of b
    (c) both a and b are 1
    (d) The only common factor of a and b is 1, i.e. GCF (a, b) = 1.

19. GCF(x^2, y^2) = 1. The prime factorizations of x and y share no primes. In x^2 and y^2 those same primes occur, just twice as often, so still none are common.

20. 496 is the sum of the cubes of 1,3,5, and 7. 8128 is the sum of the cubes of the odd numbers 1 through 15.

21. 5, 6

22. 136 miles

23. LCM(3, 4, 5) = 60 so 60 minutes after 11 was the first time all 3 dogs barked together again.

24. 90 since $90 = 2^1 \times 3^2 \times 5^1$, there are $(1+1)(2+1)(1+1) = 12$ factors.

25. 60 has 12 factors.

26. $23 \cdot 28 \cdot 33 = 21,252$

27. $494 \div 13 = 38$. $100a + 10b + a = 100a + 10(13 - a) + a = 91a + 10 \times 13 = (7a + 10)13$

28. $4 + 9 + 3 + 7 + 7 + 7 + 5 = 42$, $4,937,775 = 5 \times 5 \times 3 \times 65,837$, and $5 + 5 + 3 + 6 + 5 + 8 + 3 + 7 = 42$.

29. (a) 4
    (b) 8
    (c) $(\dfrac{m + n}{GCF(m, n)} - 1) \times GCF(m, n)$

30. $1729 = 12^3 + 1^3 = 10^3 + 9^3$

31. 377 and 233. Any pair of consecutive Fibonacci numbers beyond the 12th one. Other answers are possible.

32. Many students may have seen the abbreviation LCD which stands for Lowest Common Denominator. This is actually the same thing as the LCM of the denominators in a fraction problem. GCD means Greatest Common Divisor, and that is the same as GCF.

Problems related to the NCTM Standards and Curriculum Focal Points

1. By knowing the division facts you can quickly identify factors of a number and can then see common factors of multiple numbers in order to find the GCF. Similarly, quick recall of multiplication facts help in finding multiples of numbers and thus the LCM is easier to find.

2. When adding or subtracting fractions, a lowest common denominator is often needed. The LCM is the same as the lowest common denominator. Simplifying fractions requires dividing out common factors between the numerator and denominator. Thus the GCF can be used to simplify fractions.

3. When you need to solve equations like $x^2 - 6x - 91 = 0$, knowing whether or not 91 is prime or can be factored and what the factorization might be is critical. As mentioned before, LCMs and GCFs are also used in working with fractions in algebra.

Chapter Review

Problems for Writing/Discussion

1. The tests for divisibility by 3 or 9 involve finding the sum of the digits. However, this rule does not apply for divisibility by other factors, such as 2, 4, or 6, which have their own rules. For example, the sum of the digits of 765 is 18. Hence 765 is divisible by 3 and 9, but none of 2, 4, or 6 divide it.

2. The best way to proceed would be to look at the square root of the number, then move up (or down) from there, dividing until you find a factor. For example, the square root of 68370 is about 261.5, so you might try dividing by 261, 260, and so on until you found a number that divided 68370 evenly. In fact, $68370 = 258 \times 265$. Also, $261^2 = 68,121$.

3. The tests for divisibility by 5 and 7 are different. A number is divisible by 5 if and only if the last digit is a 5 or 0. However,

numbers divisible by 7 can have any number for a last digit. Try counting by 7; the last digits of your answers are, in order, 7, 4, 1, 8, 5, 2, 9, 6, 3, and 0. This cycle of numbers repeats indefinitely.

4. A number of shortcuts can be taken. For example, if you find 47 is not divisible by 2 or by 3, then you know it cannot be divisible by 6, which is the product of 2 and 3. In fact, once you know it is not divisible by 2, you know it is not divisible by any even number. Furthermore, once you reach the square root of 47, which is less than 7, you know you will be able to stop looking for factors. Therefore, you would have to check the numbers from 2 to 5. All of them can be quickly eliminated using tests for divisibility.

5. The LCM of 48 and 66 would be the product of all the factors shown, i.e., $2 \times 2 \times 2 \times 2 \times 3 \times 11 =$ 528. The GCF of 56 and 91 would be 7; the LCM of those two numbers is 728.

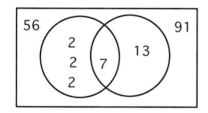

6. Both ideas still work. The GCF will still be the overlap of the three numbers (3), and the LCM can be found by multiplying all the numbers in the circles together ($2 \times 2 \times 2 \times 3 \times 3 \times 19$).

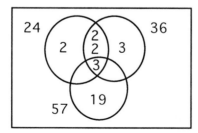

7. The multiples of 5 and 7 will lie on oblique lines that criss-cross the array. The square root of 100 is 10, but 7 is the greatest prime less than 10. Once you have crossed out all the multiples of 2, 3, 5, and 7 (the primes $\leq$ 10), you have already crossed out all multiples of 8, 9, and 10, so all the remaining numbers are primes.

8. If 1 were considered a prime, then one person might give the prime factorization of 35 as 7×5, but another might say it was $7 \times 5 \times 1$. The Fundamental Theorem of Arithmetic says the prime factorization of numbers is unique: there is only one possible answer, except that the factors can be rearranged. But in the given example, one person is giving 2 factors while the other person gives 3. Disallowing 1 as a prime eliminates this contradiction.

9. $12 = 3 \times 4$, so if a number is divisible by 3 and by 4, it will be divisible by 12. To be more specific, if the sum of the digits of the number is divisible by 3 *and* the number represented by the last two digits is divisible by 4, then the number will be divisible by 12. For example, 84 is divisible by 12 since (i) $3 \mid (4+8)$ and (ii) $4 \mid 4$.

10. Probably your answer to problem 9 was a conjecture. To turn it into a theorem, you would have to provide a proof where each step could be justified by known results.

Chapter 6

Section 6.1

1. (a) 5/8   (b) 3/10
   (c) 4/6   (d) 9/4

2. (a) (i)

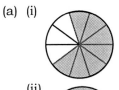

   (ii)

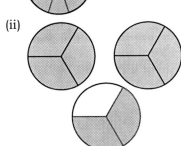

   (b) (i)

   (ii)

   (c) (i)

   (ii)

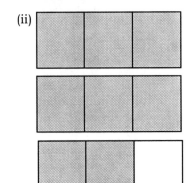

   (d) (i)

   (ii)

3. (a)

(b)

(c)

4. Yes. The shaded rectangles represent ½ and the shaded triangles represent ¼. Thus, the shaded region represents ¾.

5. (a) 9/40   (b) 5/40   (c) 7/40

6. (a) False, total days not the same for each month
   (b) True
   (c) False, each part (month) not equivalent size

7.

The same amount is shaded in both figures.

8. (a) F   (b) F
   (c) T   (d) T

9. (a) and (d)

10. (a) 21/17   (b) 14/3
    (c) 5/7   (d) 29/2

11. (a) $5\dfrac{28}{111}$ (b) $62\dfrac{1}{3}$

12. (a) 7/13 < 14/25 < 4/7
    (b) 2/9 < 3/11 < 5/18 < 7/23

13. $\dfrac{ad+bc}{2bd}$ is midway between $\dfrac{a}{b}$ and $\dfrac{c}{d}$ since it is the average of the two.

14. Only fractions in (a) are equal.
    In (b) $\dfrac{1516}{2312} < \dfrac{4196}{5202} < \dfrac{2653}{2890}$.
    In (c) $\dfrac{516}{892} < \dfrac{1892}{3268} < \dfrac{1376}{2376}$

15. (a) $\dfrac{20}{230}, \dfrac{9}{100}$ (b) $\dfrac{4}{20}, \dfrac{20}{100}$

(c) $\dfrac{17}{230}$, $\dfrac{7}{100}$ (d) $\dfrac{7}{17}$, $\dfrac{41}{100}$

$\dfrac{1666}{6664}$, $\dfrac{2666666}{6666665}$, $\dfrac{1999}{9995}$

16. Both

17. Mr. Roberts' s class

18. There are many correct possibilities. One is shown for each case.

(a)

(b)

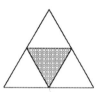

(c)

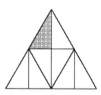

(d)

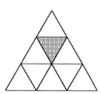

(e)

20. Yes, this process can continue. No, there is no smallest fraction greater than 0.

21. The size of the unit is different so comparison cannot be made.

22. (a) 672   (b) 11,193

23. Greater than - the fraction is always closer to one.

24. For example, 2001/6000, 2002/6000,..., 2999/6000

25. $80,000,000,000

26. 8/17

27. $2,800

28. Approximately 9.3 km

29. (a) In order, from nearest to farthest: Kelly, Janet, Cathy, Rose, Ann
    (b) 2.5 K

30. (a)

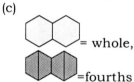

= whole,   = thirds

= whole,   = thirds

(b)

= whole,   = sixths

(c)

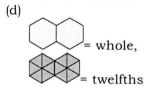

= whole,

=fourths

(d)

= whole,

= twelfths

19. (a) (i) $\dfrac{16}{64} = \dfrac{1}{4}$ (ii) $\dfrac{19}{95} = \dfrac{1}{5}$

(iii) $\dfrac{26}{65} = \dfrac{2}{5}$

(iv) $\dfrac{199}{995} = \dfrac{1}{5}$

(v) $\dfrac{26666}{66665} = \dfrac{2}{5}$

(b) Answers will vary here, but some examples are:

31. Many correct answers are possible. If the child can use a calculator, one way would be to show 3/4 = .75 and 3/5 = .60. So that any number like .61, .62, etc. would be "between." If the child is not comfortable with calculators or decimals yet, one could find equal fractions with like denominators. 3/4 = 15/20 and 3/5 = 12/20, so 13/20 or 14/20 would be between the two numbers.

32. These activities highlight that the wholes can be different shapes, the parts are always equal and most importantly, it provides a bridge from the concrete representation of a picture to the abstract representation of numerals.

Problems related to the NCTM Standards and Curriculum Focal Points

1. Three possible ideas are: 1) the denominator represents the number of pieces a whole is cut into, 2) those pieces are all of equal size, and 3) the numerator represents how many of those pieces are of interest.

2. One possible representation is an area model cut into equal sized pieces and a certain number of them shaded. Another representation is a set of objects where some of the objects have different attributes than the rest. A number line is also a possible representation. Answers may vary.

3. "Parts of unit wholes" is shown in Set A #1a. A "part of a collection" is shown in Set A #1c. A location on a number line is represented in SetA #2. An example of division of whole numbers occurs when one thinks of dividing 3 brownies evenly among 4 people. More abstractly, this is dividing 3 by 4.

Section 6.2

1. (a)

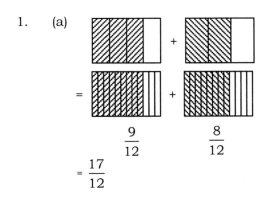

$$= \frac{17}{12}$$

(b) $\frac{3}{4} + \frac{2}{3} = 1\frac{5}{12}$

2.
$$\frac{5}{8} + \frac{1}{6} = \frac{15}{24} + \frac{4}{24} = \frac{19}{24}$$
$$\frac{5}{8} + \frac{1}{6} = \frac{30}{48} + \frac{8}{48} = \frac{38}{48} = \frac{19}{24}$$
$$\frac{5}{8} + \frac{1}{6} = \frac{45}{72} + \frac{12}{72} = \frac{57}{72} = \frac{19}{24}$$
$$\frac{5}{8} + \frac{1}{6} = \frac{90}{144} + \frac{24}{144} = \frac{114}{744} = \frac{19}{24}$$

Other correct answers are possible.

3. (a)

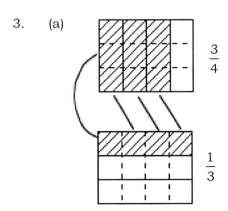

Using the comparison approach, $\frac{5}{12}$ are left.

(b)

$3\dfrac{1}{3}$

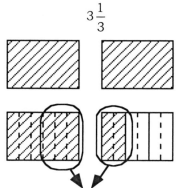

Take away $\dfrac{5}{6}$

leaves $2\dfrac{1}{2}$

4. (a) $\dfrac{5}{2^2 \times 3^3}$

    (b) $\dfrac{(5^3 \times 29) + (3^2 \times 7)}{3^2 \times 5^3 \times 7^3 \times 29}$

    (c) $\dfrac{(3^2 \times 13) + (5^3 \times 7^5)}{3^2 \times 5^4 \times 7^5 \times 13^3}$

    (d) $\dfrac{11^5 + [17 \times 53^5 \times 67^4]}{11^5 \times 17^3 \times 53^5 \times 67^{13}}$

4. (a) $11\dfrac{2}{3}$

    (b) $4\dfrac{3}{4}$

    (c) $8\dfrac{1}{6}$

    (d) $3\dfrac{2}{5}$

5. (a) $5/12 + 4/12$

    0   9/12   1

    (b) $1/5 + 7/15$

    0   2/3

    (c) $1/3 + 5/12$

    0   3/4   1

6. (a) (i) 41/24   (ii) 41/24
        (iii) 3/8   (iv) 1/24
    (b) Addition of fractions is
        associative, but subtraction of
        fractions is not.

7. (a) $11\dfrac{2}{3}$

    (b) $4\dfrac{3}{4}$

    (c) $8\dfrac{1}{6}$

    (d) $3\dfrac{2}{5}$

8. (a) $77/45 = 1\dfrac{32}{45}$

    (b) $511/24 = 21\dfrac{7}{24}$

    (c) $21\dfrac{22}{45}$

    (d) $6\dfrac{1}{24}$

9. (a) 554/675   (b) 73/156

10. (a) $1\dfrac{5}{8}$

    (b) $3\dfrac{2}{15}$

    (c) $9\dfrac{2}{11}$

11. (a) $5\dfrac{4}{9} - 3 = 2\dfrac{4}{9}$

    (b) $9\dfrac{2}{6} - 3 = 6\dfrac{1}{3}$

    (c) $21\dfrac{5}{7} - 9 = 12\dfrac{5}{7}$

    (d) $5\dfrac{8}{11} - 3 = \dfrac{8}{11}$

12. (a) (i) 11 to 13   (ii) 12
    (b) (i) 12 to 14   (ii) 14
    (c) (i) 17 to 20   (ii) 18

13. (a) $6 + 6\dfrac{1}{2} = \dfrac{1}{2}$

    (b) $8 + 5\dfrac{1}{2} = 13\dfrac{1}{2}$

(c) $8 + 2\frac{1}{2} + 7 = 17\frac{1}{2}$

14. $\sim 4 \cdot 6 = 24$

15. (a) $1\frac{29}{30}$ (b) $\frac{18}{35}$

17. 8

18. 8

19. 52 bags

20. 45 minutes

21. $35'\frac{1}{2}"$

22. Amy: $2\frac{1}{2}$ Robert: $\frac{7}{15}$
    Review simpler problems, meaning of mixed numbers, use diagrams.

23. (a) $8^2 + 15^2 = 17^2$, 17
    (b) (i) $\frac{1}{7} + \frac{1}{9} = \frac{16}{63}$,
    $16^2 + 63^2 = 65^2$
    (ii) $\frac{1}{11} + \frac{1}{13} = \frac{24}{143}$,
    $24^2 + 143^2 = 145^2$
    (iii) $\frac{1}{19} + \frac{1}{21} = \frac{40}{399}$,
    $40^2 + 399^2 = 401^2$
    (c) The third number, c, is two more than the denominator of the sum.
    (d) $\frac{1}{2n-1} + \frac{1}{2n+1} = \frac{4n}{4n^2-1}$ and
    $(4n)^2 + (4n^2 - 1)^2 = (4n^2 + 1)^2$

24. 11/23

25. (a) 7/8, 15/16, 31/32,
    (b) 7   (c) 1

26. (a) 1/5 - 2/5 is not a fraction
    (b) 3/4 - 1/4 ≠ 1/4 - 3/4
    (c) (4/5 - 3/5) - 1/5 ≠ 4/5 - (3/5 - 1/5)

27. (a) $\frac{1}{6}$ $\frac{1}{30}$ $\frac{1}{60}$ $\frac{1}{60}$ $\frac{1}{30}$ $\frac{1}{6}$

    $\frac{1}{7}$ $\frac{1}{42}$ $\frac{1}{105}$ $\frac{1}{140}$ $\frac{1}{105}$ $\frac{1}{42}$ $\frac{1}{7}$

    (b) The first number in the nth row is $\frac{1}{n}$.
    (c) Each fraction in the triangle is the sum of the two fractions directly below it. For example,
    $\frac{1}{30} + \frac{1}{20} = \frac{1}{12}$.

28. (a) 5/12 - 1/3 = 1/12 and
    11/12 - 1/3 = 7/12
    (b) 6/12 - 1/6 = 1/3 and
    2/3 - 6/12 = 1/6

29. One way would be to use an area model for fraction addition.

30. This rearrangement is impossible.

31. You might start by agreeing with the student that in the real world the word *fraction* often means a small part. However, when we are writing numerical fractions, they can be quite large. For example, how big is 5/2? That's bigger than 1. 99/100 is a proper fraction, but it is much closer to 1 than to 1/2 or 0.

32. Since the denominator of a fraction describes the size of pieces the whole is cut into, two fractions with different denominators have different sized pieces. In order for each fraction to represent the same sized pieces, they are rewritten with a common denominator.

Problems related to the NCTM Standards and Curriculum Focal Points

1. One important concept in adding fractions is recognizing the need for the two fractions being added or subtracted to have the same

size pieces. Having the same size pieces is the same as having a common denominator.

2. One possible meaning is for students to be able to sketch an area, set or number line model to represent each fraction. They can then combine or compare the representations of the individual fractions to find the sum or difference.

3. From the student's experience, they should have or develop a good sense of whether a fraction is close to a half or one. This knowledge can then be used to estimate addition and subtractions of fractions by rounding to the nearest half or whole.

Section 6.3

1. (a)
$$\frac{1}{5} \quad \frac{1}{5} \quad \frac{1}{5}$$
of 2 of 2 of 2

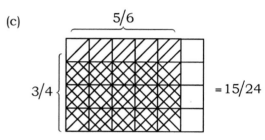

(b)
$$\frac{3}{5} \qquad \frac{3}{5}$$

2. (a)

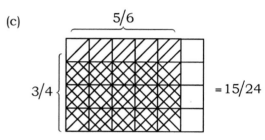

(b)

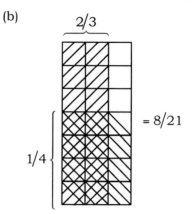
= 8/21

(c)

5/6

= 15/24

3. (a) $\dfrac{2}{3} \times \dfrac{4}{5} = \dfrac{8}{15}$

(b) $\dfrac{3}{4} \times \dfrac{7}{12} = \dfrac{21}{48}$

4. (a) 4/13   (b) 4/13

5. (a) 3/16, 5/8, 9/10, 7/5
(b) 5/7,   10/9, 8/5,   16/3
(c) They are reversed.

6. (a) Distributive
(b) Associative
(c) Commutative and Associative

7. (a)

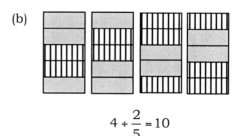

$$2 \div \frac{2}{3} = 3$$

(b)

$$4 \div \frac{2}{5} = 10$$

(c)

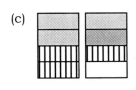

$$1\frac{3}{4} \div \frac{1}{2} = 3\frac{1}{2}$$

8.   (a)

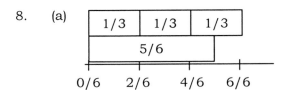

(b)

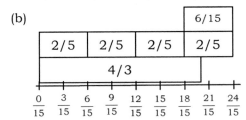

(c)

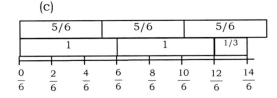

9.   (a) $\dfrac{5}{8} \div \dfrac{3}{8} = \dfrac{5}{3}$

     (b) $\dfrac{12}{13} \div \dfrac{4}{15} = \dfrac{12}{4} = 3$

     (c) $\dfrac{13}{15} \div \dfrac{28}{30} = \dfrac{26}{30} \div \dfrac{28}{30} = \dfrac{26}{28} = \dfrac{13}{14}$

10.   (a) $\dfrac{12}{15} \div \dfrac{4}{5} = \dfrac{3}{3} = 1$

     (b) $\dfrac{18}{24} \div \dfrac{9}{6} = \dfrac{2}{4} = \dfrac{1}{2}$

     (c) $\dfrac{30}{39} \div \dfrac{6}{13} = \dfrac{5}{3} = 1\dfrac{2}{3}$

     (d) $\dfrac{28}{33} \div \dfrac{14}{11} = \dfrac{2}{3}$

11.   (a) $\dfrac{3}{4} \div \dfrac{6}{9} = \boxed{}$ so

        $\dfrac{6}{9} \times \boxed{} = \dfrac{3}{4}$

$$\frac{9}{6} \times \frac{6}{9} \times \boxed{} = \frac{9}{6} \times \frac{3}{4}$$

$$\boxed{} = \frac{27}{24} = 1\frac{1}{8}$$

(b) $\dfrac{10}{7} \div \dfrac{8}{11} = \boxed{}$ so

     $\dfrac{8}{11} \times \boxed{} = \dfrac{10}{7}$

     $\dfrac{11}{8} \times \dfrac{8}{11} \times \boxed{} = \dfrac{11}{8} \times \dfrac{10}{7}$

     $\boxed{} = \dfrac{110}{56} = 1\dfrac{27}{28}$

(c) $\dfrac{5}{6} \div \dfrac{2}{3} = \boxed{}$ so

     $\dfrac{2}{3} \times \boxed{} = \dfrac{5}{6}$

     $\dfrac{3}{2} \times \dfrac{2}{3} \times \boxed{} = \dfrac{3}{2} \times \dfrac{5}{6}$

     $\boxed{} = \dfrac{15}{12} = 1\dfrac{1}{4}$

12.   (a) $\dfrac{4}{3} = 1\dfrac{1}{3}$

     (b) $\dfrac{8}{4} = 2$

     (c) $\dfrac{4}{3} = 1\dfrac{1}{3}$

13.   (a)   4/15   (b)   3/5
     (c)   77/1,000,000
     (d)   8/9
     (e)   34/35   (f)   103/105
     (g)   26/35   (h) $41\dfrac{8}{35}$

14.   (a)   3/4   (b)   18

15.   (a) $1\dfrac{77}{445}$ (b) $104\dfrac{5}{24}$

     (c) $114\dfrac{32}{45}$ (d)   183/328

     (e) $31\dfrac{7}{20}$ (f) $88\dfrac{13}{164}$

16.   (a)   1   (b)   88/217

17.   (a)   52(1/2) = 26

(b) $\dfrac{5}{8} + \left(\dfrac{2}{5} + \dfrac{3}{5}\right) = \dfrac{5}{8} + 1 = 1\dfrac{5}{8}$

(c) $\left(\dfrac{3}{7} \times \dfrac{7}{3}\right) \times \dfrac{1}{9} = 1 \times \dfrac{1}{9} = \dfrac{1}{9}$

(d) $7 + 23\left(\dfrac{3}{7} + \dfrac{4}{7}\right) = 7 + 23(1) = 30$

18.   (a) $20 \times 5\dfrac{1}{2} = 110$

      (b) $75 \div 25 = 3$

      (c) $56 \div 8 = 7$

      (d) $25 \times 4 = 6$

19.   (a)   36   (b)   27

20.   (a) $50 \times 246 = \dfrac{24,600}{2} = 12,300$

      (b) $84,602 \times 50$

            $= \dfrac{8,460,200}{2}$

            $= 4,230,100$

      (c) $75 \times 848 = \dfrac{3}{4} \times 84,800$

            $= 3 \times 21,200$

            $= 63,600$

      (d) $420 \times 75 = 42,000 \times \dfrac{3}{4}$

            $= 10,500 \times 3$

            $= 31,500$

21.   (a)   Yes   (b)   No

22.   (a)   15/14   (b)   5/2

      (c)   7/2   (d)   3/50

23. $\dfrac{2}{7} < \dfrac{2+3}{7+8} < \dfrac{3}{8}$ and

     $\dfrac{16}{56} < \dfrac{20}{56} < \dfrac{21}{56}$

24.   125.4 billion

25.   270 bottles

26. $4\dfrac{1}{2}$ yards, $2\dfrac{1}{4}$ yards

27.   \$2100,   \$3200

28. $1\dfrac{1}{3}$ pounds

29.   \$0.50

30.   1/3

31.   3/4

32.   Abigail: 4/12 = 1/3

      Harold: 24/20 = 6/5

33.   (a)   96 eggs   (b)   12 days

      (c)   9 chickens

34.   Top row: $2\dfrac{2}{3}$

      Second row: $2\dfrac{1}{2}$, $3\dfrac{1}{2}$,   1/4

      Third row: 1/2

      Bottom row: $15\dfrac{5}{9}$

35. $x + y = 18$ $xy = 40$

     $\dfrac{1}{x} + \dfrac{1}{y} = \dfrac{y+x}{xy}$

     $(x + y)^2 = x^2 + 2xy + y^2$

     (a)   18/40 = 9/20

     (b) $18^2 = x^2 + y^2 + 80$, thus

          $x^2 + y^2 = 244$.

36.   (a) $6 + 1\dfrac{1}{5} = 6 \times 1\dfrac{1}{5}$

          $7 + 1\dfrac{1}{6} = 7 \times 1\dfrac{1}{6}$

     (b)   Using a variable, check to see

          that $x + 1\dfrac{1}{x} = x \times 1\dfrac{1}{x}$.

37.   (a) $\dfrac{a}{b} < \dfrac{c}{d}$ means for some nonzero

          $\dfrac{m}{n}$, $\dfrac{a}{b} + \dfrac{m}{n} = \dfrac{c}{d}$ and

          $\dfrac{c}{d} < \dfrac{e}{f}$ means for some nonzero

          $\dfrac{p}{q}$, $\dfrac{c}{d} + \dfrac{p}{q} = \dfrac{e}{f}$. Replacing

$\frac{c}{d}$ in the second equation

yields $(\frac{a}{b} + \frac{m}{n}) + \frac{p}{q} = \frac{e}{f}$,

or $\frac{a}{b} + (\frac{m}{n} + \frac{p}{q}) = \frac{e}{f}$, where

$\frac{m}{n} + \frac{p}{q}$ is a nonzero fraction, so

$\frac{a}{b} < \frac{e}{f}$ by the alternative

definition.

(b) $\frac{a}{b} < \frac{c}{d}$ means for some

nonzero $\frac{m}{n}$, $\frac{a}{b} + \frac{m}{n} = \frac{c}{d}$, so

$\frac{c}{d} + \frac{e}{f} = (\frac{a}{b} + \frac{m}{n}) + \frac{e}{f}$

$= (\frac{a}{b} + \frac{e}{f}) + \frac{m}{n}$. Thus

$\frac{a}{b} + \frac{e}{f} < \frac{c}{d} + \frac{e}{f}$, by the

alternative definition.

(c) As in parts (a) and (b), show

that $\frac{a}{b}\frac{e}{f} + \frac{m}{n}\frac{e}{f} = \frac{c}{d}\frac{e}{f}$, thus

$\frac{a}{b}\frac{e}{f} < \frac{c}{d}\frac{e}{f}$.

38. 60

39. (a) 2 3/4 + 5 7/8 = 2 + 3/4 + 5 + 7/8 = 2 + 7/8 + 5 + 3/4 = 2 7/8 + 5 3/4

(b) (2 + 3/4) × (5 + 7/8) ≠ (2 + 7/8) × (5 + 3/4)

40. Since 9 ÷ 6 can be rewritten as 9 × $\frac{1}{6} = \frac{9}{6}$ and 6 ÷ 9 can be rewritten as 6 × $\frac{1}{9} = \frac{6}{9}$, it looks as if this will always work. In general, the answer is "Yes." The only exception is division by zero. For example, 3 ÷ 0 and 0 ÷ 3 are not reciprocals because 3 ÷ 0 is undefined.

Problems related to the NCTM Standards and Curriculum Focal Points

1. One possible example is the representation in Figure 6.23 which shows the division of fractions from a partitive perspective. Answers may vary.

2. When using the common denominator method for division of fractions, you may need to first get both fractions in terms of a common denominator. Rewriting fractions with a common denominator requires an understanding of equivalent fractions. Answers may vary.

3. From the student's experience, they should have or develop a good sense of whether a fraction is close to a half. This knowledge can then be used to estimate multiplication by fractions close to a half by just dividing by 2. Answers may vary.

Chapter Review

Problems for Writing/Discussion

1. Multiplying the numerator and denominator by the same number, like 5 for instance, is like multiplying the fraction by $\frac{5}{5}$ which equals 1. It is true that multiplying by 1 does not change the value of a number. Adding the same number to the numerator and denominator of a fraction is quite different. Take $\frac{2}{5}$, for example. If you add 3 to the numerator and denominator, the result is $\frac{5}{8}$, which is not equal to $\frac{2}{5}$.

2. Getting common denominators for addition, subtraction, and division

is helpful. However, it complicates multiplication.

3. In the example $5y$, there is an implied multiplication: $5y$ means $5 \times y$. When we write a number and a fraction together, as in $3\frac{1}{4}$, the implied operation is addition: $3\frac{1}{4}$ means $3 + \frac{1}{4}$. $2\frac{3}{5}x$ is an awkward expression. It means $(2 + \frac{3}{5})x$. Rewriting it as $\frac{13}{5}x$ would make it a little easier to read.

4. It is important to learn how to change improper fractions into mixed numbers. In $3\frac{7}{9}$, $\frac{7}{9}$ is a proper fraction.

5. Using money, if you consider how many $\frac{1}{2}$ dollars are in \$6, the answer 12 shows that dividing by a (proper) fraction produces a larger number.

6. Sometimes teachers or professors add point counts this way for grades. If the grading is based on the total number of points correct out of the total number of points assigned, then a student who had 87/100 on a test and 16/20 on a quiz would then have accumulated 103 out of 120 total points as his current grade. Getting a common denominator would make the quiz count as much as the test (which in this case would lower the grade).

    Actually, this in an example of adding ratios which are studied in the next chapter.

7. Rewriting $\frac{5}{6} \times \frac{7}{10} \times \frac{3}{14}$ as

$(5 \times \frac{1}{6}) \times (7 \times \frac{1}{10}) \times (3 \times \frac{1}{14})$ enables us to use the commutative and associative properties to rearrange the 6 numbers as we choose. So we can rewrite the product as

$(5 \times \frac{1}{10}) \times (7 \times \frac{1}{14}) \times (3 \times \frac{1}{6})$.

8. The two pizzas have different areas, so 1/4 of one would not equal 1/4 of the other. The first pizza covers an area of 64 sq. in., so 1/4 of it would be 16 sq. in. The second pizza has area 144 sq. in., so 1/6 of it would be 24 sq. in. Altogether Marilyn ate 40 sq. in. out of a total of 208 sq. in., so her fraction of the pizzas was 5/26, not 5/12.

9. When the heights of the two pizzas are equal, their volumes will be in ratio with their areas. In the former problem, we assumed, without mentioning it, that the heights were equal.

10. It would be possible to draw two circles, one divided into three equal parts and one divided into four equal parts. However, neither picture would have any shaded areas.

Chapter 7

Section 7.1

1. (a) 70.05003   (b) 3000.89
   (c) 0.025001

2. (a) (i) $5(\frac{1}{10}) + 2(\frac{1}{100}) + 5(\frac{1}{1000})$

   (ii) $\frac{525}{1000}$

   (b) (i) $3 \times 10 + 4 + \frac{7}{1000}$

   (ii) $\frac{34007}{1000}$

   (c) (i) $5 + \frac{102}{100000}$

   (ii) $\frac{50102}{10000}$

3. (a) 0.000746
   (b) 746,000.000746
   (c) 746,000,000.746

4. (a) Seventy-eight billionths.
   (b) Seven thousand five hundred eighty-nine and twelve thousand three hundred forty-five hundred thousandths.
   (c) One hundred eight-seven thousand two hundred thirteen and two thousand three hundred thousandths.
   (d) One billion one million two thousand three and one hundred thousand two ten hundred millionths.

5. Either it is read "point zero five nine" or "fifty-nine thousandths."

6. (a) and (c)

7. (a) R   (b) T, 4 places
   (c) T, 9 places   (d) T, 23 places
   Explanation: Highest power of 2 and/or 5.

8. (a) 3.078, 3.08, 3.087, 3.80
   (b) 8.0019929, 8.010019, 8.01002
   (c) 0.5, 0.5005, 0.505, 0.55

9. (a) 5/7, 10/13, 4/5
   (b) 4/11, 2/5, 3/7
   (c) 7/13, 5/9, 11/18
   (d) 17/29, 3/5, 11/18

10. (a) $\frac{1}{2} < \frac{5}{8} < \frac{17}{23}$

    (b) $\frac{2}{3} < \frac{3}{4} < \frac{13}{16}$

    (c) $\frac{8}{5} < \frac{50}{31} < \frac{26}{15}$

11. No

12. (a) $7 \times 10 = 70$
    (b) $26.58 - 9 = 17.58$
    (c) 0.00491
    (d) $6 + 6.16 = 12.16$
    (e) $5.7 + 8 = 13.7$
    (f) 67,320
    (g) 639
    (h) $72 + 6 = 78$

13. (a) $230 \times 1/10 = 23$
    (b) $36 \times 1/4 = 9$
    (c) $82 \times 1/2 = 41$
    (d) $125 \times 4/5 = 100$
    (e) $175 \times 1/5 = 35$
    (f) $3/5 \times 35 = 21$

14. (a) 1264.16
    (b) 0.00000078752
    (c) 8.25×10^{27}
    (d) 8.25×10^{13}

15. (a) $30 \times 3 = 90$ to $40 \times 4 = 160$, $35 \times 4 = 140$
    (b) 39
    (c) 60, 60 to 140
    (d) 10

16. (a) $125 \div 5 = 25$
    (b) $90 \times 8 = 720$
    (c) $400 \div 5/4 = 320$
    (d) $350 \times 2/5 = 140$
    (e) $1/4 \times 48 = 1200$
    (f) $3600 \div 3/5 = 3600 \times 5/3 = 6000$

17. (a) 321.09
    (b) 12.162
    (c) 4.009
    (d) 2.0

(e) 2.00

18. (a) Change 1.4 to 0.6.
     (b) Magic

19. D = 5, O = 2, N = 6, A = 4, L = 8, G
     = 1, E = 9, R = 7, B = 3, T = 0

20. This method for determining
     whether or not a decimal will
     repeat works only if the fraction
     under consideration has been
     written in simplest form first.
     42/150 can be simplified to 7/25.
     The factors of the denominator,
     25, are limited to 2's and 5's (in
     this case only 5's), so it is a
     terminating decimal, .28.

**Problems related to the NCTM
Standards and Curriculum Focal Points**

1. Just as the place values to the left
    of the decimal point represent 1,
    10, 100, 1000, and so forth, the
    place values to the right represent
    10ths, 100ths, 1000ths etc. In this
    way non-whole numbers are
    represented using fractions with
    denominators that are powers of
    ten.

2. Any finite decimal representation
    can be rewritten as a fraction with
    a denominator which is a power of
    10.

3. Fractions can be compared by first
    converting them to their decimal
    representation and then
    comparing the decimal numbers.

Section 7.2

1. (a) 101.782   (b) 28.135
    (c) 0.2034   (d) 21.901

2. (a) 45.92   (b) 0.1248
    (c) 148   (d) 31.2

3. (a) 23,278.9504   (b) 1279.43
    (c) 232,917.471   (d) 390.009

4. (b) and (c)

5. (a) 0.623   (b) 8.61
    (c) 0.798

6. (a) 8.6×10^2
    (b) 4.52×10^3
    (c) 2.6×10^7
    (d) 3.15×10^5
    (e) 1.084×10^9
    (f) 5.4×10^{13}

7. (a) 3.574×10^9 sec
    (b) 4.73×10^9 sec
    (c) 154,500,000,000 sec
         One hundred fifty-four billion
         five hundred million seconds

8. (a) 8.05×10^6
    (b) 6.278×10^{10}
    (c) 4.1×10^2
    (d) 8.3×10^4

9. (a) 5.9×10^{23} (b) 9.431×10^4

10. (a) 3.468×10^{40} (b) 9.5×10^{14}
    (c) 4.6656×10^{55}

11. 19.522 kilometers

12. (a) 1.2×10^{14} kilograms
    (b) 2.48×10^{18} dollars
    (c) About 290,000 times.
    (d) About $29,000 per person.
         Note: In 2001, we owed
         $21,500 each – a 35%
         increase!

13. (a) $0.3\overline{50}$ (b) $0.\overline{14}$
    (c) 0.4531596

14. (a) 0.317431743174
    (b) 0.317400000000
    (c) 0.115912311591

15. (a) 5/9
    (b) 78/99 = 26/33
    (c) 123/999 = 41/333
    (d) 123/990 = 41/330
    (e) 177/9900 = 59/3300
    (f) 123,333/999,000 =
         41,111/333,000

16. Not equal,
    $0.2\overline{525} = 0.25252525$ is smaller
    than $0.252\overline{5} = 0.2525525525$
    from the 100-thousandths place.

17. x, z, y

18. (a) 24.3, 27.5
    (b) 92.1984, 129.07776
    (c) 0.000555, 0.0005555
    (d) 9.6, 14.5
    (e) $0.8\overline{3}$, $0.8\overline{57142}$

19. (a) (i) 2 steps   (ii) 3 steps
        (iii) 1 step   (iv) 8 steps
    (b) Many answers are possible.
    One answer is 4.87.

20. (a) (i) 1/9   (ii) 1/99
        (iii) 1/999
        (iv) 1/9999
    (b) 1/999,999,999
    (c) $0.\overline{01}$

21. 1. Since $1/3 = 0.\overline{3}$, three times
    both sides of this equations
    yields $1 = 0.\overline{9}$.

22. (a) $a_{n+1} = a_n + 9/10^{n+1}$ and
    $1 = a_{n+1} + 1/10^{n+1}$
    (b) Since $1 = a_{100} + 1/10^{100}$,
    $1 - a_{100} = 1/10^{100}$.
    Therefore, $1 - a_n < 1/10^{100}$
    whenever $n > 100$.
    (c) Use idea in part (b).
    (d) Essentially $0.\overline{9}$ is greater than
    any number less than 1 and
    $0.\overline{9}$ does not exceed 1, hence
    $0.\overline{9} = 1$.

23. (a) $0.\overline{142857}$, $0.\overline{285714}$,
    etc. The repetends have 6
    digits and they share the same
    digits.
    (b) The repetends for 1/13, 3/13,
    4/13, 9/13, 10/13, 12/13
    use same digits and the rest
    use same digits. All have
    repetends with 6 digits.

24. $\dfrac{y}{10^n} + \dfrac{x}{99999} \cdot \dfrac{1}{10^n} = \dfrac{99999y + x}{(99999)(10^n)}$,
    where $0 \le y < 10^n$ and
    $1 \le x \le 99{,}998$

25. $999 \div 22 = 45$ with 9 remaining,
    so the 999th digit is 7.

26. (a) 1   (b) 7

27. After taking 1/2 of 16 1/2, the
    final correct step is to find 1/2 of
    12, not 1/2 of 12 1/2.

28. (a) 28.6650 g   (b) 28.6749 g

29. (a) 257.6 mi   (b) 7.8 in.

30. $2528.24

31. $43.71

32. 55 mph

33. $3,750

34. $31.63

35. There are 3 digits in the repeating
    pattern. Thus, Henry must
    multiply by 1000, which is 10^3, in
    order to get the numbers to line
    up for subtraction. If he does
    that, he will get $999n = 7445$, or n
    $= \dfrac{7445}{999}$.

36. Barry is rounding $0.\overline{3}$ (which
    equals $\dfrac{1}{3}$) to 0.3. Rather than
    multiply by 0.3, which equals
    3/10 not 1/3, he might remember
    that multiplying by 1/3 is the
    same as dividing by 3. $54 \div 3 =$
    18, which is quite different from
    16.2.

**Problems related to the NCTM
Standards and Curriculum Focal Points**

1. When adding whole numbers it is
   important to add tens to tens and

hundreds to hundreds. Similarly, when adding decimal numbers, tenths need to be added to tenths and hundredths to hundredths. This is done by lining up the decimal point.

2. When multiplying 0.43 and 0.7, these number could be rewritten as the fractions $\frac{43}{10^2} \times \frac{7}{10^1}$. The exponents on the denominators indicate how many digits are to the right of the decimal. Thus, the denominators would be multiplied together by adding the exponents of the powers of ten which the same as counting the number of digits to the right of the decimal.

3. Because our numeration system is base ten, multiplying by a power of 10 is equivalent to moving the decimal point. Thus if the product 3.7×10^7 were computed, the decimal would be moved 7 places to the right yielding 37,000,000.

Section 7.3

1. (a) 2:5   (b) 6.18:100   (c) 3:4
    (d) 5:1   (e) 1:2   (f) 9:16

2. Each is an ordered pair. For example, (a) measures population density.

3. (a) 1/7   (b) 2/7   (c) 25/17

4. (a) No   (b) No

5. (a) $\frac{32}{29}$

    (b) $\frac{37}{86}$

    (c) Mandarin : Hindi/Urdu

    (d) $\frac{167}{500}$

    (e) $\frac{507}{1000}$

6. (a) 2 1/2   (b) 1
    (c) 320   (d) 5.1

7. (a) 56   (b) 116.67

(c) $\frac{2}{3}$ (d) 96

(e) $\frac{30}{17}$ or ≈1.76   (f) $\frac{24}{11}$ or ≈ 2.18

8. $\frac{35 \text{ mi}}{87.5 \text{ mi}} = \frac{2 \text{ hrs}}{5 \text{ hrs}}$,

    $\frac{2 \text{ hrs}}{35 \text{ mi}} = \frac{5 \text{ hrs}}{87.5 \text{ mi}}$,

    $\frac{87.5 \text{ mi}}{35 \text{ mi}} = \frac{5 \text{ hrs}}{2 \text{ hrs}}$

9. (a) 26:6 = 52:12 = 104:24
    (b) 84:6 = 42:3 = 210:15
    (c) 40:12 = 10:3 = 30:9
    (d) 27.50:1.5 = 55:3 = 110:6
    (e) 750:12 = 250:4 = 1000:16

10. 88 kph

11. (a) 60 oz for 29 cents
    (b) $45 for 10 yards
    (c) 18 oz for 40 cents

12. Model *XL*

13. About 148 minutes

14. About 87 gallons.

15. About $2085

16. Just over 7 weeks.

17. (a) 105 miles, 350 miles, 35*n* miles
    (b) About 28 3/5 inches

18. 8572 seeds

19. About 2.3 miles

20. (a) 5 1/2 cups
    (b) 5 gallons
    (c) 6 liters
    (d) $2.71/lb

21. About 206.1 mph

22. (a) 134
    (b) 70

23. (a) 6.48 runs
    (b) About 29 runs

24. (a) 11/32 inch
    (b) 29,500 miles

25. (a) A and C
    (b) 20 : 21
    (c) 12 : 11
    (d) No, adding using equivalent ratios does not give same result.

26. 6 inches

27. (a) F = 170 2/3, D = 576, A = 864, E = 1296, B = 1944
    (b) D = 288, E = 324, F = 341 1/3, G = 384, A = 432, B = 486
    (c) 1.125 = 9/8
    (d) 1.333 = 4/3

28. Ferne - 39
    Donna - 21
    Susan - 12

29. 54 feet

30. 31 eggs

31. No. Consider the following: Joleen bats 1 for 10 and Maureen bats 0 for 1. Then Joleen bats 1 for 1 and Maureen bats 1 for 2. At the end of the season, Joleen's average is 1/11 and Maureen's is 1/3.

32. 4, 7, 28, $3n - 2$

33. 9:4

34. The problem is mismatched units. The proportion needs to be
    $$\frac{feet}{feet} = \frac{feet}{feet} \text{ or } \frac{inches}{inches} = \frac{feet}{feet} \text{ or}$$
    $$\frac{feet}{inches} = \frac{feet}{inches}.$$ This latter proportion yields $\frac{4}{15} = \frac{tree}{144}$, or the height of the tree is 38.4 feet.

Problems related to the NCTM Standards and Curriculum Focal Points

1. The student is looking at the problem additively instead of multiplicatively. He thinks that because there are 2 more cans of OJ, then there should be 2 more cans of water. However, in order to be proportional, he needs to see that there are 3 times as many cans of OJ so there needs to be 3 times as many cans of water.

2. In Problem Set B #13 and #14, rates are used. In #13, the rate is kilometers per minute or kilometers per hour and in #14 the rate is gallons per week or gallons per year. Answers may vary.

3. When mixing orange juice, there are typically 3 cans of water for each can of orange juice so the scale is 3. If 4 cans of OJ are used, then the scale of 3 will help determine that $3 \times 4 = 12$ cans of water are needed. Answers may vary.

Section 7.4

1. $\frac{6666}{10000}$, 0.6666; $\frac{3}{1000}$, 0.3%;

   0.025, 2.5%; $\frac{1}{20}$, 5%; $\frac{160}{100}$, 0.016;

   0.01, 1%; $\frac{1}{100000}$, 0.001%;

   $\frac{17}{200000}$, 0.000085

2. (a) 400, 350, 25%, 250
   (b) $1.00, $15.00, $40.00
   (c) 0.06, 0.36, 0.03, 0.45

3. (a) 98   (b) 61   (c) 50%
   (d) 1462   (e) 125%   (f) 142
   (g) 500   (h) 0.1%   (i) 350

4. (a) 1.6   (b) 10   (c) 30
   (d) 150   (e) 6   (f) 44
   (g) 7.5   (h) 360

5.   (a   90
     (b) 11
     (c) 3/4 × 320 = 240
     (d) 1/3 × 210 = 70
     (e) 2/5 × 250 = 100
     (f) 1/8 × 400 = 50
     (g) 2/3 × 660 = 440
     (h) 1/5 × 120 = 24

6.   (a) 1/5 × 35 = 7
     (b) 2/5 × 60 = 24
     (c) 1/4 × 60 = 15
     (d) 200% × 85 = 170
     (e) 15% × 42 = 6.3
     (f) 10% × 430 = 43
     (g) 1/2 × 26 = 13
     (h) 2/5 × 150 = 60

7.   (a) $1.65   (b) $2.25
     (c) $5.25   (d) $3.60

8.   (a) What percent of 95 is 67?
     (b) 18.4 is 112% of what number?
     (c) What is $16\frac{2}{3}$% of $3\frac{1}{2}$?
     (d) 2.8 is what percent of 0.46?
     (e) 0.05% of what number is
          4200?
     NOTE: Other answers are
     possible.

9.   (a) 370.8   (b) 41.0%
     (c) 216.7%   (d) 350
     (e) 2400   (f) 75.6%

10. (a) 4400   (b) 22%
     (c) 1250   (d) 125
     (e) 650%

11. (a) 30.6   (b) 90.72
     (c) 190   (d) 62.5
     (e) $101.70   (f) $105.60

12. (a) $194.05   (b) $111.48
     (c) $1011.88   (d) $312.88

13. 68.75%
     Enter 80 as the whole and 55 as
     the part.

14. $12.91
     Guess and Test. By entering a
     value for the Whole and 70 for the
     Percent, we can add the Part and

the Whole searching for a sum of
$21.95. The best guess on the
eManipulative is $12.90.

15. 66%

16. $11\frac{2}{3}$%

17. $349.50

18. Rent, Utilities $2320, Tuition
     $2100, Food $1520, Other $660,
     Transportation $640, Clothes,
     Health $400, Books, Supplies
     $360

19. $36.\overline{1}$%

20. 150 games

21. (a) About 71%
     (b) About 99.6%

22. $1600

23. $7.80 to $12.00

24. (a) 12.1%
     (b) 18.4%
     (c) No, gas consumption increased
          at a higher rate as the
          number of less efficient SUV's
          on the road increased.

25. $795

26. Both

25. (a) (i) $237.22   (ii) $799.56
          (iii) $187.74
     (b) $4505

28. 750%

29. 4% less

30. 49%

31. (a) $4515   (b) $174,418.61
     (c) $78,070.18
     (d) 202,272.73 pounds

32. At least 12 passes

33. They are equal.

34. 1 pencil, 9 erasers, 90 paper clips

35. Use Guess and Test; Tom = 7 and Carol = 13

36. 3. Cut open all of the links of one chain and use them to link the remaining chains together.

37. 1111

38. 20. Yes. $n \rightarrow n + 20 \rightarrow 10(n+20) \rightarrow 2(n + 20) \rightarrow n + 20 \rightarrow 20$

39. $133,156.49

40. (a) Investment (2) - at 6.1% compounded annually.
    (b) He must invest $3553.28 at the rate in (a).

41. (a) Net loss $5.50
    (b) Net loss $2.00
    (c) Strategy b

42. 15%

43. 45

44. The 35% is taken on the original price, not the sale price. Since you don't know the original price, you need to remember that if you saved 35%, you paid 65%. So the sale price is 65% of the original price. You can find the original price by dividing the sale price by 0.65. The original price was $210.77.

Problems related to the NCTM Standards and Curriculum Focal Points

1. If you answered 27 out of 40 questions correct on a test and wanted to find the percent correct, a proportion could be set up as follows:
$$\frac{27}{40} = \frac{x}{100}$$
Solving this proportion would yield 67.5%. Answers may vary.

2. Some possible commonly used fractions, decimals and percents are:

$$\frac{1}{2} = 0.5 = 50\%$$

$$\frac{3}{4} = 0.75 = 75\%$$

$$\frac{3}{8} = 0.375 = 37.5\%$$

$$\frac{4}{5} = 0.8 = 80\%$$

3. It means that regardless of what is given in a problem – fraction, decimal or percent – a student could use it or convert it to the most convenient form for solving the problem.

Chapter Review

Problems for Writing/Discussion

1. Calculators cannot always show all places of a decimal. You might want to divide 12 by 17 on paper to show at what point the repeat pattern begins.

2. If there are 3 parts oil to 4 parts vinegar, then there are 7 parts altogether. So 3/7 is oil and 4/7 is vinegar. 3/7 is about 43%, which is less than 50%.

3. The numbers to be compared are 45/100 and 5/10. Using common denominators, we have 45/100 and 50/100. Thus, 50/100 is larger. With decimals, adding a zero (or zeros) helps. Here you would compare 6.45 and 6.50.

4. Using lattice multiplication we get 05508. The question is where to place the decimal. Adding up the total number of decimal places in the original numbers, we get 3. So the correct answer is 5.508.

5. Caroline has been done in by successive rounding. If she had looked at the hundredths place in the original number and then

looked at the place just to the right, she would have seen a 4, not a 5.

6. When rounding down, the succeeding numbers are simply dropped. For example, 35.62 rounded down to tenths place would become 35.6.

7. There is not universal conformity as to how to represent the decimal. Some European countries use a comma instead of a period. Thus, this is just a different custom, not a matter of right and wrong.

8. The calculator shows 0.6666667 because it has rounded up. We would represent the answer as $0.\overline{6}$, but the calculator cannot do that. Students should always be reminded that the calculator has some limitations, and that students have to use it as a tool in conjunction with their own thinking.

9. Many possible answers. Many people take 10% of the bill, then find half of that amount, then add those two amounts together. That's like saying 10% + 5% = 15%, an equation which is true only if the percents are all being taken on the same amount, which in this case they are. Example: If the bill is $37.48, you take 10% which is approximately $3.75, you take half of that, which is approximately $1.90, and you add the two amounts together, which is $5.65.

10. Inches per month and miles per hour are ratios. One can use the scaling method to get from one to the other. Scientists often use a method that involves multiplying by 1 and canceling units. For example, if you multiply a fraction

by $\dfrac{1 \text{ foot}}{12 \text{ inches}}$, you haven't really changed its value, only its units.

$$\dfrac{0.5 \text{ in}}{1 \text{ mo}} \cdot \dfrac{1 \text{ ft}}{12 \text{ in}} \cdot \dfrac{1 \text{ mi}}{5280 \text{ ft}}$$
$$\cdot \dfrac{1 \text{ mo}}{30 \text{ day}} \cdot \dfrac{1 \text{ day}}{24 \text{ hr}}$$

Now by multiplying across and canceling units, you will find the answer in miles per hour:

1.096×10^{-8} mph. This technique is often referred to as dimensional analysis (which is studied in Chapter 13).

Chapter 8

Section 8.1

1. Only (b); (b) is positive.

2. (a) 1   (b) - 4   (c) 5   (d) - 3

3. (a) RRR

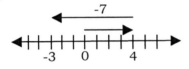

    (b) BBBBBB

4. (a) $-a$ (b) b
    (c) $-(a + b)$ (d) $b - a$

5. (a) $\{-1, -2, -3, -4,...\}$
    (b) $\{1, 2, 3, 4,...\}$ (c) W

6. (a) BBBBRRRRRRR = -3

    (b) RRR RRRRR = -8

7. (a) $14 + (-6) = (8 + 6) + (-6) =$
        $8 + [6 + (-6)] = 8 + 0 = 8$
    (b) $21 + (-41) = 21 + [(-21) + (-20)]$
        $= [21 + (-21)] + (-20) = 0 + -20$
        $= -20$

8. (a) Associative Property for Integer
        Addition
    (b) Additive Identity

9. (a) 3117   (b) 33

10. (a) Start with RRR and add 3 zero
        pairs to obtain BBBRRR RRR.
        Take away 6 reds to get
        BBBRRRRRR = 3
    (b) Start with 0 and add 4 zero
        pairs to obtain BBBBRRRR.
        Take away 4 red to get
        BBBBRRRR = 4

11. (a) -14   (b) 52
    (c) 14   (d) 6

12. (a) -231   (b) -56
    (c) 986   (d) -555

13. (a) -5   (b) -7   (c) -13
    (d) 9   (e) -3   (f) 0

14. (d)

15. (a) opposite of negative five
    (b) Ten minus the opposite of
        negative two
    (c) opposite of p

16. (a) 3   (b) 7   (c) $-x$
    (d) $-x$ (e) x (f) x

17. Top: 42; Second: 16 26;
    Middle: -6 22 4

18. (a) Gained 9 yards
    (b) Loss of 2 points
    (c) Gained $200

19. (b)

20. Philadelphia: 28   Cheyenne: 44
    Bismarck: 11

21. The result $-a$ represents "the
    opposite of a". Thus, when a is
    negative, $-a$ is positive.

22. 98 -28

23. (a) -8, 3   (b)   -7, 4
    (c) 0, 8

24. Top: 9; Third 25 -15 14;
    Bottom: 33 -8 -7 21

25. (a) (i) 1 2 3 4 ...
        (ii) 1 2 3 4 . . .
             -1 -2 -3 -4. . .
             0 1 2 3 . . .
        (iii) . . . 6 4 2 0 1 3 5 . . .
              . . . -3 -2 -1 0 1 2 3 . . .
    (b) Both sets have same number
        of elements

26.

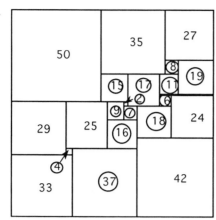

27. If the student subtracts the numbers as they stand, the problem will become 4 - (-6) which equals 10. This is incorrect. What was intended (but not said) was that one should find the difference between two numbers "without their signs." Thus, 6 - 4 = 2, so the answer is -2,

28. Most people recognize that the word "unique" means "one of a kind." But in the phrase "*there is a unique integer*" there is also a guarantee that every integer has an additive inverse. So the phrase means that every integer has "at least one and at most one" additive inverse.

Problems related to the NCTM Standards and Curriculum Focal Points

1. Problem 1: At 10:00 pm the temperature was 7 degrees and it dropped 15 degrees overnight. What is the new temperature in the morning?
   Problem 2: Reno gained 17 yards on his first run of the football game and lost 5 yards on his second run of the game. How many yards did he gain in his first two carries?
   Answers may vary.

2. Rule: When adding numbers with the same sign, the absolute values of the numbers can be added and

the common sign will the sign of the sum.
Context: In the context of temperature change, if the temperature decreases twice, you know that the total change will have to be a decrease so the sum of two negative numbers has to be negative.

Section 8.2

1. (a)

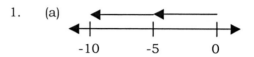

    -10   -5   0

    (b)

    -12   -8   -4   0

    (c)

    -10 -8 -6 -4 -2 0

2. (a) -5 × (-1) = 5   -5 × (-2) = 10
        5 × (-3) = 15
    (b) -8 × (-1) = 8   -8 × (-2) = 16
        -8 × (-3) = 24
        Negative times negative equals positive

3. (a) -30   (b) 420
    (c) -230   (d) 0

4. (a) BBBB BBBB BBBB
        RRRR RRRR RRRR = -12
    (b) RRRR RRRR = -8
    (c) BBRR = 2

5. Distributivity, additive inverse, multiplication by 0

6. (a) -6x - 12   (b) -5x + 55
    (c) -3x + 3y   (d) xa - xb
    (e) -xa + xb (f) x^2 - x - 6

7. (a) 3   (b) -86
    (c) -34   (d) 907

8. (a) 0   (b) 4   (c) 36

9. (a) -1872 (b) 8134
   (c) 224,409 (d) -243,984
   (e) -31 (f) 123
   (g) -58 (h) -1

10. No

11. (a) Negative (b) Positive
    (c) Negative (d) Positive
    (e) Positive (f) Negative
    (g) Positive (h) Negative

12. Always positive: c, d, e
    Always negative: f

13. (a) $\dfrac{1}{16}$ (b) $\dfrac{1}{32}$ (c) $\dfrac{1}{343}$

14. (a) $\dfrac{1}{729}$ (b) $\dfrac{1}{729}$ (c) 15,625
    (d) Yes

15. (a) $\dfrac{1}{512}$ (b) $\dfrac{1}{512}$ (c) $\dfrac{1}{50625}$
    (d) Yes

16. (a) 5^5 (b) 3^{16}
    (c) 4^5 or 2^{10} (d) $\dfrac{1}{6^4}$

17. (a) 0.000009
    (b) 0.000000000000126

18. (a) 6.91×10^{-7}
    (b) 3.048×10^{-13}
    (c) 8.071×10^{-20}

19. (a) 2.6936×10^{-20}
    (b) 4.4×10^{23}
    (c) 3.93×10^{-20}
    (d) 5.4×10^{-14}
    (e) 2.046×10^{-9}
    (f) 1.6×10^{-9}

20. (a) -7 + 4 = -3 (b) -6 + 11 = 5
    (c) -23 + 6 = -17

21. (a) < (b) > (c) >
    (d) > (e) > (f) >
    (g) = (h) <

22. (a) < (b) <

23. Second row: 8, 18
    Third row: -2
    Bottom row: 2, -2, -9
    Also,
    Second row: -8, -18
    Third row: 2
    Bottom row: -2, 2, -9

24. (a) -3, -2, and -1 (b) No
    (c) -3

25. (a) No, no, yes (-1), no
    (b) Yes (0), no, no, yes (1)

26. (a) $pq = - |p||q|$
    (b) $pq = |p||q|$

27. (a) $p/q = - |p| / |q|$
    (b) $p/q = |p| / |q|$

28. No; $-3 < -2$, but $(-3)^2 > (-2)^2$.

29. Yes; $x < y$ means $y = x + p$ for
    some $p > 0$, $z - y = z - (x + p)$
    $= z - x - p$. Therefore, $z - y + p$
    $= z - x$ which means $z - y < z - x$.

30. 8.38×10^{-26} grams

31. 6.508×10^{-7} meter

32. (a) 1.1×10^{-22} kilograms
    (b) Approximately 1.62×10^{-27}
    kilograms.

33. (a) 2.31×10^6 corpuscles
    (b) About 1.08×10^7 seconds or
    125 days.

34. True. From problem 23 in part A,
    squares must be a multiple of 3 or
    one more than a multiple of 3. If
    neither of x nor y is a multiple of
    3, then $x^2 + y^2 = (3m + 1) +$
    $(3n + 1) = 3(m + n) + 2 = z^2$. But
    z^2 must be of the form $3r$ or $3r +$
    1. Thus, one of x or y must be a
    multiple of 3.

35. 1806

36. If $(a - b)c = 0$, then $a - b = 0$ or $c = 0$. Because c was assumed to be nonzero, $a - b = 0$, or $a = b$.

37. In general, this equation is false. If we multiply $(a + b)(a + b)$ using the distributive property, we get the answer $a^2 + 2ab + b^2$. So the problem becomes "When does $a^2 + b^2 = a^2 + 2ab + b^2$? " That reduces to "When does $2ab = 0$?" The Zero Divisors Property tells us that this is true when $2 = 0$, $a = 0$ or $b = 0$. So the ultimate conclusion is that the equation is rarely, but sometimes, true.

Problems related to the NCTM Standards and Curriculum Focal Points

1. Rule: A positive number multiplied by a negative number is a negative number.
    Context: For 5 consecutive hours, the temperature changes by -3 degrees each hour. What is the total temperature change after the 5 hours? It can be seen that this is just 5 groups of -3 degrees which would be -15. Answers may vary.

2. When writing very large numbers, positive powers of 10 can be used instead of writing many zeros. Similarly very small numbers can be represented using negative powers of 10 because they are the same as $\frac{1}{10}$ to positive powers.
    Thus a number like 0.0000000057, which is $\frac{57}{10,000,000,000}$, can be rewritten as 5.7×10^{-9}. Answers may vary.

3. Using integers to compare temperatures is common. For example, which is colder -5 or -7 degrees? Similarly, which is warmer -4 or 2 degrees? Answers may vary.

Chapter Review

Problems for Writing/Discussion

1. It is usually a good idea to differentiate the words "minus" and "negative," using "minus" only for the operation of subtraction. "Negative 3 minus negative 2 equals negative 3 plus 2 which equals negative 1."

2. The minus sign between the - 5 and 7 is probably being read *both* as a subtraction sign and as a negative sign. -5 - 7 = -5 + (-7) = -12.

3. Since n is a variable, it can take on many values. If n is a positive number, like 4, then $-n$ is -4. However, if n is a negative number, say -7, then $-n$ is - (- 7) which is 7. That is, $-n = 7$. If $n = 0$, then $-n$ equals 0; in this case $-n$ is neither positive nor negative.

4. Misha's calculator is giving him the answer to $(-7)^2$, which is different from $-(7^2)$, the way Joe's calculator does the problem. Joe is getting the correct answer since the exponent takes precedence over the opposite sign.

5. Many calculators give answers in scientific notation when the answer is too large for the display. In this case, 2^{42} gives the answer 4.398046511 12, which should be read $4.398046511 \times 10^{12}$. Mary Lou, however, interpreted the display to mean 4.398^{12}, which is how she got her incorrect answer. The actual answer is more than 4 *trillion*.

6. The negative sign signals a reciprocal, so we need to find $(\frac{1}{3})^7$. Also one could find 3^7, then take the reciprocal of that answer.

7.   Many possible answers:
     temperatures below zero, owing
     money, bank debits, driving a car
     in reverse, running a film
     backward, below sea level, etc.

8.   Many possible answers. Here is
     one example using cars and
     motion picture cameras. Cars can
     drive forward (+) and backward (-).
     Film can be played forward (+) and
     backward (-). By considering all
     possible combinations of these +'s
     and -'s, we can model the product
     of two negatives. First we film the
     car driving forward and backward.
     Then we play back the film in both
     modes to see the resulting image.

Car	Film	Image moves
forward (+)	forward (+)	forward (+)
backward (-)	forward (+)	backward (-)
forward (+)	backward (-)	backward (-)
backward (-)	backward (-)	forward (+)

9.   The student said two correct
     things, but they don't go together.
     It is true that a negative times a
     negative gives a positive, but this
     is not a multiplication problem.
     It is also true that 4 - (-3) is the
     same as 4 + 3. However, the
     reason that should connect those
     two statements should connect
     addition and subtraction. For
     example, "Subtracting a number is
     the same as adding its opposite;
     that's why 4 - (-3) = 4 + 3."

10. The significant number which
     determines whether or not to
     reverse the inequality is the
     number you are multiplying or
     dividing by. In this case, the
     student is dividing both sides by
     7, so the inequality should *not* be
     reversed. The student should
     check by substituting values for x
     in $7x > -28$. Trying -3, -4, and -5,
     for example, should be enough to
     convince the student that the
     values that make the original
     inequality true will be numbers
     that are greater than -4.

Chapter 9

Section 9.1

1. (a) 7 and 3 are integers
   (b) $7\frac{1}{8} = \frac{57}{8}$ and 57 and 8 are integers.
   (c) $-3 = \frac{-3}{1}$; -3 and 1 are integers.

2. (a) True (b) False

3. (a) -2/3 (b) 5/7
   (c) -4/9 (d) -8/9

4. (a) -1/2 (b) -41/36
   (c) -2/3 (d) 1/24

5. -5/-6, - (-5/6), - (5/-6)

6. (a) 17/23 (b) 6/29

7. (a) 2/7 (b) 5/16

8. (a) 2/3 (b) -33/28
   (c) 29/36 (d) -1/12

9. (a) -2/7 (b) -1
   (c) 3/2 (d) -1/3

10. (a) 8/5 (b) 0
    (c) 5/6 (d) -23/27

11. (a) - 4 (b) -3/5
    (c) 8/9 (d) 2/3

12. (a) -164/837 (b) -19/528

13. (a) $1\frac{313}{826}$ (b) $-1\frac{580}{627}$

14. (a) > (b) <
    (c) = (d) <

15. (a) $\frac{475}{652} < \frac{-308}{-421}$
    (b) $\frac{372}{487} < \frac{-261}{319}$

16. (a) F,Q (If division by 0 is not allowed.)
    (b) W,F,I,Q (c) W,F,I,Q

    (d) I,Q (e) F,Q

17. (a) Associative - multiplication
    (b) Commutative - addition
    (c) Property of Less Than and Addition
    (d) Property of Less Than and Multiplication by a Negative

18. (a) $x < -18/35$ (b) $x > -43/35$

19. (a) $x < -5/2$ (b) $x < -35/16$

20. (a) $x > 5/2$ (b) $x < -56/15$

21. (a) -16,261 (b) -86,266,944

22. (a) -113/217 < -163/314, -92/177
    (b) -545/522 < -812/779, -1357/1301

23. There are many possible solutions
    (a) For example, -11/9, -16/13, and -21/17.
    (b) For example, -2/21, -3/31, and -3/32.

24. (a) $a/b + c/d = (ad + bc)/bd$

    (definition of addition) = $(bc + ad)/bd$ (commutativity of integer addition) = $bc/bd + ad/bd$ (definition of addition with a common denominator)
    $= c/d + a/b$ (simplification)
    (b) An argument similar to part (a)

25. (a) holds.
    (b) 3 - 1 ≠ 1 - 3
    (c) (4 - 2) - 1 ≠ 4 - (2 - 1)
    (d) $a - 0 = a$, but $0 - a \ne a$.
    (e) There is no inverse since there is no identity.

26. Add $-e/f$ to both sides of the equation.

27. (a), (c), and (d) are true; (b) is false; 1/3 - 1/2 = -1/6.

28.　$(a/b)(c/d - e/f)$
　　$= (a/b)[c/d + (-e/f)]$
　　$= (a/b)(c/d) + (a/b)(-e/f)$
　　$= (ac)/(bd) + (-ae)/(bf)$
　　$= (ac)/(bd) - (ae)/(bf)$
　　$= (a/b)(c/d) - (a/b)(e/f)$

29.　For simplicity, assume that the denominators are positive. First get common denominators. Then $adf/bdf < cbf/bdf$ and $cbf/bdf < ebd/bdf$. Thus $adf < cdf$ and $cbf < ebd$. Therefore, $adf/bdf < ebd/bdf$, or $a/b < e/f$.

30.　(a) $ad < bc$ and $ef > 0$. By Properties of Ordering Integers $adef < bcef$ and thus $a/b \times e/f < c/ \times e/f$ by the Cross Multiplication Property of Inequality.
　　(b) Similar argument

31.　If $\dfrac{a}{b} < \dfrac{c}{d}$ then $\dfrac{ad}{bd} < \dfrac{bc}{bd}$ so $ad < bc$. Thus, $ad + 1 \le bc$ and $2ad + 2 \le 2bc$, so $2ad + 1 < 2bc$. Hence
　　$\dfrac{ad}{bd} = \dfrac{2ad}{2bd} < \dfrac{2ad+1}{2bd} < \dfrac{2bc}{2bd} = \dfrac{bc}{bd}$ So $\dfrac{e}{f} = \dfrac{2ad+1}{2bd}$ is one fraction that satisfies $\dfrac{a}{b} < \dfrac{e}{f} < \dfrac{c}{d}$.

32.　Let n be an odd number, the first of the Pythagorean triple. Then n^2 is its square. Next, $(n^2 - 1)/2$ is the second number and $(n^2 - 1)/2 + 1$ is the third.
　　$n^2 + [(n^2 - 1)/2]^2 =$
　　$n^2 + (n^4 - 2n^2 + 1)/4 =$
　　$(n^4 + 2n^2 + 1)/4$ and
　　$[(n^2 - 1)/2 + 1]^2 = [(n^2 + 1)/2]^2 = (n^4 + 2n^2 + 1)/4$.

33.　The sum $\dfrac{3}{7} + \dfrac{2}{5}$ is $\dfrac{3 \times 5 + 7 \times 2}{7 \times 5}$, or $\dfrac{29}{35}$, which has integers as its numerator and denominator and a nonzero denominator since both 7 and 5 are nonzero. Thus, $\dfrac{29}{35}$ satisfies the definition of a rational number.

Problems related to the NCTM Standards and Curriculum Focal Points

1.　With rational numbers you can take the properties of addition and multiplication of integers and combine them with the properties of addition of fractions to add negative and positive non-integer rational numbers. For example, $\dfrac{-3}{4} + \dfrac{2}{3} = \dfrac{-3 \cdot 3}{4 \cdot 3} + \dfrac{2 \cdot 4}{3 \cdot 4}$ applies the concept of finding a common denominator with fractions and $\dfrac{-3 \cdot 3}{4 \cdot 3} + \dfrac{2 \cdot 4}{3 \cdot 4} = \dfrac{-9 + 8}{12} = \dfrac{-1}{12}$ applies the properties of integer multiplication and addition to find the sum. Answers may vary.

2.　Example 1: The problem $-6\left(\dfrac{2}{3} + \dfrac{5}{6}\right) = -4 + -5 = -9$ applies the distributive property to eliminate the fractions before adding.
　　Example 2: The problem $\dfrac{2}{5} + \left(-5 + \dfrac{-2}{5}\right) = \left(\dfrac{2}{5} + \dfrac{-2}{5}\right) + -5 = -5$ applies the commutative and associative properties to add compatible numbers first and simplify the problem. Answers may vary.

3.　"Develop algorithms" means to use your understanding of the meaning of the operations and the properties of the numbers to develop strategies for doing algorithms that make sense and are efficient for each student. Answers may vary.

Section 9.2

1.　(a) Rational　　　　(b) Irrational
　　(c) Rational　　　　(d) Irrational

(e) Rational   (f) Irrational
(g) Rational   (h) Irrational

2.   The number 1.414 is a rational
     number approximately equal to
     $\sqrt{2}$.

3.   (a) $\sqrt{10}$ (b) $\sqrt{13}$
     (c) $\sqrt{18} = 3\sqrt{2}$

4.   (a) $\sqrt{8} = 2\sqrt{2}$
     (b) $\sqrt{9} = 3$
     (c)

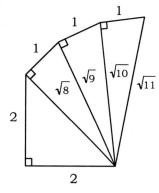

5.   (a) $x = \sqrt{13}$, $y = \sqrt{8} = 2$
     (b) $a = \sqrt{20} = 2\sqrt{5}$,
         $b = \sqrt{24} = 2\sqrt{6}$,
         $c = \sqrt{33}$

6.   (a) $2\sqrt{10}$ (b) $4\sqrt{5}$
     (c) $6\sqrt{5}$

7.   (a) 56   (b) 71

8.   (a) $4\sqrt{3} - \sqrt{3} = (4-1)\sqrt{3} = 3\sqrt{3}$
         Distributive Property

     (b) $5\sqrt{7} + \left(\sqrt{35} + 7\sqrt{7}\right)$
         $= 5\sqrt{7} + \left(\sqrt{5}\sqrt{7} + 7\sqrt{7}\right)$
         $= \left(12 + \sqrt{5}\right)\sqrt{7}$
         Distributive Property

     (c) $\sqrt{32} + \sqrt{50}$
         $= 4\sqrt{2} + 5\sqrt{2} = 9\sqrt{2}$
         Distributive Property

9.   (a) 6   (b) 9   (c) $12\sqrt{5}$
     (d) $-4\sqrt{2}$ (e) $7\sqrt{2}$ (f) $4\sqrt{5}$

10. (a) 5   (b) 4
     (c) 7/2   (d) 3/5

11. $0.\overline{876} < 0.8766876667... <$
     $0.8\overline{766} < 0.\overline{876} <$
     $0.876787667788... <$
     $0.876787677876... < 0.\overline{876}$

12. For example,
     $0.577757777577777...$.

13. $\sqrt{5}$, $\sqrt{6}$, $\sqrt{7}$, $2.373373337...$ for
     example.

14. (a) $2.2^2 < 5 < 2.3^2$
         $2.23^2 < 5 < 2.24^2$
         $2.236^2 < 5 < 2.237^2$
         $\sqrt{5} \approx 2.24$
     (b) $4.3^2 < 19.1 < 4.4^2$
         $4.37^2 < 19.1 < 4.38^2$
         $4.370^2 < 19.1 < 4.371^2$
         $\sqrt{19.1} \approx 4.37$
     (c) $0.2^2 < 0.05 < 0.3^2$
         $0.22^2 < 0.05 < 0.23^2$
         $0.223^2 < 0.05 < 0.234^2$
         $\sqrt{0.05} \approx 0.22$
     (d) Because 0.05 and 5 differ by a
         factor of 100, $\sqrt{0.05}$ and $\sqrt{5}$
         differ by a factor of 10.

15. $r_1 = 5$
     $s_1 = 24 \div 5 = 4.8$
     $r_2 = \dfrac{r_1 + s_1}{2} = 4.9$
     $s_2 = 24 \div 4.9 \approx 4.8979591$
     $r_3 \approx 4.8989795$
     $s_3 \approx 4.8989794$
     $r_3 - s_3 = 0.00000001$
     so $\sqrt{24} \approx 4.898979$

16. No.

17. (a) $0.5041 < 0.71$
     (b) $0.9604 < 0.98$

The squares of numbers between 0 and 1 are smaller than the number.

18. (a) 6   (b) 27   (c) 9
   (d) -8   (e) 27   (f) 729

19. (a) -2   (b) -6
   (c) Does not exist

20. (a) 1.5874 (rounded)
   (b) 2.1746 (rounded)
   (c) 344.061 (rounded)
   (d) 6.36 (rounded)

21. (a) $\sqrt[5]{7^2}$ (b) π to the $\sqrt{2}$ power

22. (a)

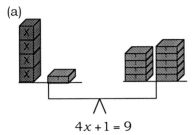

$$4x + 1 = 9$$

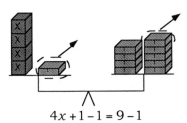

$$4x + 1 - 1 = 9 - 1$$

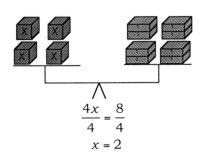

$$\frac{4x}{4} = \frac{8}{4}$$
$$x = 2$$

(b)

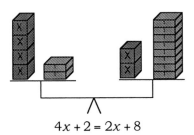

$$4x + 2 = 2x + 8$$

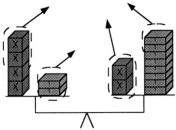

$$4x + 2 - 2x - 2 = 2x + 8 - 2x - 2$$
$$2x = 6$$

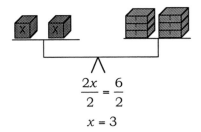

$$\frac{2x}{2} = \frac{6}{2}$$
$$x = 3$$

23. (a) $-4\sqrt{6}$ (b) $9\sqrt{3} + \sqrt{2}$
   (c) $\sqrt{3}$ (d) $-5/\pi$

24. (a) $x = -14$ (b) $x = 1/12$
   (c) $x = 13/3$ (d) $x = 3$
   (e) $x = 5$ (f) $x = 12$

25. (a) $x > 9/6 = 1.5$ (b) $x \geq -7/2$
   (c) $x \leq 4$ (d) $x < 5$

26. True. Reason, by analogy, from the proof that $\sqrt{2}$ is irrational.

27. Let $\sqrt{6} = a/b$. Then $6b^2 = a^2$ o $2 \times 3 \times b^2 = a^2$. If we consider the number of times the prime factor 2 occurs on both sides we arrive at a contradiction.

28. Assume it is rational. Simplify and then count factors of q on both sides.

29. Let $\sqrt[n]{2} = a/b$. Then $2b^n = a^n$. The prime factor 2 occurs a multiple of n times on the right, but 1 more than a multiple of n times on the left. This is a contradiction of the Fundamental Theorem of Arithmetic

30. (a) Irrational. If $\sqrt[3]{p} = a/b$, the $b^3 \cdot p = a^3$ for integers a and b. But a^3 has a multiple of 3 factors of p whereas $b^3 p$ has one more than a multiple of 3 factors of p. This is impossible since they are equal.
    (b) Irrational. Justification is similar to that in (a).

31. (a) (i) Irrational. Proof: If $r + p$ is rational, say $r + p = t$ for some rational number t. Then $p = t - r$, which states that p is rational because $t - r$ is the difference of two rationals. A contradiction.
        (ii) Rational if $r = 0$. Irrational otherwise.
        (iii) Rational. ($\sqrt{2} + (-\sqrt{2})$ $= 0$) or irrational ($\sqrt{2} + \sqrt{2} = 2\sqrt{2}$).
        (iv) Rational ($\sqrt{2} \times \sqrt{2} = 2$) or irrational ($\sqrt{2} \times \sqrt{3} = \sqrt{6}$.
    (b) In (ii), $r = 0$ yields a rational number.

32. (a) $0.10110111... + 0.20220222...$ $= 0.30330333...$
    (b) $0.10110111... + 0.01001000...$ $= 0.11111111...$
    (c) $\sqrt{2} \times \sqrt{3} = \sqrt{6}$
    (d) $\sqrt{2} \times \sqrt{2} = 2$

33. (a) No   (b) No
    (c) No   (d) No

34. (a) They are equal.
    (b) $a + (1 - a)$ are the two numbers. Show that $a^2 + (1 - a) = (1 - a)^2 + a$.

35. (a) C = 261.63, C# = 277.19, D = 293.67, D# = 311.13, E = 329.63, F = 349.23, F# = 370.00, G = 392.00, B = 493.88, C = 523.25
    (b) Ratio is within 0.002 of 1.5
    (c) Within 0.002

36. Build the school at town A.

37. The sums are always the same.

38. 3 and 1/3, or -3 and -1/3

39. $47, $33, $13, $1
    There are other possible answers; for example, $282, $198, $78, $6.

40. 33

41. The student is likely thinking (incorrectly) that the square roots increase by 1 as the numbers increase by 1. A few minutes with a calculator having a square root key should dispel this misconception.

42. Since the number of Pythagorean triples is infinite, you won't be able to give her a complete list. You might write down a few of the common triples, like 3-4-5 or 5-12-13 or 7-24-25 or 8-15-17 and suggest that their multiples would also work (6-8-10, for example). Third, you might suggest she do some research to find some expressions that are Pythagorean triple generators. Finally, you might urge her to find applications of the Pythagorean theorem where many non-integral solutions (decimal approximations to real numbers) will likely arise.

Problems related to the NCTM Standards and Curriculum Focal Points

1. A balance scale is a common model to illustrate solving equations. It helps to emphasize the concept of maintaining equality in the equation.

2. A mathematical expression might be something like $2x$ or $\frac{2}{3}x - \sqrt{5}$ but an equation has an equal sign in it like $2x = \frac{2}{3}x - \sqrt{5}$.

3. If the square root of a positive number, x, is computed and then the result is squared, the original number, x, will be the final output. These are inverses because one function undoes the other.

Section 9.3

1. (a) x-axis   (b) I   (c) II
    (d) y-axis   (e) III   (f) IV

2. (a) II   (b) I
    (c) I and IV

3. $\{(x, y) \mid 1 \le x \le 3$ and $-2 \le y \le 2\}$

4. (a) (i) 1   (ii) 2   (iii) 3
    (b) Domain: $-2 \le x \le 6$
        Range: {1, 2, 3, 4}
    (c) $2 \le x < 3$; none.
    (d) Step function

5. (a) Quadratic
    (b) A(4) ≈ 12.57
        A(12) ≈ 113.1
    (c)

    (d) The diameter, d, must be positive.

6. (a)

x	0	1	-1	2	-2
$f(x)$	-2	1	-5	4	-8

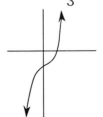

(b)

x	0	4	8	12	16
$g(x)$	9	6	3	0	-3

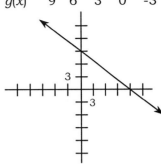

(c)

x	0	1/2	1/4	1/6	1/12
$c(x)$	25	85	55	45	35

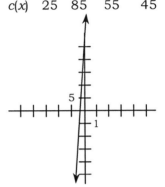

7. (a)

x	0	1	-1	2	-2
$f(x)$	0	-3	5	-4	12

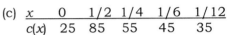

(b)

x	0	1	-1	2	-2
$f(x)$	1	1/2	2	1/4	4

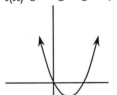

(c)

x	0	1	-1	2	-2
$f(x)$	-4	$-3\frac{1}{3}$	$-4\frac{2}{3}$	$1\frac{1}{3}$	$-9\frac{1}{3}$

8. (a) (ii)

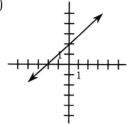

(ii)

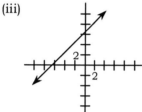

(iii)

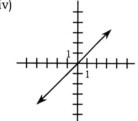

(iv)

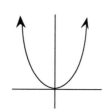

(b) The constant term determines where the graph intersects the *x*-axis

9. (a) A straight line going up to the right that passes through the origin.
    (b) The value of *b* is where the line hits the *y*-axis. As *b* changes, the graph moves up or down with the same slope.

10. (a) (i)

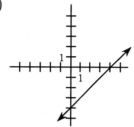

(ii)

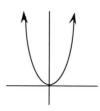

(iii)

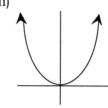

(iv)

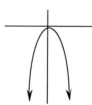

(b) Positive coefficients greater than one have the effect of narrowing the graph. Positive coefficients between 0 and 1 have the effect of broadening the graph. Multiplying by -1 has the effect of reflecting the graph in the *x*-axis. Thus the coefficient -3 would narrow the original graph and reflect it in the *x*-axis.

(c) The 5 makes the parabola in (i) 'narrower'. The 1/3 makes the parabola in (i) 'wider' and the 2 shifts it to the right 2 units.

11. (a) The parabola narrows.
    (b) A horizontal line.
    (c) The parabola opens down instead of up.

12. (a) (i)

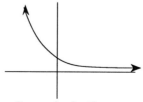

Same in both cases.

(ii)

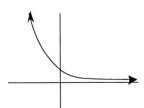

Same in both cases.

(iii)

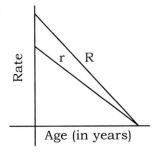

Same in both cases.

(b) Their graphs are the same because they represent the same function.

13. (a) It's a lot steeper on the right.
    (b) It is a horizontal line $y=1$.
    (c) The graph decreases to the right.

14. (a)

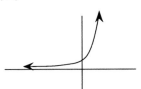

    (b) Between 123.5 and 152
    (c) Heart rates go down. The graph shows this information by falling from left to right.

15. (a) (i) 3   (ii) -18
        (iii) -4   (iv) -1

(b)

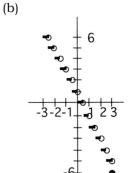

16. (a)

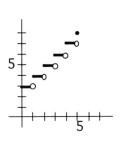

(b)

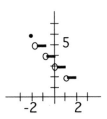

(c)

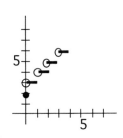

(d)

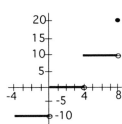

17. (a) linear   (b) step
    (c) quadratic   (d) exponential

18. (a) Function
        Domain: $-5 \le x \le 4$
        Range: $-2.5 \le y \le 4$
    (b) Not a function

19. (a) The distance varies according to time.
    (b) D(8) = 1.5. D(8) is the number of miles to the lightning if 8 seconds have elapsed.
    (c) $D(t) = \dfrac{3}{16}t$

20. (a)
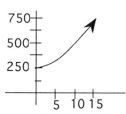
    (b) About $342
    (c) About 16.5 years
    (d) About 11 years

21. (iii)

22. (a) $20 and $60
    (b) $2000 to $2499.99
    (c)

n	B
500	20
750	20
1000	40
1250	40
1500	60
1750	60
2000	80

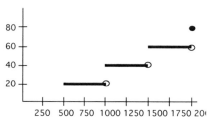

    (d) $B(n) = 20\ [[\ \dfrac{n}{500}\ ]]$

23. $T(n) = \dfrac{n}{4} + 4$

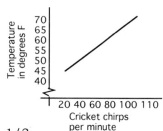

24. 1/3

25. Each successive y value is increased by a multiple of 3 and the value of y can be expressed as $2(3^{x-1})$. Thus, the graph will be that of an exponential.

26. If the common difference of the arithmetic sequence were negative, then the line would slope downward; for example, consider the sequence 6, 4, 2, 0, -2, . . . where the common difference is -2. If the common ratio of the geometric sequence were a positive fraction less than one, the curve would move downward; for example, consider the sequence 20, 10, 5, 2.5, 1.25, . . . where the common ratio is 0.5. As a point of interest, if the common ratio of a geometric sequence is negative, the graph does not proceed downward in an orderly fashion, but bounces back and forth between positive and negative values; for example, the sequence 20, -10, 5, -2.5, 1.25,... where the common ratio is -0.5.

Problems related to the NCTM Standards and Curriculum Focal Points

1. Three common ways of representing linear equations are tables, graphs and equations. Students should be comfortable with all three representations and be able to move flexibly between them.

2. Example 9.15 involves a linear equation about a base salary with addition commission. The y-intercept of $1200 represents the base salary that a salesman will make regardless of the number of sales. The slope is the percent commission, 5%, of the sales. If the percent commission were larger, the slope of the graph would be steeper.

3. With a linear equation, for each change of 1 unit of the x variable, the y variable will change by the

same fixed amount depending on the slope. With an exponential equation, however, each change of 1 unit of the x variable will yield a different change in the y variable. Thus, when the x variable changes from 1 to 2 both the linear equation and exponential equation may change by 4 units in the y variable. However, when the x variable changes from 4 to 5, the y variable of the linear equation will still change by 4 units but the exponential equation may change by 4000 units.

Chapter Review

Problems for Writing/Discussion

1. $\frac{6}{7} \div \frac{3}{14} = \frac{6}{7} \times \frac{14}{3} = \frac{6}{3} \times \frac{14}{7} = \frac{6}{3} \div \frac{7}{14}$. If you know that $2 \div \frac{1}{2} = 4$, then the problem $\frac{6}{3} \div \frac{7}{14}$ might be considered to be easier.

2. As you go through school, you expand your knowledge of numbers, and the sets of numbers you consider expand with you. When your last year's teacher said you couldn't subtract 3 - 5, he was thinking of the set of whole numbers in which there are no negative numbers. He wasn't wrong, he was just thinking of a smaller set of numbers. Your next year's teacher might tell you that you can find $\sqrt{-4}$ and say the answer is $2\boldsymbol{i}$, but that will be because she is thinking of a bigger set of numbers than the real numbers, the complex numbers. But this year we are only looking at the real numbers, and in the real numbers, there is no answer to $\sqrt{-4}$.

3. The 5 is in the denominator of the exponent. So if you raise 32 to the third power first, you then have

$(32768)^{(1/5)}$, not $(32768)^5$. If you find the fifth root of 32768, you'll find your answer is 8, the same answer you got for the first way you tried it.

4. It is true that if you had $5^4 \times 5^6$ you would know what to do: you could keep the base and add the exponents, which would give you 5^{10}. But Claudia is only sometimes right. Although there is nothing to be done with $3^4 \times 5^6$, sometimes there is a way to rewrite the problem. For example, in the problem $7^9 \times 2^9$ the bases are different but the exponents are the same, so this problem could be rewritten as $(7 \times 2)^9$ or 14^9. If you had a problem like $4^6 \times 8^3$, both bases could be written as powers of 2, so the problem would become $2^{12} \times 2^9$, which equals 2^{21}.

5. $3.25 = 3\frac{25}{100}$ and $3.5 = 3\frac{5}{10} = 3\frac{50}{100}$ Thus $3.25 < 3.5$ since $\frac{25}{100} < \frac{50}{100}$ To compare two decimals, you should add zeros to one until it has the same number of decimal places as the other. Then it will be easier to compare. Since 3.5 = 3.50, Erik should see that 3.25 < 3.50.

Similarly, 6.2 = 6.20, and 20 > 4, so 6.2 > 6.04.

6. One way to explain would be to use the method for changing repeating decimals to fractions, but Chuck might be convinced by other methods as well. For example, if he agrees that .3333333... is equal to 1/3, then ask what would be 3 times

.3333333..., and what would be 3 times 1/3.

7. One way is to just use the natural numbers as the decimal places: 0.123456789101112131415... This number will go on forever and never repeat or terminate. Another example can be constructed by using a pattern that keeps getting bigger: 0.12122122212222122222...

8. Carol Ann is thinking that if you take the square root of both sides, you'll get $x + 4 = 7$. However, $\sqrt{x^2 + 4^2}$ is *not* equal to $x + 4$.

9. The negative, the four, and the 1/3 all represent operations to be performed on the 125. They can be done in any order. And there are 6 different orders. All six ways give the same answer, 1/625 or .0016, although some ways are easier than others to execute.
(- , 4, 3): Take the reciprocal of 125 first, raise it to the 4th power, then take the cube root of your answer.
(- , 3, 4): Take the reciprocal of 125 first, take the cube root of that number, then raise your answer to the 4th power.
(4, - , 3): Raise 125 to the 4th power first, take the reciprocal of the answer, then take the cube root of that.
(4, 3, -): Raise 125 to the 4th power first, take the cube root of the answer, then take the reciprocal of that.
(3, 4, -): Take the cube root of 125 first, raise that answer to the 4th power, then take the reciprocal of that.
(3, - , 4): Take the cube root of 125 first, take the reciprocal of that answer, then raise that to the 4th power.

10. Ask him to check that on his calculator to see if the calculator agrees. Would $3^4 + 3^7 = 3^{11}$?

$(2268 = 177147?)$ How about $3^4 \times 3^7 = 3^{11}$? What's different about the two problems? A rule that works for multiplication doesn't seem to work for addition.

Chapter 10

Section 10.1

1. (a) 45, 56, 64, 71, 73, 74, 76, 82,
        83, 83, 84, 85, 87, 91, 92, 92,
        92, 95, 96
    (b) 45, 96
    (c) 92
    (d)

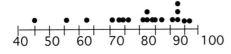

    (e)

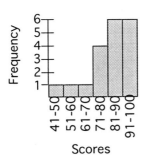

    (f)

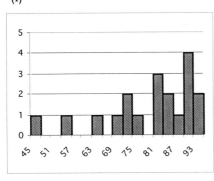

2. (a) 12. 15 25 40 45 50 50 50
        80 80 85
    (b)
        | 12.0 | |
        | 12.1 | 5 |
        | 12.2 | 5 |
        | 12.3 | |
        | 12.4 | 0 5 |
        | 12.5 | 0 0 0 |
        | 12.6 | |
        | 12.7 | |
        | 12.8 | 0 0 5 |
        | 12.9 | |
    (c) The plot in part (b) since it
        shows the spread of the data
        better.

3. (a)

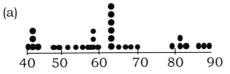

(b)

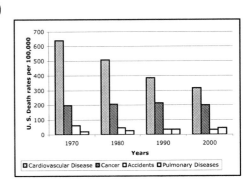

4. (a)

Class 1		Class 2
	3	1
5 1	4	3 6 6
6 4	5	
5 5	6	5 7
8 7 7 6 6	7	4 5 6 8 9
9 6 6	8	2 4 5 7
4 3 0	9	2 8

    (b) It is difficult to determine
        which class is better in this
        case.

5. (a) Yes, no   (b) Yes, no
    (c) Vertical scale does not begin
        at 0

6. (a)

    Chrysler New Yorker
    Lincoln Mark VII
    Cadillac DeVille
    Oldsmobile Lss
    Buick Riviera
    Ford Taurus

    (b) Look for the shortest bar
        which means the best braking.
        It is the Lincoln Mark VII.

7. (a)

(b) Cardiovascular diseases and accidents

(c) Most resources should be targeted for cardiovascular diseases and cancer.

8. (a) $0, $21, $47.50, $112.50, $188.50, $275.50, $373.50, $481.50

(b)

Tax (in dollars) vs Income (in dollars)

9. (a) 108 °   (b) 72 °
    (c) 54°   (d) $1800, $600, $600

10. (a) (i)   29%   104°
        (ii)   38%   137°
        (iii) 15%   55°
        (iv)   18%   64°

(b)

Pie chart:
> 4 yrs College 18%
< 4 years HS 29%
1-3 yrs College 15%
4 years HS 38%

11. (a) About 2 million
    (b) About 6.6 million
    (c) About 5.5 million
    (d) The height of all of the bars would be cut in half.
    (e) The range from 4,000 to about 6.6 million makes it difficult to have an amount for the symbol to represent.

12.

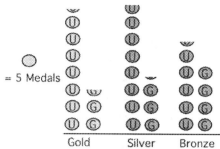

U.S.A and Germany medal count for Sydney 2004

= 5 Medals

Gold   Silver   Bronze

13. (a) and (c)

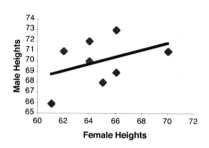

Dating Heights

(b) There are not any outliers.
(d) There is no change since there are no outliers.

14. (a) and (b)

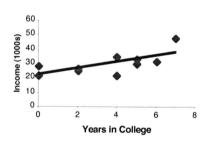

Education vs. Income

(c) Answers will vary depending on the method used to sketch your regression line in part (b).

15. (a) and (b)

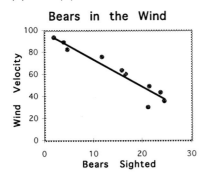

Bears in the Wind

(c) It should look similar but may look slightly different depending on the strategy used to find it by hand.

16. (a) and (b)

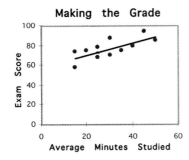

Making the Grade

(c) It should look similar but may look slightly different depending on the strategy used to find it by hand.

17. (a) Approximately 1150
    (b) Approximately 1400

18. (a)

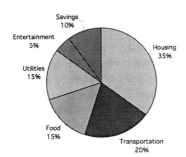

Monthly Budget

(b) The sector representing savings almost doubles and the rest of the sectors are smaller to accommodate it.

(c) $300

19. (a) Circle graph because the values are parts of a total or bar graph because it allows for comparison.
    (b) Circle graph:

Mail Handled in 2006

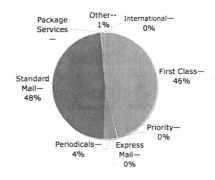

20. (a) Multiple circle because parts make up the whole population or multiple bar graphs for comparison.
    (b) Multiple bar graph:

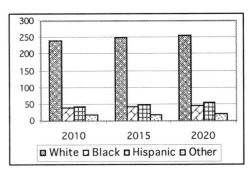

21. (a) Circle graph because values are parts of a whole or bar graph for comparison.
    (b) Circle graph:

Federal Budget Expenses 2006

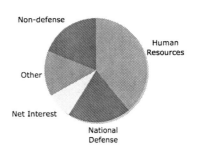

22. (a) Line graph to show trend.
     (b)

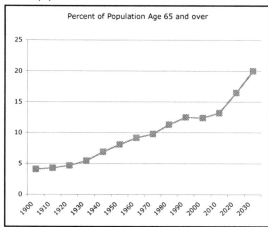

23. (a) Pictograph or bar graph to
          show trend and comparisons.
     (b) Bar graph:

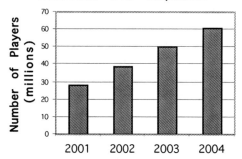

24. (a) Circle graph or bar graph
     (b) Circle graph:

25. (a) and (b)

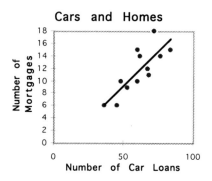

     (c) About 9 home mortgages

26. About $196,000,000,000

27. Histograms are often used to
     represent intervals of numbers.
     Since numbers of pets are to be
     represented, a bar graph would be
     the proper choice.

28. Create a scatterplot of the data
     and, by using a regression line,
     make a guess at the student's
     final score.

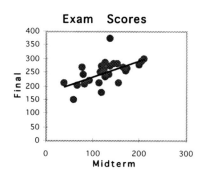

     Based on the scatterplot of the
     data, a student with a midterm
     score of 180 should probably get a
     final exam score of 275. This
     prediction is reasonably good but
     it could be surer if the data were
     closer together around the
     regression line.

Problems related to the NCTM Standards and Curriculum Focal Points

1. When constructing a stem and leaf plot, the stem is one place value and the leaves are the next smaller place value(s).

2. Double Bar - Section 10.1 Set A #7 is a good example of data for a double-bar graph because for each city, you can construct two bars, one for each year, and compare them.

   Ordered pairs – Ordered pairs are graphed on a scatterplot. Thus, any pair of data that might be correlated are good for ordered pairs. For example a person's height and arm span are an ordered pair of data.

3. A histogram is used when the data set is a continuous set of numbers like that are listed with different frequencies.

Section 10.2

1. (a)

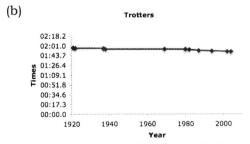

   (b)

   Putting the baseline at 1:50.0 as opposed to 0 makes the changes more dramatic.

2. (a)

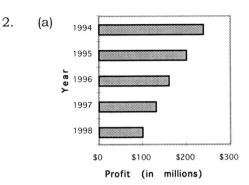

   (b) It appears as if the profit decreased over time, which is a more accurate representation.

3. (a) Oil companies want the increase to appear less dramatic so the range of the y-axis is larger.

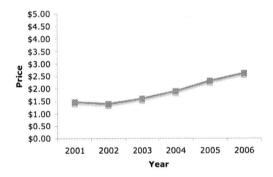

   (b) Consumer groups want the increase to appear more dramatic, so the range of the y-axis is small.

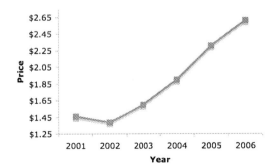

4.

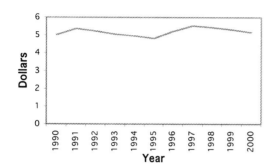

5.

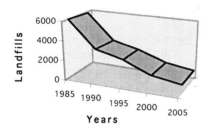

6.

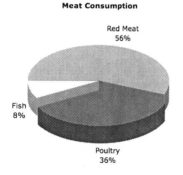

7. Because of the perspective, sectors B and D appear to be significantly larger than sectors A and C.

8.

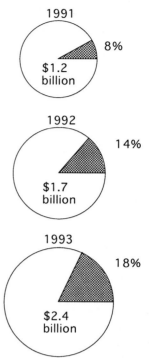

9.

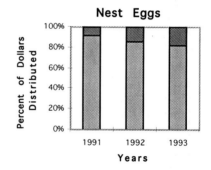

It appears as if the difference between 1992 and 1993 is small.

10. If the length of the bars (lasagna noodles) is measured from the right side of the fork and we assume that the "less often" bar is accurate, then the "once/twice a month" bar should be about 15%, the "once/twice a week" bar should be about 35%, and the "three times a week" bar should be about 29%. If the length of the bars is measured from the left side of the fork, then the bars are even less accurate at representing their corresponding percents.

11. No, the graph is not accurate. The radius has been tripled making the areas 9 times larger.

12. Exploding a sector; changing 3D perspective; incomplete labels; sectors don't add to 100%. Answers may vary.

13. Population-1000 coins in chest; Sample-20 coins taken from top.

14. Population-students taking mathematics classes; Sample-the 82 students in the three classes.

15.

16.

Average Carbon Monoxide Pollutant Concentration

17.

Average Carbon Monoxide Pollutant Concentration

18. (a)

Robberies with Guns

(b)

Robberies with Guns

19. (a)

Employees with good Job Security

(b)

Employees with good Job Security

20. Population-all of the professor's students; Sample-the students in the selected class; Bias- (i) the professor selected the class, (ii) the students would be discouraged from writing their true feelings because of his presence.

21. Population-all of the student body; Sample-the students at the coffee house and the gym; Bias-the students at the coffee house are participating in a social activity and the students at the gym are participating in a sporting activity so they are likely to choose candidates Johnson and Jackson respectively.

22. Celeste is correct. Depending on the situation, the vertical axis can be cropped as long as there is some indication, like a "squiggle" mark, that it has been done.

23. Cesar needs to convert the time he spends doing each activity into a percent by dividing by 24. As long as he accounts for all of the 24 hours, the percents will add up to 100 and a circle graph can be constructed.

Problems related to the NCTM Standards and Curriculum Focal Points

1. If a survey of 50 people is conducted in a school of 800 students, and 15 people responded in a certain way, then the proportion $\frac{15}{50} = \frac{x}{800}$ can be used to estimate how many students in the school feel the same way.

2. It is difficult to get a sense of a list of data by looking only at the numbers. However, if the numbers are organized into some kind of graph, it becomes easier to see trends and relationships.

3. Many possible answers.

Example 1: If the vertical axis on a line or bar graph is cropped, it may be inferred that the changes are greater than they really are.

Example 2: In an exploded circle graph, the isolated piece of the graph appears larger than it really is.

Section 10.3

1. (a) 0,0,0
   (b) 0, -0.5, no mode
   (c) 0, -0.05, no mode
   (d) $5 + \sqrt{2}$, $5 + \sqrt{2}$, no mode

2. (a) $\sqrt{2}/2$, $2\sqrt{2}$, $3\sqrt{2}$
   (b) π, π, $4 + \pi$
   (c) $\sqrt{3}/3 + \pi$, $(\sqrt{2} + \sqrt{3})/2 + \pi$, $\sqrt{3} + \pi$

3. 2.87

4. 26 students

5. No. $27 \times 70 = 21 \times 90$. Thus, 21 scores above ninety would yield a total that would exceed 27×70.

6. (a) {1, 3, 8, 9, 9}; answers may vary.
   (b) {1, 1, 5, 9, 9}; answers may vary.

7. (a) Lowest score = 50, lower quartile = 59, median = 73, upper quartile = 82, highest score = 97.
   (b) 20, 40, 60

8. (a)

   (b) Class 2 performed better since most statistics except the lowest score are higher than their counterparts from Class 1.

9. (a) The lower quartile: 21
    (b) The upper quartile: 42
    (c) The lower quartile: 25

10. (a) 0,0   (b) 59.3, 7.7
    (c) 11.7, 3.4   (d) 11.1, 3.3

11. (a) 8; $\sqrt{8}$ (b) 8; $\sqrt{8}$ (c) 8; $\sqrt{8}$
    (d) 16; 4. Adding/subtracting a constant amount does not change the variance or standard deviation.

12. 18, 18.5, 19, 2.6, 1.612

13. .03, .38, -.66, -.84, -.31, .21, -1.01, -1.19, 1.26, 2.13

14. (a)

stem	Leaves (× 100)
5	1 2 3
6	0 0 1 0 1 4 5 6 7 7 7 8
7	0 1 2 1 2 3 3 3 4 4 5 6 7 9
8	0 1 2 1 2 4 7 7 8
9	0 0 1 0 1 2 3 5 7 8 9 9
10	1 3 8 3 8 8
11	4 8 8
12	3
13	3

(b) Gaps occur mostly at the ends from 53-60 and 123-133. The biggest gaps at the upper end. Clusters occur in the middle, primarily in the sixties.
(c) There are no outliers
(d) East:
Lowest value = 6100
Lower quartile = 7500
Median = 9100
Upper quartile = 10300
Highest value = 13300
Outlier = None

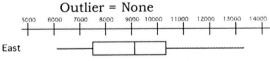

West (including LA and MN):
Lowest value = 5100
Lower quartile = 6650
Median = 7300
Upper quartile = 7800
Highest value = 9800
Outlier = None

All measures for the east are higher than corresponding measures for the west.

15. (a)

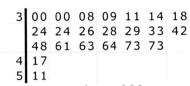

3	00 00 08 09 11 14 18
	24 24 26 28 29 33 42
	48 61 63 64 73 73
4	17
5	11

Lowest value = 300
Lower quartile = 314
Median = 328.5
Upper quartile = 363
Highest value = 511
Outlier = 511

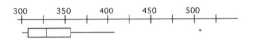

(b) Young's total is an extreme outlier.

16. (a) Fiftieth Percentile
    (b)

z-SCORE	PERCENTILE
-2	2
-1	15 or 16
1	84 or 85
2	98

17. A: test score >95
    B: 85 < test score ≤ 95
    C: 65 < test score ≤ 85
    D: 55 < test score ≤ 65
    F: test score ≤ 55

18. (a) 59th percentile   (b) 41%

19. 77%-78%

20. 65, 55, 75

21. Approximately 113.2

22. 11 girls

23. 87.9 (to nearest tenth)

24. All the numbers are equal.

25. (a) For example, {1,2,3,4,5} and {1,1,3,5,5}
     (b) For example, {1,2,3,4,5} and {6,7,8,9,10}

26. 63 (rounded to 2 places)

27. (a) No
     (b) Yes (if all scores are equal, then all z-scores are zero).

28. (a) 32.5   (b) 30; no.

29. (a) $s = 1.41$, $s_{n-1} = 1.58$ (to 2 places)

     (b) Yes, $s_{n-1} = \dfrac{\sqrt{n}}{n-1} \cdot s$

     whenever $s_{n-1} \neq 0 \neq s$

30. Although the number 3.9 has a 3 in it, it is really much closer to 4 than 3, so that is more positive than neutral. More importantly, a median 5 indicates that at least half of the class gave lavender a 5. A few negative votes have a more powerful effect on the mean than on the median, but these figures indicate the class is quite happy with the new color.

Problems related to the NCTM Standards and Curriculum Focal Points

1. To construct a stem and leaf plot, each data value must be broken into the stem part and the leaf part. The point where the values are broken is between two place values like the tens and ones or the ones and tenths. Thus and understanding is essential to constructing a stem and leaf plot. Other answers are possible.

2. The measures of central tendency – mean, median, and mode – as well as the measures of dispersion – variance and standard deviation – are all used to analyze and summarize data. The topic of z-scores combine central tendency and dispersion to indicate how a single value fits with the rest of the values. Finally, the normal distribution can indicate how a set of data all fit together. Answers may vary.

3. All three of the mean, median and mode typically used to indicate the "middle" of a set of data. The mean is most impacted by an outlier that is particularly large or small. The median is above half of the values and below the other half and not impacted by outliers. Since the mode is the value with the highest frequency, it will usually be in the middle but could be the lowest or highest value if it occurs most often. Answers may vary.

Chapter Review

Problems for Writing/Discussion

1. The median, $105,000, is the better representative because it is within the cluster of prices. The mean, $127,800, is greater than all but one of the prices, but doesn't really represent any of them.

2. When stores are restocking merchandise, they need to be attentive to which sizes are selling fastest.

3. With the double stem and leaf, all the original data points can be reconstructed, whereas with the box and whisker plot, the median, the upper and lower quartiles, and the range are the only specifics displayed. On the other hand, the box and whisker plot gives a good visual sense of where the "heft" of each set is located, since the box illustrates where the middle half of each set is located. The box and whisker plot also makes comparison easier between two sets of unequal size.

4. The state-licensing bureau would have the information on 30 year olds in the state who have drivers' licenses. Assuming you could get access to that information, you would then have to determine how to contact a certain number of these drivers.

5. In a normal distribution the mean, median, and mode are all equal. If the median is greater than the mean, it means that more than half of the test scores were "above average." We say the distribution is "skewed to the left." If most of the scores are high, it takes some very low scores to bring the mean below the median.

6. You would want to know the data for each year to see if there was a pattern. You would want to talk to sociologists and other experts to see if they have an explanation for the increases in 1990 and 1995. You would want to determine to what extent the cause of the increases in those years was still operating in the culture. You could then base your prediction on the sociological and mathematical patterns you inferred.

7. If the average of 24 students was 75%, then the total number of points earned was 24 ´ 75, or 1800 points. If the average of 25 students is 76%, then the new total would be 25 ´ 76, or 1900 points. The absent student must have gotten 100!

8. In the following picture, the cars are shown in a 3:1 format.

    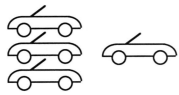

    It is clear that where there was one, there are now three.

In the next picture where the car seems to have enlarged three times in two dimensions, the actual areas of the images are in the ratio of 9:1. This is deceptive.

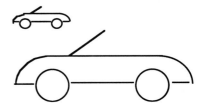

9. He was referring to the fact that many people try to bend statistics to suit their own ends. Statistics in themselves don't lie, but people can use them to deceive.

10. If the student earned 79%, that means he had earned a total of 592.5 points during the quarter. An 80% would represent a total of 600 points. So the student really missed an 80 by 7.5 points, not just one.

Chapter 11

Section 11.1

theoretical probability, but answers may vary.

1. (a) Gift B or E
   (b) Gift A or C
   (c) No one

2. (a) {HH, HT, TH, TT}
   (b) {H1, H2, H3, H4, H5, H6, T1, T2, T3, T4, T5, T6}
   (c) {RG, RW, BG, BW}

3. (a) {R,G,B,Y,W}
   (b) {RR,RG,RB,RY,RW,GR,GG,GB, GY,GW,...,WR,WG,WB,WY,W} (25 pairs)
   (c) {RG,RB,RY,RW,GR,GB,GY,GW, BR,BG,BY,BW,YR,YG,YB,YW, WR,WG,WB,WY}

4. (a) {H1, H2, H3, H4, H5, H6, T1, T2, T3, T4, T5, T6}
   (b) {H1, H2, H3, H4, H5, H6}
   (c) {H3, T3}
   (d) {H2, T2, H4, T4, H6, T6}
   (e) {H5, H6}
   (f) {T1, T2, T3, T4, T5, T6, H5}

5. (a) C   (b) P   (c) I

6. P | (H, P) (T, P)
   G | (H, G) (T, G)
   Y | (H, Y) (T, Y)
   _____
         H   T

7. (a) 75/1000 = 0.075
   (b) 150/1000 = 0.15
   (c) 275/1000 = 0.275
   (d) 375/1000 = 0.375

8. (a) 1/2   (b) 11/12
   (c) 5/12   (d) 13/18
   (e) 5/18
   (f) In general, the answers for 500 rolls should be closer to the theoretical probability, but answers may vary.

9. (a) 0.5   (b) 0.25
   (c) 0.875   (d) 0.375
   (e) In general, the answers for 500 rolls should be closer to the

10. (a) 7/12   (b) 1   (c) 1/2

11. (a) 1/2   (b) 3/13
    (c) 10/13   (d) 3/26

12. (a) 37/75   (b) 64 times

13. (a) 7/22   (b) 3/22
    (c) 5/22   (d) 3/22
    (e) 15/22   (f) 9/22

14. (a) 5/9   (b) 27/38
    (c) 9/19   (d) 18/19

15. (a) 1/3   (b) 1/3
    (c) 1/3   (d) 1
    (e) 1/2, 1/8, 3/8, 1; yes.

16. (a) 1/6   (b) 5/6
    (c) 1/2   (d) 1/2
    (e) 2/3   (f) 1/3

17. (a) 7/13   (b) 3/4
    (c) 7/13   (d) 25/52

18. (a) 1/2   (b) 1/3   (c) 1/6
    (d) 1   (e) 7/12

19. (a) Either two or three heads appear; 1/2
    (b) Number of heads is not 2; 5/8
    (c) The second coin lands tails; 1/2
    (d) Two heads appear, one of which is on second coin; 1/4

20. (a) The probability of getting a spade or a face card.
    (b) The probability of getting a jack, queen, or king of spades.
    (c) The probability of not getting a face card.

21. (a) Each state not equally likely, since populations not equal.
    (b) Intersection of two events is not empty set, so property 4 does not apply. Probability cannot be greater than 1.
    (c) Winning and losing are complementary events, but 1/2 + 1/3 ≠ 1.

22. (a) 1/3   (b) 2   (c) 4

23. (a) 6; 1/2   (b) 30;7/30
    (c) 20;1/20

24. $\dfrac{100^2 - \pi(40)^2}{100^2} \approx 0.497$

25. $91/216 \approx 0.42$

26. Shirley has to consider the fact that each day has its own probability. The probability of no rain on the first day is .6. The probability of no rain on the second day is .6. So the probability that it would not rain on the first two days is (.6)(.6) = .36. The probability that it would not rain on <u>any</u> of the 7 days she will be there is $(.6)^7$ = .0279936 or only about 3%.

27. Although the probability of getting 50 heads out of 100 tosses is the most likely, the probability of getting 48 or 49 or 51 or 52 or other numbers close to 50 is slightly less, but very close to the probability of getting 50. Since these outcomes have similar probabilities, a different outcome could occur on each of a small number of trials.

Problems related to the NCTM Standards and Curriculum Focal Points

1. An experiment with outcomes that are not equally likely is dropping a thumbtack to see if it will land point up or point down. An experiment with equally likely outcomes is tossing a coin. Answers may vary.

2. Probability is the fraction of the number of elements in an event divided by the number of elements in the sample space. Since an event is always a subset of the sample space, it is impossible to for the fraction to have a numerator that is larger than the denominator. Thus, the probability will always be less than or equal to one.

3. Two events are mutually exclusive if they have no elements in common. If two events are mutually exclusive then the probability of the union of these two events can be computed by simply adding the probabilities of the individual events.

Section 11.2

1. (a) (b) (c) (d)

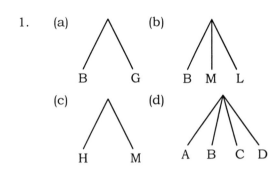

2. (a)

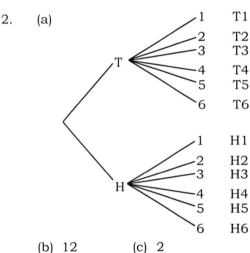

(b) 12   (c) 2
(d) 6   (e) 2 × 6 = 12

3.

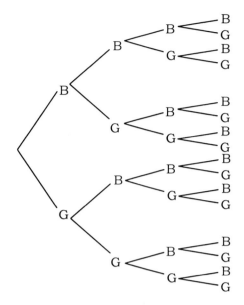

(c) 4/25 + 6/25 + 6/25 = 16/25
(d) 1 - 9/25 = 16/25

10. (a)   (b)

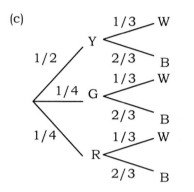

(c)

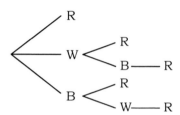

4.

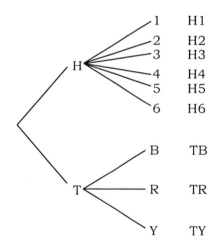

11. (a), (b) and (c)

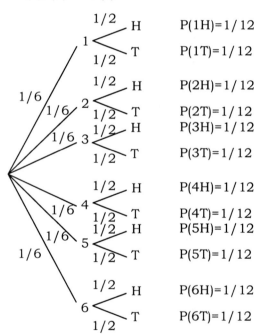

5.

6.   20 ways

7.   36

8.   (a) R - 1/4, W - 1/4, B - 1/2
      (b) R - 1/5, W - 1/5, B - 3/5
      (c) R - 1/3, W - 1/6, B - 1/2

9.   (a) Y = 2/5, R = 3/5 appropriate
           for each branch
      (b) 4/25, 6/25

(d) P(even and head)
     = P(2H) +P(4H) + P(6H)
     = 1/12 + 1/12 + 1/12 = 1/4

12.   (a) and (b)

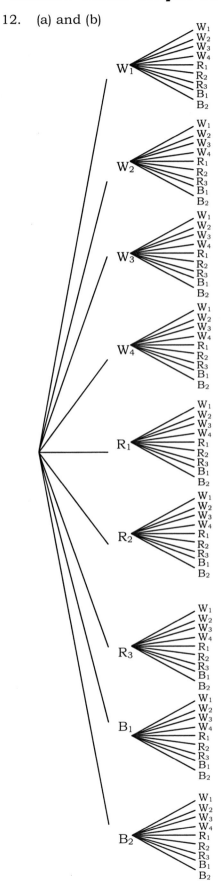

(c) Label each of the 9 branches in the first stage of the outcome tree with 1/9 and each of the 81 branches in the second stage with 1/9.

The probability of each of the 81 outcomes is
$1/9 \times 1/9 = 1/81$

(d) P(red and white) = $P(R_1W_1)$ + $P(R_1W_2)$ + $P(R_1W_3)$ + $P(R_1W_4)$ + $P(R_2W_1)$ + $P(R_2W_2)$ + $P(R_2W_3)$ + $P(R_2W_4)$ + $P(R_3W_1)$ + $P(R_3W_2)$ + $P(R_3W_3)$ + $P(R_3W_4)$ + = $12/81$

13.   (a)

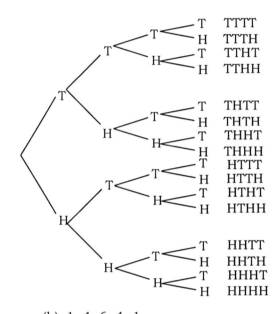

(b) 1, 4, 6, 4, 1
(c) same as 1, 4, ... row

14.   (a) $10 \times 10 \times 10 \times 10$
= 10,000
(b) 10
(c) 10/10,000 = 1/1000
(d) 7/10,000

15.   (a) $2 \times 26 \times 26 \times 26 = 35,152$
(b) $1/35,152 \approx 0.00003$

16.   (a) $8 \times 3 \times 2 \times 5 = 240$
(b) 120
(c) 1/2
(d) 16/240 = 1/15

17. (a) 1, 5, 10, 10, 5, 1
    (b) 5
    (c) 10
    (d) 5/16, 1/2

18. (a)

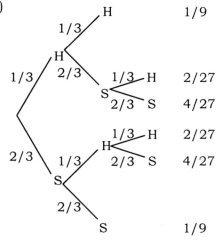

    (b) 1/9, 4/9   (c) 4/9
    (d) 2/27   (e) 20/27

19. (a)

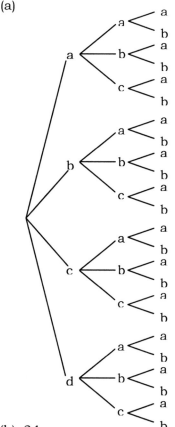

    (b) 24
    (c) 4 × 3 × 2 = 24, yes
    (d) 1/24

20. (a) $(0.343)^3 \approx 0.04$
    (b) $(0.657)^3 \approx 0.28$
    (c) $1 - 0.28 = 0.72$
    (d) $3(0.343)(0.657)^2 \approx 0.45$

21. (a)

    (b) 1/2, 1/4, 1/8, 1/16
    (c) 1/32

22. (a)

    (b)   0.7

23. A = 3%, B = 16%, C = 31%,
    D = 31%, E = 16%, F = 3%

24. If the prisoner places one white
    ball in one box and the remaining
    balls (9 white and 10 black) in the
    other box, his chance of going free
    would be (1 + 9/19)/2 = 0.737 or
    73.7%.

25. Switch! For curtains *A*, *B*, and *C*,
    suppose that the prize is behind *A*.
    Here are the possibilities:

    Choose *A* first. Then *B* or *C* is
    shown. Stay wins, switch loses.

    Choose *B* first. Then *C* is shown.
    Stay loses, switch wins.

    Choose *C* first. Then *B* is shown.
    Stay loses, switch wins.

26. (a) 1/3   (b) 4/11

27. Let a, b, $a + b$, $a + 2b$ be four consecutive Fibonacci numbers. Then $(a + b)^2 - b^2 = a^2 + 2ab$, and $a(a + 2b) = a^2 + 2ab$. Thus, they are always equal.

28. As noted in the previous problem, P(K *and* heart) = P(K) ´ P(heart). Maxwell is correct that the probability of getting a king *or* a heart can be represented by the sum of the two probabilities, with the exception that one particular card, namely the king of hearts, will have been counted twice. To adjust for that, P(K *or* heart) is given as P(K) + P(heart) - P(king of hearts). This equals 16/52, not 17/52. The 16 equals all of the hearts plus the kings of spades, clubs, and diamonds. In general, we have to subtract the items that are in the intersection of the two sets in question because we don't want them to be counted twice, so P(A *or* B) = P(A) + P(B) - P(A *and* B).

Problems related to the NCTM Standards and Curriculum Focal Points

1. If a sample space were written out for this experiment, there would be three possible equally likely outcomes, R, R, and W. The definition of theoretical probability assumes that all of the outcomes are equally likely in order to write P(Red) =2/3. Suppose, however that the two red marbles were very small and difficult to find, then a sample space of equally likely outcomes could not be written and the theoretical probability could not be determined. Answers may vary.

2. If a two stage tree diagram with 3 outcomes in the first stage and 4 outcomes in the second stage were constructed, there would be a total of 12 branches. The number of possible outcomes could also be determined by using the

Fundamental Counting Principle and multiplying 3 by 4.

3. Since each birth is independent and the probability of getting a boy on any given birth is $\frac{1}{2}$, the probability having 4 boys in a family of 4 children could be found by using the multiplicative property of probability. We can compute $\frac{1}{2} \cdot \frac{1}{2} \cdot \frac{1}{2} \cdot \frac{1}{2} = \frac{1}{16}$.

Section 11.3

1. (a) $\frac{20!}{15!} = 20 \cdot 19 \cdot 18 \cdot 17 \cdot 16$
   $= 1,860,480$
   (b) $(n + 1)(n)(n - 1)$
   (c) $\frac{57!}{55!} = 57 \cdot 56 = 3192$

2. (a) $m = 23$, $n = 4$
   (b) $m = 11$, $n = 2$

3. (a) $\frac{10!}{7!3!} = \frac{10 \cdot 9 \cdot 8}{3 \cdot 2 \cdot 1} = 120$
   (b)
   $$\frac{23 \cdot 22 \cdot 21 \cdot 20 \cdot 19 \cdot 18 \cdot 17 \cdot 16 \cdot 15 \cdot 14}{10 \cdot 9 \cdot 8 \cdot 7 \cdot 6 \cdot 5 \cdot 4 \cdot 3 \cdot 2 \cdot 1}$$
   $= 1,114,066$
   (c) $\frac{50 \cdot 49 \cdot 48 \cdot 47 \cdot 46}{5 \cdot 4 \cdot 3 \cdot 2 \cdot 1}$
   $= 2,118,760$

4. (a) $m = 16$, $n = 4$
   (b) $m = 33$, $n = 28$

5. (a) $_6P_2$ (b) $_{12}P_2$
   (c) $_{12}P_2$ (d) $_{12}P_2$

6. (a) 90 (b) 45 (c) 45
   (d) 30 (e) 27

7. (a) 26^4
   (b) $26 \cdot 25 \cdot 24 \cdot 23 = 358,800$
   (c) 26^3

8. $8!$

9.   (a) $_{10}C_7 = 120$ (b) $_8C_5 = 56$

10. $_{11}C_7 = 330$

11. (a) 1, 20, 190, 1140
     (b) 1, 21, 210, 1330
     (c) 210 = 20 + 190
         1330 = 190 + 1140

12. (a) 15/64
     (b) 20/64 = 5/16
     (c) 1/64

13. $\dfrac{17!}{20!} = \dfrac{1}{6840}$

14. $\dfrac{_{16}C_3 \times _{13}C_5}{_{19}C_6 \times _{13}C_5} = \dfrac{20}{969}$

15. $\dfrac{7}{_{10}C_4} = \dfrac{1}{30}$

16. (a) $n = 9$ (b) $n = 12$

17. $\dfrac{12}{_{14}C_3 \times _{11}C_5} = \dfrac{1}{14014}$

18. $\dfrac{_4C_2 \times _4C_2}{_{52}C_5} = \dfrac{3}{216580}$

19. (a) $3 \cdot 13! = 18,681,062,4000$
     (b) $3(_{13}C_3 + _{13}C_2 + _{13}C_1 + _{13}C_0) = 1134$

20. $5,428,503,678,976$
     $\approx 5.4285 \times 10^{12}$

21. (a) 5!
     (b) $6! - 2 \times 5! = 4 \times 5! - 480$

22. $_{30}P_6 = 427,518,000$

23. $11! = 39,916,800$

24. 3 - Yes, 4 - Yes, 5 - No

25. (a) $(_4C_2 + _3C_2 + _2C_2)/_{10}C_2$
         $= (6 + 3 + 1)/45 = 2/9$
     (b) $(_4C_1 \times _6C_1)/_{10}C_2 = 24/45$
         $= 8/15$
     (c) $(_4C_1 \times _6C_1 + _4C_2 \times _6C_0)/_{10}C_2$
         $= (24 + 6)/45 = 2/3$

     (d) $(_4C_0 \times _6C_2/_{10}C_2 = 15/45$
         $= 1/3$

26. (a) $2 \times 6! = 1440$
     (b) $7! - 2 \times 6! = 3600$
     (c) $6 \times 5! = 720$

27. $12! = 479,001,600$
     $5! \times 4! \times 3! \times 6 = 103,680$

28. (a) $_8C_0 \times _6C_4 + _8C_1 \times _6C_3 +$
         $_8C_2 \times _6C_2 + _8C_3 \times _6C_1 +$
         $_8C_4 \times _6C_0 = 1265$
     (b) $_8 C_2 \times _8C_2 = 784$
     (c) $_8C_4 = 70$ (d) $_6C_4 = 15$

29. No, Julio is not correct. Since
     there are 4 different condiments,
     which can either be on or off (2
     choices) of the sandwich, there are
     $2^4 = 16$ choices of condiments.
     There are two choices of bread and
     only one choice of meat so there
     are only 32 sandwich
     combinations.

30. If permutations were used, then
     the order of selection would be
     taken into account. Lowell is
     correct because the order in which
     the committee members are
     selected does NOT matter, so
     combinations are the correct way
     to count the committees.

**Problems related to the NCTM
Standards and Curriculum Focal Points**

1.   Sometimes the sample space of an
     experiment is too large to write out
     so the number of elements in the
     sample space or in an event can
     be determined by using
     permutations or combinations.

2.   If there are a lot of outcomes for
     any stage of an experiment, then
     drawing a tree diagram can be
     overwhelming. Thus,
     combinations or permutations can
     be used to find the number of
     branches on a tree diagram or the
     number of elements in an event.

Section 11.4

1. Answers will vary.

2. Answers may vary but should be around 7 packages.

3. (a) Answers will vary.
    (b) The theoretical number is 21.74 or 22 pennies.

4. Step 1: Yes   Step 2: 2
    Step 3: 44
    (a) .88 (theoretical solution .63)

5. (a) Place pieces of paper corresponding to the chocolate candies in a bag. Draw out 2 pieces of paper and record the results.
    (b) Answer should be near
        $\frac{150}{812} \approx 0.185$, but will vary.
    (c) Place 5 ones, 7 twos, 8 threes, 5 fours, and 4 fives in the bin and draw 2. After 30 trials, the probability should be near 0.185.

6. Read the digits on the table and record numbers 1-6 as rolls. Ignore 0, 7, 8, 9. Starting on the top row, the first twenty rolls would be 1, 3, 1, 1, 2, 1, 2, 5, 2, 2, 3, 6, 5, 5, 2, 1, 6, 5, 2, 4.

7. 0.8

8. 4/5 (In long run such a sample will average just under one defective microscope.)

9. (a) $40,000   (b) $25
    (c) Scholarship A

10. Make $2,200

11. They are the same since they both reduce to 3:2.

12. (a) (i)   6:30 or 1:5
        (ii) 33:3 or 11:1
        (iii) 18:18 or 1:1
    (b) (i) 5:1   (ii) 1:11   (iii) 1:1

13. (a) 3:10   (b) 3:1
    (c) 1:51   (d) 10:3

14. (a) 3:5   (b) 7:1
    (c) 7:1   (d) 3:5

15. (a) 1:7, 7:1   (b) 2:3, 3:2

16. (a) 1/9   (b) 3/8   (c) 5/11

17. For example, the sum is...
    (a) not 8, 9, or 10
    (b) 6, 7, or 8
    (c) not 2.

18. (a) 10/21   (b) 1/3
    (c) 11/21   (d) 3/7
    (e) 3/10   (f) 5/11
    (g) 1/2   (h) 3/11
    (i) 3/7

19. (a) 1/4   (b) 1/5
    (c) 1/6   (d) 1/3

20. (a) 1/2, 3/4   (b) 1/2, 1/4

21. (a) 1/3   (b) 2/4 = 1/2
    (c) 3/5   (d) 1/2
    (e) 1   (f) 1/3

22. (a) 13/16   (b) 13/21
    (c) 15/16   (d) 5/14
    (e) 1   (f) 1/2

23. (a) and (b) Answers will vary.
    (c) 176/1024

24. Use a deck of 52 cards. Draw until 2 aces appear. Count and record the number of draws needed. Repeat n times, for your choice of n, say $n = 100$. Then compute the average number of draws needed. Theoretical expected value is 21.2.

25. Use slips of paper, numbered from 1 to 20. Call your number 1, for example. Draw 12 slips from a hat; this is the first jury. Replace all 12 slips and draw 12 slips again. This is the second jury. Repeat this n times, say $n = 100$. Count the number of times out of n that your number came up on

one (or both) of the juries. It should be around 80% of the time. Theoretical probability = .84.

26. Switches should win about 2/3 of the time.

27. Answers will vary.

28. Click on the numbers 1, 2, 3, 4, 5, 6 to put in the box. Press Start. When each of the numbers 1-5 have been drawn, press Pause and record the number of draws. Repeat 100 times.

29. True. Let the row sum be m. Then the sum of all numbers must be the sum of three rows, or $3m$, a multiple of 3.

30. (a) Set the "Longest run in heads" to 4 and the "Probability of heads" to 0.5. Start tossing until you get 4 heads in a row and record how many tosses it took. Repeat this 20 times and average the number of tosses it took to get 4 heads in a row.
    (b) A reasonable answer would be around 25 to 30 tosses.

31. Assuming that the five hits were counted as part of the .333, the odds of a hit on Julio's next at bat would be P(hit):P(no hit). That is, 0.333:0.667 or 1:2.

32. Yes. Simulation is a good idea when you need to run a large number of trials. For example, if you want to toss a coin 1000 times, it would be faster to use a random number table, or better still to use a computer simulation, to ascertain the number of heads or tails in the outcome rather than actually tossing the coins.

Problems related to the NCTM Standards and Curriculum Focal Points

1. When drawing cards from a standard 52-card deck, the theoretical probability says the probability of drawing a spade is $1/4$. If a simulation of drawing a single card is done 60 times, the following proportion could be used to determine how many times a spade is expected. $1/4 = x/60$. Answers may vary.

2. Theoretical probability is the ratio of the number of elements in an event compared to the number of elements in the sample space. The odds of an event, on the other hand, is the ratio of the number of elements in the event compared to the number of elements in the complement of the event.

3. For some experiments, the theoretical probability is difficult to determine. In those cases a simulation can be done to determine the experimental probability of an event. If the experimental probability were, for example, 3/8, and the same experiment were done 40 times, the proportion $3/8 = x/40$ could be used to make a conjecture about the number of times an event would occur in the 40 experiments.

Chapter Review

Problems for Writing/Discussion

1. No! There are 36 possible outcomes when tossing a pair of dice. A 2 can occur in only one way out of the 36, that is, if you get a 1 on both dice. Thus P(2) = 1/36.

2. The possible sums would go from 2 to 16 and there are $8^2 = 64$ possible outcomes. The sum with the highest probability would be 9 because there are 8 ways you could get a 9. Thus P(9) = 8/64 = 1/8.

3. The number of ways of choosing the correct 6 numbers out of 50 is the same as the ways of choosing 6 committee members out of 50 people, 50!/(6!44!) = 15,890,700. (See Topic 3 for a complete

discussion of combinations.) Only one of those choices would win the lottery. So your probability of holding a winning ticket is $1 \div 15{,}890{,}700$ or about .00000006293.

If the jackpot is \$13,000,000, the expected value of a ticket would be 82¢, the product of 13,000,000 and 1/15,890,700.

4. The following diagram would represent the situation, that it would take a maximum of 5 single moves to get Home.

Irene					Home

The 8 possible outcomes are 1-1-1-1-1, 1-1-1-2, 1-1-2-1, 1-2-1-1, 2-1-1-1, 1-2-2, 2-1-2, 2-2-1. Their probabilities, respectively, are $(1/2)^4$, $(1/2)^4$, $(1/2)^3$, $(1/2)^3$, $(1/2)^3$, $(1/2)^3$, $(1/2)^3$, and $(1/2)^2$. (These probabilities can be ascertained from a tree diagram by looking at the number of times a decision was made to achieve a particular outcome.) Note that once Irene is at the square next to Home, there is no choice to be made since she could only move 1 square. The answer to the question asked in the problem is found by summing the 4 probabilities that involve four moves: $1/16 + 1/8 + 1/8 + 1/8 = 7/16$.

5. You could make a chart of the 8 possible outcomes. Then by tossing a coin successively, you would see if you got HHHHH, HHHT, HHTH, etc. Once you have completed one of the paths of the tree diagram, you could add 1 to the appropriate column of your chart. Using a die, you might decide to make the three odd numbers represent heads and the three even numbers represent tails. Using a deck of cards, you

might decide to let the red suits represent heads, and the black suits represent tails. A computer simulation would be able to make 9600 trials quickly and easily.

6. $8{,}388{,}608 = 2^{23}$ where 23 is the number of random choices that were made between two possibilities as each of your parents donated half of their 46 chromosomes to create you.

7. The number of possible outcomes for the 10-item true/false test would be 2^{10}. The number of instances in which there would be 7 correct and 3 incorrect answers would be 120 (ways of choosing 7 out of 10). So the probability of a 70% would be $120/2^{10} = .1172$. The chance of getting 8 correct would be $45/2^{10}$, 9 correct would be $10/2^{10}$, and 10 correct would be $1/2^{10}$. So the probability of 70% <u>or better</u> would be the sum of these probabilities, $176/2^{10} = 0.1719$ or about 17%. One way to look at this is that on a ten-item true/false test you would have about 1 chance in 6 of passing if you guessed at random.

8. Mortality tables are constructed from the actual data of births and deaths. Insurance companies need them to figure out how little to charge people for life insurance and still maintain a profit margin. In the computer age, these tables can be made very specific to allow for differences in life expectancy in different areas of the country or the world. As to the change in your life expectancy as you age, "the longer you live, the longer you *will* live." If you are still surviving 20 years from now, you will have outlived all the people in your age cohort who died in the meantime. Their deaths are what brought the average down to 75, so with them

gone, your expected age at death will go up.

9. This is a good problem in which to look at the probability that you do *not* get what you want. The probability that you would *not* get a 5 or a jack on the first draw is 44/52, on the second is 43/51, and on the third is 42/50. So the probability that none of the first three cards was a jack or a 5 is the product of those probabilities, 0.599276. Thus there is roughly a 60% chance that none of the first three cards is a jack or a 5. The person who bets that one of the two cards *will* show up in the first three cards chosen is at a disadvantage because this will happen only about 40% of the time.

10. The probability of a 7 is 6/36, of 11 is 2/36, of 2 is 1/36, of 3 is 2/36, and of 12 is 1/36. The sum of those probabilities is 12/36 or 1/3. So there are 2 chances out of 3 that the gambler neither wins nor loses on his first roll.

Chapter 12

Section 12.1

1. (a) Level 1
   (b) Level 0
   (c) Level 0

2. (a) None
   (b) 7
   (c) 2, 3, 4, 7
   (d) 5, 6
   (e) Level 3

3. (a) {1, 2, 7} and {3, 4, 5, 6, 8, 9}. Shapes 1, 2, and 7 all have 4 congruent sides and the rest of the shapes do not. Answers may vary.
   (b) {4, 6, 8, 9} and {1, 2, 3, 5, 7}. Shapes 1, 2, 3, 5, and 7 all have at least two parallel sides and the rest of the shapes do not. Answers may vary.
   (c) Level 1
   (d) Level 1

4. 9 rectangles

5. (a) 13   (b) 15   (c) 15

6.

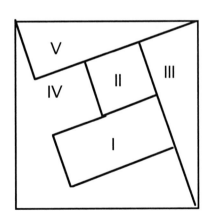

7. (a)

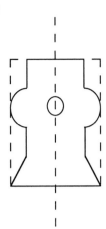

   (b)

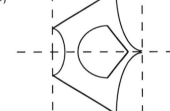

8. (a)

   (b)

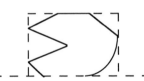

Figures here show the fold line at the bottom. They could also be drawn with the fold line at the top.

9.

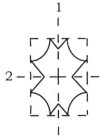

10.

11. (a) a, b, e, j
     (b) b, e, g, i, j
     (c) b, c, d, g, h, i, j
     (d) c, g, j

12. (a) ABRI, IRGH, IBMG
     (b) RDFG
     (c) IDEG
     (d) ABI, IBR, BMR, IRG, IGH,
          GRM, DEF
     (e) ICG
     (f) JOPQ
     (g) CGHI
     (h) IJB, JCG, LMG etc.
     (i) BCG, GRN, etc.
     (j) ACEH, BCEG, GRDE, etc.
     (k) DEGM, GIKL

13. (a) reflect over vertical line.
     (b) rotate 1/4 turn.

14. Yes.

15. Lengths x and y are the same in each case.

16. (a) 3   (b) 4

17. All of them.

18. (a) 6   (b) 6
     (c) 8   (d) $2n$, where $n \leq m$

19. (a)

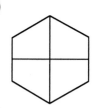

     (b)

20. (a) 7: $\mathbf{3} \times 2^2 + \mathbf{4} \times 1^2 = 16$
          8: $\mathbf{1} \times 3^2 + \mathbf{3} \times 2^2 + \mathbf{4} \times 1^2$
               $= 25$
          9: $\mathbf{9} \times 1^2 = 9$
               $\mathbf{1} \times 4^2 + \mathbf{4} \times 2^2 + \mathbf{4} \times 1^2$
               $= 36$
         10: $\mathbf{2} \times 2^2 + \mathbf{8} \times 1^2 = 16$
               $\mathbf{1} \times 4^2 + \mathbf{9} \times 1^2 = 25$
         11: $\mathbf{1} \times 3^2 + \mathbf{2} \times 2^2 + \mathbf{8} \times 1^2$
               $= 25$
               $\mathbf{2} \times 3^2 + \mathbf{3} \times 2^2 + \mathbf{6} \times 1^2$
               $= 36$
         12: $\mathbf{1} \times 5^2 + \mathbf{11} \times 1^2 = 36$
               $\mathbf{3} \times 3^2 + \mathbf{9} \times 1^2 = 36$
         13: $\mathbf{1} \times 2^2 + \mathbf{12} \times 1^2 = 16$
               $\mathbf{4} \times 2^2 + \mathbf{9} \times 1^2 = 25$
         14: $\mathbf{1} \times 3^2 + \mathbf{1} \times 2^2 + \mathbf{12} \times 1^2$
               $= 25$
               $\mathbf{2} \times 3^2 + \mathbf{2} \times 2^2 + \mathbf{10} \times 1^2$
               $= 36$
         15: $\mathbf{7} \times 2^2 + \mathbf{8} \times 1^2 = 36$
               $\mathbf{1} \times 4^2 + \mathbf{2} \times 2^2 +$
               $\mathbf{12} \times 1^2 = 36$
         16: $\mathbf{16} \times 1^2 = 16$
               $\mathbf{3} \times 2^2 + \mathbf{13} \times 1^2 = 25$
     (b) See (a)
     (c) 9 and 16

21. These children's comments seem to reflect Van Hiele Level 0, the visual level. Bernie does not recognize that straight sides are a property of triangles, and Chandra is visualizing a stereotypical triangle with slanted sides (which she calls "angles") and a horizontal base (which she calls "straight").

22. Since a square satisfies the definition of a rhombus, the set of squares is a subset of the set of rhombuses. Every square is a rhombus, although some rhombuses are not squares.

Problems related to the NCTM Standards and Curriculum Focal Points

1.   Identifying shapes is a level 0 activity unless students use

properties to make the
identification.

2. Describing shapes could be at a
level 0 or level 1 depending on the
level of detail of the descriptions. If
they use properties in their
descriptions, they are at a level 1.

3. The analysis in this focal point
would indicate that students at
grade 3 should have now moved to
a level 1.

Section 12.2

1. (a) Reflections over both
diagonals, half turn rotation
around the center of the
square.
   (b) 1/2 turn around the center of
the square.

2. (a) 72°, 144°, 216°, 288°
   (b) 60°, 120°, 180°, 240°, 300°
   (c) 51.4°, 102.9°, 154.3°, 205,7°,
257.1°, 308.6°
   (d) 45°, 90°, 135°, 180°, 225°,
270°, 315°
   (e) $\dfrac{x \cdot 180°}{n}$, for $x = 1, ..., n-1$

3. (a) A,H,I,M,O,T,U,V,W,X,Y
   (b) B,C,D,E,H,I,K,O,X

4. (a) Rotation, 180° about center of
circle.
   (b) Reflection, vertical line
through center; rotation, 120°
or 240° degrees about center
of circle.
   (c) Reflection, vertical line.
   (d) Reflection, 12 lines through
center; rotation, 30° and
multiples.

5. No. When the paper is folded along
one line the ends of the other line
match.

6. Yes. When the paper is folded so
the ends of one line match, the
ends of the other line also match.

7. (a) S, C   (b) None
   (c) None   (d) S

8. Yes

9. (a)

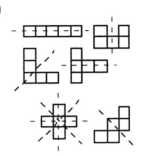

(b)

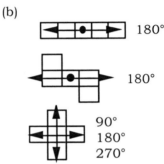

180°

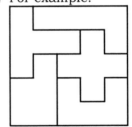

180°

90°
180°
270°

10. Refer to answer to exercise 6.
Shapes 2, 4, 5, 6, 9, 10, 11, 12.
    (a) For example, in answer 6 put
shape 5 onto shape 8. Rotate
shape 7 through 1/2 turn and
fit on top of shape 5.
    (b) For example:

    (c) One of many solutions

11. (a) (iii) Rectangles are inner set.
    (b) (ii) Note that the intersection
is squares.
    (c) (iii) Squares inside rectangles.
    (d) (i)

12. Rotate 1/2 turn around the center, E. Then $\overline{AE}$ of the tracing coincides with $\overline{CE}$, and $\overline{BE}$ of the tracing coincides with $\overline{DE}$.

13. Rotate 1/2 turn around the center.

14. Rotate 1/2 turn around the center. Then opposite sides will coincide.

15. (a) Fold on the dashed line.

    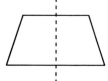

    (b) They are congruent.

16. (a) Pentagon: 1/5, 2/5, 3/5, 4/5and 1 full turn around the center. Hexagon: 1/6, 1/3, 1/2, 2/3, 5/6, and 1 full turn around the center.

    (b) *n.*

17. A – Parallelogram
    B – Trapezoid
    C – Rhombus
    D – Square
    E – Rectangle
    F – Kite
    G – Quadrilateral

18. While it is true that many figures have both types of symmetry, it is possible to have one without the other. Just as the parallelogram in the problem above has rotation symmetry, but not reflection symmetry, there are figures that have reflection symmetry, but not rotation symmetry, such as the one shown below.

    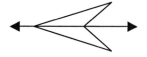

Problems related to the NCTM Standards and Curriculum Focal Points

1. Rotational symmetry, reflection symmetry, perpendicular lines, parallel lines, convex and so on.

2. Opposite sides being parallel could be used to determine if the quadrilateral were a parallelogram or a trapezoid. If the adjacent sides are perpendicular then the quadrilateral may be a square or a rectangle. Answers may vary.

3. Paper folding works well for determining reflection symmetry. Paper tracing works well for determining rotation symmetry. Both of these tasks are appropriate for elementary students.

Section 12.3

1. (a) {L, M, N, R}, {Q, P, R}, {M, O, Q}
   (b) $\{\overleftrightarrow{LO}, \overleftrightarrow{MO}, \overleftrightarrow{NO}\}$
       $\{\overleftrightarrow{MN}, \overleftrightarrow{ON}, \overleftrightarrow{PN}\}$
       $\{\overleftrightarrow{OP}, \overleftrightarrow{QP}, \overleftrightarrow{NP}\}$

2. $\overline{AB}, \overline{AC}, \overline{AD}, \overline{AE}, \overline{AB}, \overline{AF}, \overline{BC}, \overline{BD},$
   $\overline{BE}, \overline{BF}, \overline{CD}, \overline{CE}, \overline{CF}, \overline{DE}, \overline{DF}, \overline{EF}$

3. (a) $\angle LOM, \angle MON, \angle NOP, \angle NOQ,$
       $\angle POQ$
   (b) $\angle LOP, \angle LOQ, \angle MOP, \angle MOQ$
   (c) $\angle LON$
   (d) $\angle LOM$ and $\angle MON$
       $\angle MON$ and $\angle NOP$
       There are many others.

4. (a) 60°   (b) 30°   (c) 120°

5. (a) m($\angle C$) = 38°, m($\overline{AC}$) = 7 cm
   (b) m($\angle C$) = 55°,
       m($\overline{AC}$) = 6.4 cm
       Note: Answers will vary due to measurement error.

6. (a) ∠*LTO* and ∠*XVO*
   ∠*MUN* and ∠*XWV*
   ∠*NUX* and ∠*VWQ*
   There are many others.
   (b) ∠*STX* and ∠*XVO*
   ∠*NTX* and ∠*XVW*
   ∠*NUX* and ∠*XWR*
   ∠*TUX* and ∠*XWV*

7. (a) Yes (b) No (c) No

8. (a) 28 (b) 5 (c) 8
   (d) 15 = 28 - (5 + 8)

9. For example:
   (a)
   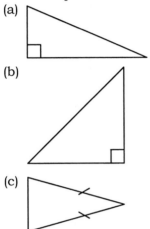
   (b)

   (c)

10. m(∠*AOB*) = 83°, m(∠*BOC*) = 7°

11. m(∠*X*) = 123°

12. m(∠1) = 47°, m(∠2) = 47°,
    m(∠3) = 106°, m(∠4) = 133°

13. (a) *l* || *m* , given; m(∠3) =
    m(∠4), Alternate Interior
    Angles Property; m(∠3) =
    m(∠1), vertical angles have
    same measure; m(∠1) =
    m(∠4).
    (b) m(∠3) = m(∠6), given; m(∠4)
    = m(∠6), vertical angles have
    the same measure; m(∠3) =
    m(∠4); *l* || *m*, Alternate
    Interior Angles Property.

14. (a) Equals 180°.
    (b) m(∠1) + m(∠3) = 180°, given;
    m(∠1) + m(∠2) = 180°, form
    straight angle;

m(∠1) + m(∠3) = m(∠1) +
m(∠2);
m(∠3) = m(∠2), subtraction;
l || *m*, Alternate Interior
Angles Property

15. The sum of the measures of any
    two consecutive angles of a
    parallelogram is 180°. Any two
    opposite angles of a parallelogram
    are congruent.

16. (a) (i)   (ii)
    (iii)   (iv)
    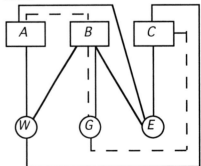
    (b) 6 points

17. (a) *a* + *b* + *c* = 180° since the three
    angles form a straight angle.
    (b) A rectangle with a base half as
    long as $\overline{AC}$.
    (c) Yes, the results are the same.

18. 4 points → 6 lines
    5 points → 10 lines
    6 points → 15 lines

    n points → $\dfrac{n(n-1)}{2}$ lines

19. (a) No, there will always be at
    least one house not connected
    to one of the utilities.
    (b) Yes, one solution is shown
    next.

The problem stated above is related to a branch of mathematics called graph theory.

20. In this context, the word 'vertical' is an adjective derived from the word *vertex*. Vertical angles are formed when a pair of lines intersect in one point, the vertex. The lines don't have to be vertical.

Problems related to the NCTM Standards and Curriculum Focal Points

1. If the angles of a quadrilateral are measured, it can be determined of they are right angles or if consecutive ones are supplementary. In the first case it may indicate a rectangle and in the second case, it indicates parallel sides. Sides can be measured to see if all sides are congruent (rhombus) or opposite sides are congruent (parallelogram). Answers may vary.

2. The bottom (straight) edge is placed along one side of an angle with the center point of the protractor placed on the vertex of the angle. The second side of the angle can be seen under the curved part of the protractor. The number over the second side is the measure of the angle.

3. Concurrent lines: Where two walls meet each other and meet the floor, three lines are created. Those three lines are concurrent in the corner of the floor.
Collinear points: The top corner of the three hinges on a door are collinear because the edge of the door is a straight line.
Parallel lines: The top and bottom of a door are parallel lines
Many other answers are possible.

Section 12.4

1. (a) 720°
   (b) 900°

2. (a) 122°
   (b) 68°, 112°
   (c) 115°, 115°, 120°, 120°

3. (a) 154.3°, 25.7°, 25.7°
   (b) 160°, 20°, 20°
   (c) 170°, 10°, 10°
   (d) 171.4°, 8.6°, 8.6°

4. 18 sides

5. (a) 12   (b) 15
   (c) 60   (d) 180

6. (a) 3   (b) 30
   (c) 24   (d) 72

7. (a) 20   (b) 10   (c) 120

8. (a) 40°   (b) 24°
   (c) $(180 - x)°$

9. (a) 144°   (b) 60°
   (c) $(180 - a)°$

10. (a)

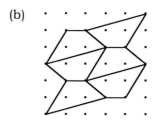

    (b)

11. E and D are midpoints of $\overline{AB}$ and $\overline{AC}$, respectively. Lines $\overleftrightarrow{ED}$ and $\overleftrightarrow{BC}$ do not meet in the tessellation (extended), so are parallel. Since ED = BF = FC, we have BC = 2ED.

12. (a) Trapezoid, isosceles triangle.
    (b) No

13.   (a)   Kites

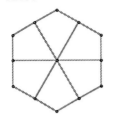

(b)   Triangles

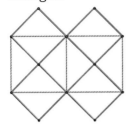

(c)   Pentagons

14. $a_1/a_2 = b_1/b_2$. In this case a_1/a_2 = 1/2.

15.   (a) (4, 8, 8)   (b) (4, 6, 12)
      (c) (3, 3, 3, 3, 6)   (d) (3, 3, 4, 3, 4)
      (e) (3, 4, 6, 4)
      (f) (3, 3, 3, 3, 4, 4)
      (g) (3, 12, 12)   (h) (3, 6, 3, 6)

16.   (a) (4, 4, 4, 4), (3, 3, 4, 12),
          (3, 3, 6, 6), (3, 4, 4, 6),
          (3, 4, 3, 12), (3, 6, 3, 6),
          (3, 4, 6, 4)
      (b) (3, 3, 3, 3, 6), (3, 3, 3, 4, 4),
          (3, 3, 4, 3, 4)
      (c) (3, 3, 3, 3, 3, 3)
      (d) no ways

17.   (a)

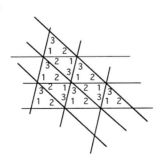

(b)   Sum of measures of vertex angles of a triangle is 180 degrees. Vertical angles have same measure.

18. $a = 45°$, $b = 45°$, $c = 65°$, $d = 80°$, $e = 30°$, $f = 70°$, $g = 20°$, $h = 55°$

19.   Divide by 180, subtraction of fractions, addition property, division by 2 and distributivity.

20.   (a) (3,7,42), (3,8,24), (3,9,18), (3,10,15), (3,12,12)
      (b) (4,5,20), (4,6,12), (4,8,8)
      (c) (5,5,10)
      (d) (6,6,6)
      (e) 10

21.   (a) 5   (b) 10   (c) 5
      (d) (5,5,5), which does not surround point E
      (e) By putting triangle or Pentagon in the center, you get the same results except for (3,12,12).

22.   (a) (4,4,4,4), (3,3,4,12), (3,3,6,6), (3,4,4,6)
      (b) (4,4,4,4)
      (c) (3,3,4,12), (3,4,3,12), (3,3,6,6), (3,4,4,6)
      (d) (3,6,3,6), (3,4,6,4)

23.   (a) (3,3,3,3,6) and (3,3,3,4,4)
      (b) (3,3,3,3,6), (3,3,3,4,4), (3,3,4,3,4)
      (c) (3,3,3,3,3,3), regular
      (d) No, angle measure would have to be less than 60° (or have fewer sides than 2 then.)

24.   If Tyrone's pentagons were really regular, there would be gaps between them in his attempted tessellation of the plane. It is possible to tessellate the plane with pentagons (for example, baseball home plates), but not *regular* pentagons. Since the interior angles of a regular pentagon are 108°, when 3 pentagons are put together around

a common vertex, these angles add up to 324°, not 360°.

25. The formula this student is using is appropriate for a *regular* pentagon where all five angles are congruent. If the four angles are not all 108°, he needs to subtract the sum of the measures of the four angles from 540° to find the measure of the missing angle.

Problems related to the NCTM Standards and Curriculum Focal Points

1. The key to constructing a tessellation is fitting polygons around a single point so that no overlaps or gaps occur. The sum of the measures of the vertex angles of the different polygons must add to 360° for this to work.

2. You could use a protractor to find the sum of the interior angles of a polygon but the most accurate way is to cut the polygon into triangles as shown in Figure 12.4 and then adding of the angles of the triangles.

3. Tiles on a floor, bricks on a wall and plywood on a roof all form tessellations. Answers may vary.

Section 12.5

1. (a) $\{\overline{BG}, \overline{CF}\}, \{\overline{CF}, \overline{DE}\}, \{\overline{BG}, \overline{DE}\}$

   (b) $\{\overline{DC}, \overline{GF}\}, \{\overline{AD}, \overline{GF}\}, \{\overline{EF}, \overline{BG}\},$
   $\{\overline{AB}, \overline{CF}\}$
   Other answers are possible.

   (c) Planes DCFE and BCFG with edge $\overline{CF}$. Other answers are possible.

   (d) Planes ADE and CFDE with edge $\overline{DE}$.

2. (a) $1/2, \sqrt{3}/2$

   (b) $\sqrt{3}/2$

   (c) AE = DE = $\sqrt{3}/2$, AD = 1

3. (a) Yes. 6 total faces – 2 triangles, 2 quadrilaterals, and 2 pentagons.
   (b) No. Faces are not polygons.
   (c) No. Not a single enclosed space.

4. (a) Triangular prism
   (b) Rectangular prism
   (c) Hexagonal prism

5. Prisms: (a) and (c); pyramid: (b)

6. (a) right triangular prism
   (b) regular tetrahedron
   (c) right rectangular prism
   (d)

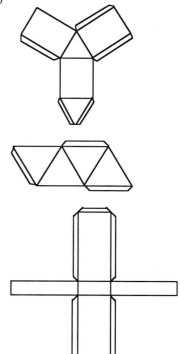

7.

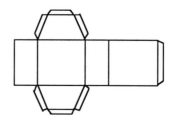

8.

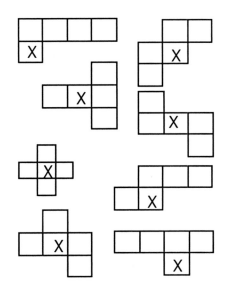

9.   (a)

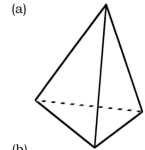

    (b)

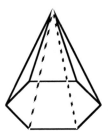

10.   (a) Triangle: 4, 4, 8, 6;
         quadrilateral: 5, 5, 10, 8;
         pentagon: 6, 6, 12, 10;
         hexagon: 7, 7, 14, 12;
         n-gon: $n + 1$, $n + 1$, $2n + 2$, $2n$
    (b) Yes

11.   (a) (i)   10, 12, 22, 20;
         (ii) 9, 9, 18, 16
    (b) Yes

12.   Truncated icosahedron: 6-6-5
      Truncated dodecahedron: 10-10-3
      Cube octahedron: 4-4-3
      Small rhombicubahedrdon: 4-4-4-3

On each polyhedron all vertex arrangements are the same, so they are all semiregular.

13.   (a)

    (b)

        Parabola

    (c)

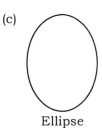

        Ellipse

14.   (a)   (b)

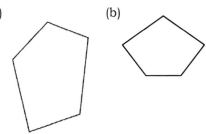

15.   (a) Either upper left or lower right.
    (b) Either, depending on perspective.

16.   34

17.   View (b). The tops in (a) and (c) should have a rectangle.

18.   (a)   Base

        Front

        Right Side

(b)
Base

Front

Right
Side

19.   Largest number = 19

2	3	2
2	2	2
2	2	2

Smallest number = 13

1	3	1
2	1	1
1	1	2

(Other base designs are possible.)

20.   (a) | Sides | 1 | 2 | 3 | 0 |
       |---|---|---|---|---|
       | Cubes | 0 | 0 | 8 | 0 |

       (b) | Sides | 1 | 2 | 3 | 0 |
       |---|---|---|---|---|
       | Cubes | 6 | 12 | 8 | 1 |

       (c) | Sides | 1 | 2 | 3 | 0 |
       |---|---|---|---|---|
       | Cubes | 24 | 24 | 8 | 8 |

       (d) | Sides | 1 | 2 |
       |---|---|---|
       | Cubes | $6(n-2)^3$ | $12(n-2)$ |

Sides	3	0
Cubes	8	$(n-2)^3$

21.   They all are possible, for example
       (h)

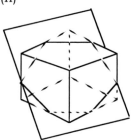

22.   Yes for all parts.

23.   (a) 6   (b) 4
       (c) 6   (d) infinite number

24.   (a) 3 of order 2 (through
           midpoints of nonintersecting
           edges); 4 of order 3 (through
           vertex and center of opposite
           face)
       (b) 5 of order 2 (through midpoint
           of edge and center of opposite
           face); 1 of order 5 (through
           centers of bases)

25.   (a) 1   (b) Infinite   (c) Infinite

26.   6

27.   Slice through BDE, BDG,
       GED, and BGE.

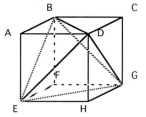

28.   The word 'right' used with a prism
       or pyramid refers to the
       orientation of its axis
       perpendicular to (forming a right
       angle with) the base, as opposed
       to an oblique polyhedron which
       'leans.' 'Right triangular pyramid'
       would usually be taken to mean a
       pyramid that has a triangular
       base, but not necessarily a right
       triangular base. Which makes one
       wonder if to specify a right
       pyramid with a right triangular

base one would need to say a
"right right triangular pyramid."

**Problems related to the NCTM
Standards and Curriculum Focal Points**

1. All of the faces of a polyhedron are
    polygons. They enclose space
    without any holes. They satisfy
    Euler's formula. Answers may
    vary.

2. It is called a dihedral angle. It is
    measured by drawing a line in
    each plane (face) of the angle that
    is perpendicular to the edge. Both
    lines also intersect need to
    intersect the edge at the same
    point. These two lines and their
    point of intersection form a regular
    angle, which can then be
    measured.

3. Polyhedra or not, regular or not,
    semiregular or not, oblique or
    right. Answers may vary.

Chapter Review

Problems for Writing/Discussion

1. It is true that the more sides a
    polygon has, the more it tends to
    resemble a circle. However, no
    polygon can be a circle since it has
    straight sides, and a circle does
    not.

2. There are two exterior angles at
    each vertex of a polygon; they are
    vertical to each other and
    therefore equal to each other.
    When we say the sum of the
    exterior angles is 360°, we are only
    considering one exterior angle per
    vertex. Jackie is probably
    summing two exterior angles per
    vertex, which is why she got 720°
    instead of 360° - an acceptable
    answer.

3. A scalene triangle, by definition,
    has no two sides congruent,
    whereas an isosceles triangle, by

definition, has at least two sides
congruent. These two definitions
are incompatible. Therefore, each
pair of words must be carefully
examined to see if they can apply
to the same triangle
simultaneously.

4. As a category, trapezoids that are
    not isosceles do not fit into any of
    the circles. However, it should be
    noted that one could have a
    specific instance of a trapezoid
    whose diagonals were
    perpendicular, or a specific
    quadrilateral, not one of the
    special figures noted, in which the
    diagonals were equal, etc.

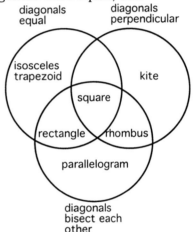

5. Students often believe that all
    polygons should have the same
    vertex angle sum. A common way
    to demonstrate this idea is not
    true is to divide a polygon into
    triangles by drawing all the
    diagonals from one vertex. Most
    students will accept the fact that a
    triangle contains 180°, so seeing a
    polygon as a set of triangles will
    often convince them that the
    number of degrees is the number
    of triangles times 180°.

6. What needs to be true about a
    pentagon for it to be able to
    tessellate the plane is that the
    angles that go together around
    any one vertex must add up to
    360°. For example, pentagons
    that look like a baseball home

plate will tessellate the plane if
their angles are, say, 90°, 90°,
150°, 150°, and 60°.   Many other
pentagons that do tessellate the
plane have been discovered.

7.   The correct definitions are almost
     identical. For the circle, however,
     it is necessary to insert the phrase
     "in a plane."

8.   An oblique prism whose bases
     have no line of symmetry will have
     no plane of symmetry.

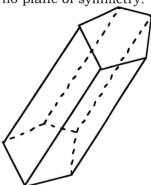

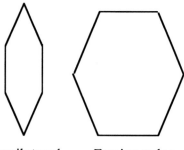

Equilateral   Equiangular

9.   At the vertex of every polyhedron
     there must be at least three
     polygons coming together. Three
     squares can come together at a
     vertex since the sum of their
     angles is 270° (which is less than
     360°).

However, when three regular
hexagons come together, their
angle sum is 360° and so they lie
flat .

10. Two such polygons can be formed
     by "stretching" or "squeezing" a
     regular hexagon as shown.

Chapter 13 - Measurement

Section 13.1

1. (a) $1\frac{2}{3}$, $1\frac{1}{4}$, $\frac{1}{4}$
    (b) 12, 12,
    (c) Whether the pencil is mechanical or wood or old. Whether the fingers are fat or skinny.

2. (a) Waist, hips, length from neck to waist or to hemline, bust or chest, length of arm.
    (b) Length and width of foot, height of arch.
    (c) Height, weight, heartbeat, blood pressure.
    (d) Height, strength, height of jump, number of sit-ups in 1 minute.

3. (a) 220   (b) 320
    (c) 640   (d) 4492.125
    (e) 512,000   (f) 1
    (g) 126   (h) 48

4. (a) 205 m   (b) 72 m
    (c) 512 km

5. (a) 10 L   (b) 200 mL
    (c) 200 L

6. (a) 25 g   (b) 7 g
    (c) 1715 kg

7. (a) -5° C   (b) 39° C

8. (a) 10 cents   (b) 1 cent
    (c) $10   (d) $1000

9. "Mega" means one million times, so winnings are millions of dollars.

10. (a) 12 m   (b) 0.03569 km
    (c) 26,000,000 cm
    (d) 0.786 m
    (e) 38.4 cm   (f) 1200 cm
    (g) 1,345,000 cm (h) 0.019 km
    (i) 46,780 km   (j) 8.9 hm

11. (a) 10,000
    (b) four places to right

(c) two places to the right
(d) two places to the left.
(e) are and hectare

12. (a) 2,000,000 cm³
    (b) 5,000,000,000 mm³
    (c) 16,000 cm³
    (d) 0.62 dm³
    (e) 0.056 m³
    (f) 1200 cm³

13. (a) 4750 mg
    (b) 0.057 hg
    (c) 32,000 mg

14. (a) 3.5 dL   (b) 0.56 L
    (c) 0.520 kL

15. (a) kg   (b) dm³, kg
    (c) mL, g

16. (a) 58°C   (b) 194°F
    (c) -22°F   (d) -88°C
    (e) -0.4°F

17. (a) 400 g/cm
    (b) 65 g/cm³
    (c) 0.972 ton/yd³
    (d) 98.2 mi/hr

18. (a) 48 farthings
    (b) 2 farthings

19. (a) 402.34 m   (b) 0.62 mi

20. (a) 750 mi/hr
    (b) 6,570,000 mi/yr

21. 1 jack = 1/8 james, 1/480 jennifers, 1/5760 jessicas; 1 james = 192 jills, 1/60 jennifers, 1/720 jessicas; 1 jennifer = 11,520 jills, 480 jacks, 1/12 jessicas; 1 jessica = 138,240 jills, 5760 jacks, 720 james

22. 261,100 watts

23. Approximately 85 ha

24. 89 kph (88.5 km/hr)
    Note: most signs are reading 88 kph, which has us drive a little slower.

25. (a) 50 days   (b) 2.7 ft/hr

26. (a) 6,278,400,000 joules
    (b) $88.39

27. $-40° C = -40° F$

28. (a) About 18 km/sec
    (b) 5.4×10^9 km

29. 3.268 light years

30. This is impossible since the car has used up all the time required for the round trip by the time it reaches the first city.

31. (a) 1 hr/roll
    (b) 18 rolls/hr or .055 hr/roll
    (c) 2600 rolls

32. Surface area about 10243 m²; Volume about 68292 m³

33. (a) 139.7 pounds
    (b) 36, 864 g
    (c) part (b)

34. One yd³ is 27 ft³ (3×3×3). 27 ft³ equals 46,656 in³ (27×12×12×12). Scotty's garden is 360 ft² in size (15×24). 46,656 ÷ 360 = 129.6 in³ of topsoil per ft² of garden. Each ft² of garden is 144 in² in size. Dividing 129.6 over 144 gives an amount of topsoil 12 in. by 12 in. by 0.9 in. So the whole garden would be covered to a depth of 0.9 in. or "about 1 inch."

Problems related to the NCTM Standards and Curriculum Focal Points

1. The height of a book; the length of a foot; the number of marbles in a bag; the height of a stack of blocks. Answers will vary.

2. It is easier to convert within a given type of measurement like meters to centimeters. It is easier to convert between different types of units like liters to cubic centimeters. Almost all other countries in the world already use the metric system. Answer will vary.

3. Foot- a persons foot; yard- one step; gallon-a gallon of milk; pound-a pound of butter; liter- a liter of soda or about a quart of milk; milligram- an ibuprofen pill usually contains 200 milligrams of medicine.

Section 13.2

1. (a) $9/2 - \sqrt{3}$ (b) $3\sqrt{3}$
   (c) 7.96   (d) 6.03

2. (a) $q - p$ (b) $\dfrac{q - p}{2}$

   (c) $p + \dfrac{q - p}{2} = \dfrac{p + q}{2}$

   (d) Yes

   (e) $\dfrac{-2.5 + 13.9}{2} = 5.7$

3. (a) -10.9   (b) -2.4

4. (a) $q - p$ (b) $\dfrac{2p + q}{3}$

   (c) $\dfrac{p + 2q}{3}$

   (d) $m = 2.9, n = 9.4$

5. (a) -10.2   (b) 11.1

6. (a) $a = 7.6$ units,
       $A = 115.52$ sq. units
   (b) $b = 12$ units, $A = 81.6$ sq. units
   (c) $b = 35.6$ units,
       $P = 99.4$ sq. units

7. (a) 25   (b) 20   (c) $22\frac{1}{2}$

   (d) Figure (a) by $2\frac{1}{2}$

8. (a) 7 units   (b) $6\frac{1}{2}$ units

   (c) 8 units

9. 92 Pieces

10. (a) 8.2 km^2 (b) 60 m^2

11. 195.6 units, 1292.9 square units

12. (a) Acute

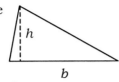

Right

Obtuse

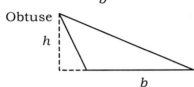

b and *h* are the same on all triangles to give equal areas.

(b) The perimeters are all different.

(c) There is no clear relationship.

13. 90 units, 418.9 square units.

14. (a) $\sqrt{13}$, 4, A$_1$ = 12, A$_2$ = 8; 5, 2, A$_1$ = 6, A$_2$ = 8

(b) Statement is false since parallelograms with the same length sides had different areas.

15. (a) (1/2)(2 + 6) = 4
(b) 4
(c) They are equal.

16. (a) $6\sqrt{7}$ (b) 16

17. No. If a parallelogram is very long and narrow, the perimeter will be large but the area will be small.

18. (a) 2   (b) 18   (c) 1:9

19. (a) 15.2 units, 30.4 units, 30.4 π units
(b) 13.4/π units, 26.8/π units, 179.56/π sq. units
(c) $2\sqrt{15}$ units, $2\pi\sqrt{15}$ units, 15π sq. units

(d) 9 π units , 18 π^2 units, 81 π^3 sq. units

20. (a) Hypotenuse of 2 by 1 right triangle
(b) 4 × 1   (c) 3 × 3
(d) 5 × 2

21. (a) $\sqrt{34}$ (b) 7

22. (a) Yes   (b) Yes   (c) No

23. (a) Slant distance (13 ft) can be more easily measured than $6\sqrt{5}$ ft.
(b) 3120 sq. ft.
(c) 260 sheets
(d) 120 sheets laid out in 15 rows by 8 rows. 10 sheets cut each into 2' by 3' pieces to be laid out end to end on top of others. 130 sheets for each half of the roof.

24. Approximately 25 meters

25. (a) $\sqrt{89} \approx 9.4$m   (b) $\sqrt{73} \approx 8.5$m
(c) $\sqrt{34} \approx 5.8$m   (d) $\sqrt{98} \approx 9.9$m

26. (a) 16, 30, 34
(b) 105, 208, 233
(c) 715, 1428, 1597
(d) 1, 1, 2, 3, 5, 8, 13, 21, 34, 55, 89, 144, 233, 377, 610, 987, 1597   Yes

27. (a) $\sqrt{3}$ units
(b) $\sqrt{3}$ square units
(c) $6\sqrt{3}$ square units

28. 250 square inches

29. A 4 × 4 and a 6 × 3 rectangle.

30. About 128 ft.

31. 40 posts

32. (a) Obtuse   (b) No
(c) Acute   (d) Acute
(e) Right   (f) No

33. (a) $\overline{RS} \parallel \overline{TU}$ since $\angle S$ and $\angle T$ (interior angles on same side) are supplementary.
    (b) $(1/2)(a + b)(a + b)$
    (c) $m(\angle RVS) + m(\angle RVU) + m(\angle UVT) = 180°$, but $m(\angle RVS) + 90° + m(\angle UVT) = 180°$, so $m(\angle RVU) = 90°$.
    (d) $(1/2)ab + (1/2)c^2 + (1/2)ab$
    (e) $(1/2)(a + b)(a + b)$
        $= (1/2)ab + (1/2)c^2 + (1/2)ab$;
        $a^2 + 2ab + b^2 = 2ab + c^2$
        $a^2 + b^2 = c^2$.

34. (a) 63.7%   (b) 78.5%
    (c) Circular plug fits better into the square hole.

35. $x = 15$ units

36. Consider the possible ways of flattening out the room. The shortest distance between two points is given by a straight line. The shortest distance is 1133 cm or 11.33 m calculated as follows:

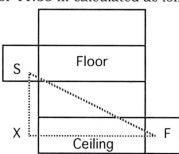

    $SX = 200$ cm $+ 400$ cm $+ 200$ cm $= 800$ cm
    $XF = 1$ cm $+ 800$ cm $+ 1$ cm $= 802$ cm
    $SF = \sqrt{(800)^2 + (802)^2} = 1132.8$

37. (a)

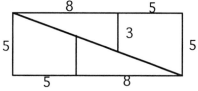

    Area of square = 64 sq. units; Area of rectangle = 65 sq. units; yes.
    (b) 169, 168, yes; 441, 442

38. $4 - \pi$ sq. units

39. Area of equilateral triangle with side 1 $= \sqrt{3}/4$ sq. units. Area of 1/6 of circle is $\pi/6$ sq. units. Area of half-petal (shaded) is $\pi/6 - \sqrt{3}/4$ sq. units. Total area of the hexafoil is $12(\pi/6 - \sqrt{3}/4) = 2\pi - 3\sqrt{3}$ sq. units.

40. The shaded areas are equal. The total area of the three smaller circles is 36π. The area of the largest circle is 36π. The unshaded areas of overlap are both subtracted from 36π, leaving the same amount remaining.

41. (a) About 5,681,818 mi
    (b) About 227 times

42. (a) No, the ratios area C: area B: area A = 5:3:1, while the point ratios are 4:2:1.
    (b) Make the points 30, 18, 6.

43. (a) $9\sqrt{3}$ square units
    (b) $A = \dfrac{s^2\sqrt{3}}{4}$

44. When P, Q, and R are collinear.

45. Yes, it works with all figures, including the fact that formulas for volume would have 3 variables.

Problems related to the NCTM Standards and Curriculum Focal Points

1. Area is the physical quantity expressing the size of a part of a surface and can be measured with squares, or triangles or any shape

that tessellates. Length is the long dimension of any object and is one-dimensional as opposed to two-dimensional like area.

2. First the equations of the areas of different triangles are developed so that a parallelogram can be split into two triangles. The equation for the areas of these two triangles is known and can be added to find the equation for the area of a parallelogram.

3. A regular polygon is inscribed in a circle and the perimeter of the polygon is determined. By inscribing polygons with more and more sides and looking at the corresponding perimeters, the equation for the circumference emerges.

Section 13.3

1. (a) 1248.1in^2 (b) 186 m^2
    (c) 792 cm^2 (d) 173 cm^2

2. (a) $SA = 60 + 30 \times 20 = 660$ sq. units
    (b) 254 sq. units

3. $864 + 432\sqrt{3} \text{ cm}^2$ or approximately 1612 cm^2

4. (a) 792 cm^2 (b) 173 cm^2

5. (a) 766 cm^2 (b) 866 cm^2

6. (a) 122 sq. units
    (b) 450 sq. units

7. $S = 564$ sq. units

8. (a) 1206 sq. units
    (b) 4825 sq. units

9. 1923 in^2

10. (a) $36\pi \text{ cm}^2$
    (b) $610.09\pi \text{ cm}^2$
    (c) 8.288 cm

11. 196π sq. units

12. Cube

13. $12 \times 8 \times 6$ units

14. 8 units

15. (a) 72 square units
    (b) 272 square units
    (c) 1640 square units

16. (a) 4:25   (b) 4:25
    (c) 4 times original surface area

17. $347,538.7 \text{ ft}^2$

18. Approximately 230 m^2

19. (a) 384 sq. units
    (b) 192 sq. units

20. Each stripe covers 1/3 of the lateral surface area, so the red stripe covers about 2094 cm^2.

21. If Mark wants to use the same size circle for both cones, he can. In the following circle, the larger sector will make the fatter shorter cone and the small sector will make a skinny taller cone. The radius of the circle becomes the slant height for each cone.

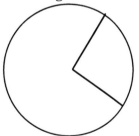

Problems related to the NCTM Standards and Curriculum Focal Points

1. When finding surface areas, one can simply break the surface into its various parts like rectangles, triangles, circles, etc., find the areas of the parts and then add them up. This is a more powerful way to find surface areas than

memorizing many different
equations.

2. The surface area of a cone has two
    parts: the base and the lateral
    surface. The area of the base can
    be found by using the equation of
    a circle. The area of the lateral
    surface can be laid out flat to see
    that it is just the sector of a circle.
    The portion of the circumference
    that the sector takes up can be
    used along with the equation of
    the area of a circle to find the
    lateral surface area.

3. Similar to the answer to question
    1, breaking the surface area into
    pieces and finding the areas of
    those pieces is a good general
    strategy for finding surface area.

Section 13.4

1. (a) 2508 in^3 (b) 148 m^3

2. 320$\sqrt{3}$ in^3

3. 2160 m^3

4. (a) 540 π cm^3 (b) 12.5 π cm^3

5. (a) About 1562 cm^3
    (b) About 1951 cm^3

6. (a) 40 cu. units
    (b) 70 cu. units

7. (a) 10 cu. units
    (b) 20 cu. units   (c) part (b)

8. (a) 18 π cu. units
    (b) 96 π cu. units

9. (a) triples
    (b) nine times larger

10. (a) 51 cu. units
    (b) 157 cu. units

11. (a) Volume = 10 cu. units
         Surface Area = 36 sq. units
    (b) Volume = 11 cu. units

         Surface Area = 38 sq. units
    (c) Volume = 21 cu. units
         Surface Area = 64 sq. units

12. (a) 296 cm^3 (b) 296 g

13. (a) All have volume 125,000 cm^3.
    (b) A 15,000 cm^2,
         B 17,500 cm^2,
         C 19,500 cm^2
    (c) No
    (d) Box A

14. (a) 120,000 cm^3 (b) 31,000 cm^2

15. (a) 3,072,000 cubic yards
    (b) 96,000 square yards

16. 4 trips

17. $h = 30/\pi \approx 9.55$ cm

18. $48.48

19. 6569 in^3

20. (a) 48%   (b) 32.5%

21. $151\frac{2}{3}$ pounds

22. (a) New volume is 8 times
         original.
    (b) New surface area is 4 times
         original.

23. (a) 4:25   (b) 8:125
    (c) 8 times original volume

24. (a) $8\sqrt{2} \approx 11.31$ inches on a side
    (b) 63.66%

25. 192 cm^3

26. Approximately 0.5 cm

27. 208/216 $\approx$ 0.963

28. 20.25 hours.

29. 160 ft

30. The one with the shorter side as height.

31. Fifty-six blocks cannot be made into a perfect cube. The nearest larger cube is 4^3 or 64. If the toy box is made so that 4-by-4-by-4 blocks can fit in it, then the 56 blocks will fit with room for 8 more later. The size of the box would be 12" on a side.

32. Spheres roll; they're hard to stack. To get them to stack well, they have to be put into prisms or cylinders, so the manufacturer probably feels he/she might as well use boxes to start with. Products that come in a spherical or near-spherical shape: oranges, peaches, apples, etc., which shows that Mother Nature is efficient with her packaging. Eggs and L'eggs come in ovoid shapes.

Problems related to the NCTM Standards and Curriculum Focal Points

1. Since the surface area and volume of a shape are not necessarily related, it is not possible to know for sure without more information. The cylinder could be short and fat, tall and skinny, or have a comparable height and diameter.

2. The relationship between the volume of a cone and a cylinder that have the same radius and height is that the cylinder is 3 times as big.

3. Since the volume a cylinder and a prism are both found using the area of the base multiplied by the height, one strategy is to break a shape into some form of cylinder or prism. Answers may vary.

Chapter Review

Problems for Writing/Discussion

1. Sometimes students who see an answer like 156 cm² believe there is "something more to do." They think the exponent is an operation that needs to be carried out. However, in this case it is just shorthand for a particular unit of measure. Some teachers prefer to have their students write out 156 *sq. cm* to avoid this problem.

2. Amy is having a common problem with units. For example, if 1 m = 100 cm, she might think that 1 m² = 100 cm². But 1 m² = 100 × 100 cm² = 10,000 cm². It's the same with the decimals. If 1 cm = 0.01 m, then 1 cm² = 0.0001 m² (0.01 × 0.01) and 1 cm³ = 0.000001 m³ (0.01 × 0.01 × 0.01).

3. First, make sure that Tyrone can really do what he says he can. If not, you show him how to do those cuts first. Then explore a parallelogram with, say, base 8 and height 4. The area of this parallelogram would be 32 units². A square with the same area would have to have a side of exactly $\sqrt{32}$, which is about 5.66. It will not be possible to turn this parallelogram into a square with one cut since its height is only 4.

4. The square, rectangle, and rhombus are already parallelograms. Two kites could be turned into a hexagon, but not a parallelogram (unless they were rhombuses).

5. The formula for the area of a trapezoid will "work" for any figure that has at least one pair of parallel sides. In other words, it will work for a parallelogram, a rectangle, a rhombus, or a square. In a square with side s, for example, we can find the area by using $\frac{1}{2}h(b_1 + b_2) = \frac{1}{2}s(s + s) = s^2$.

6. If she uses AD as the height, she will have to use CB as the base.

In the formula $\frac{1}{2}bh$, the two variables, b and h, must be perpendicular to each other. So the area is $\frac{1}{2}(5.5 \times 8) = 22$. Once she knows that, she could determine CE because the area is the same any way you compute it. So $22 = \frac{1}{2}(10)CE$ or $CE = \frac{22}{5} = 4.4$.

7. The lateral surface area could be represented by the paper label. The metal of the can itself could represent total surface area. The volume could be represented by the contents, the soup itself.

8. No. A cone has only one height, a line segment perpendicular to the base, that extends from the apex of the cone to the base.

9. The height is the perpendicular distance between the bases of the cylinder. So the height would be 10, *not* 12. This is similar to the problem with parallelograms where students may use the length of a side of the parallelogram as the height.

10. $41°F = 5°C$. $82°F \approx 28°C$. Would that mean that in Celsius it was 5 and 1/2 times as hot as in the morning? Whether in Celsius or Fahrenheit, the zero is not an absolute measure. Therefore, this type of comparison, by a *factor*, does not apply here.

Chapter 14

Section 14.1

1. $\triangle BAC \cong \triangle FEG$, $\triangle BCA \cong \triangle FGE$,
    $\triangle CAB \cong \triangle GEF$, $\triangle CBA \cong \triangle GFE$

2. (a) EFD   (b) ZYX

3. $\angle B \cong \angle H$, $\overline{BC} \cong \overline{HI}$ or
    $\angle A \cong \angle G$, $\overline{AC} \cong \overline{GI}$

4. (a) $\overline{GH} \cong \overline{ML}$ and
        $\overline{GI} \cong \overline{MN}$
    (b) $\angle H \cong \angle L$ and
        $\overline{HG} \cong \overline{LM}$ and
        $\overline{HI} \cong \overline{LN}$
    (c) $\angle I \cong \angle N$ and
        $\overline{IG} \cong \overline{NM}$ and
        $\overline{IH} \cong \overline{NL}$

5. $\angle A \cong \angle G$, $\angle B \cong \angle H$

6. (a) $\angle P \cong \angle S$, $\angle Q \cong \angle T$
        $\overline{QR} \cong \overline{TU}$, and m($\angle R$) = m($\angle U$)
        = 80°, so $\angle R \cong \angle U$.
    (b) Yes.
    (c) m($\angle R$) = 80° = m($\angle U$), so we
        can use $\angle R$, $\overline{RQ}$, $\angle Q$ and
        $\angle U$, $\overline{UT}$, and $\angle T$.

7. $\overline{BC} \cong \overline{HI}$, $\overline{CA} \cong \overline{IG}$

8. $\triangle ABC \cong \triangle FDE$ by SSS or SAS
    ($\angle C$ and $\angle F$ are right angles).

9. (a) SSS   (b) SAS   (c) ASA

10. Yes; m($\angle Y$)= 30°, m($\angle O$) = 80°,
    so $\triangle AMY \cong \triangle JON$ by ASA.

11. (a) $\overline{AB} \cong \overline{DE}$ (leg), $\angle B \cong \angle E$,
        $\overline{AC} \cong \overline{DF}$ (hypotenuse)
    (b) No
    (c) BC = EF = $\sqrt{8}$, so $\overline{BC} \cong \overline{EF}$
    (d) Yes; SAS.

12. (a) $\angle A \cong \angle X$, $\angle B \cong \angle Y$,
        $\angle C \cong \angle Z$

(b) No.
(c) No; $\triangle ABC$ and $\triangle XYZ$ would
    satisfy conditions for AAA, but
    are not congruent. This is a
    counter-example to the AAA
    property.

13.

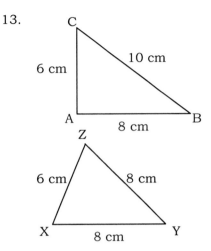

m($\angle A$) = 90₀ > m($\angle X$)

14. Since the hexagon is regular, the
    length of hypotenuses (YZ) are all
    equal. The legs are given to be
    congruent. Therefore all the right
    triangles are congruent. From the
    original congruent vertex angles,
    angles congruent to Ð Y and Ð Z
    are removed, leaving angles of the
    same size.

15. (a) For example, have 3 pairs of
        congruent angles
    (b) For example, have 3 pairs of
        congruent angles and 1 pair of
        congruent non-corresponding
        sides
    (c) See the Mathematical Morsel
        at the end of Section 14.1

16. $\triangle ABC \cong \triangle WXY$ (by SAS
    congruence property); $\angle 1 \cong \angle 5$,
    $\angle 3 \cong \angle 7$, and $\overline{AC} \cong \overline{WY}$
    (corresponding parts of congruent
    triangles); m ($\angle A$) - m ($\angle 3$)
    = m($\angle W$) - m ($\angle 7$) so $\angle 4 \cong \angle 8$
    and m($\angle C$) - m($\angle 1$)
    = m($\angle Y$) – m($\angle 5$) so $\angle 2 \cong \angle 6$;
    $\triangle ADC \cong \triangle WZY$ (by ASA
    congruence property);

$\overline{AD} \cong \overline{WZ}$, $\angle D \cong \angle Z$,
$\overline{DC} \cong \overline{ZY}$ (corresponding parts of congruent triangles); so
quad ABCD $\cong$ quad WXYZ.

17. $\overline{AB} \cong \overline{XY}$ (given), $\angle B \cong \angle Y$ (both right angles), $\overline{BC} \cong \overline{YZ}$ (Both have length $b = \sqrt{c^2 - a^2}$ by the Pythagorean Theorem) so $\triangle ABC \cong \triangle XYZ$ by the SAS congruence property

18. (a) Both a square and rhombus which is not a square could be drawn.
    (b) Both a rectangle and a parallelogram, which is not a rectangle could be drawn.
    (c) No, parts (a) and (b) have provided counterexamples.

19. This is an example of SSA which is not sufficient to prove congruence.

20. The congruence relationship $\triangle ABC \cong \triangle CAB$ means that C $\leftrightarrow$ A, A $\leftrightarrow$ B, and B $\leftrightarrow$ C. Under these correspondences, the triangles are not congruent. *But* we could say $\triangle ABC \cong \triangle BAC$ by SAS.

Problems related to the NCTM Standards and Curriculum Focal Points

1. The triangle can be drawn with a protractor and a straightedge. It can be seen by this construction that there is only one shape of triangle that can be built with these given dimensions which leads toward the ASA property of triangle congruence.

2. Examples 14.1 and 14.2 are both examples of reasoning and proof. Any problem that asks for a justification or why would require reasoning and proof to answer.

3. Inductive arguments are based on patterns seen through many examples but may not "prove" that something is true for all cases.

Deductive arguments are based on a logical sequence of statements that build on each other and can show a statement is true for all cases.

Section 14.2

1. (a) $\triangle LMN \sim \triangle OPQ$, by SAS similarity.
   (b) $\triangle RST \sim \triangle VWU$, by AA similarity.
   (c) Not similar. On one triangle, the 40° angle is between the proportional sides and on the other it is not.
   (d) $\triangle EFG \sim \triangle HJI$, by SSS similarity.

2. (a) XY = $\frac{27}{8}$ cm, VW = $\frac{128}{9}$ cm
   (b) AB = 9 in., AC = 12 in., DC = 4 in.

3. (a) BC = $\frac{65}{4}$ in., AC = $\frac{56}{9}$ in.
   (b) RQ = 6 in., PT = 16 in.

4. (a) False. Sides may be of different lengths.
   (b) False. Consider triangles whose angle measures are 80°, 80°, 20°, and 70°, 70°, 40°.
   (c) False. See part (a).
   (d) True. AA

5. 3/4 = 5/AD, so AD = 20/3.

6. (a) $\triangle ABC \sim \triangle EDC$ by AA similarity because the vertical angles at C are congruent and both are right triangles.
   (b) 45°

7. 27 feet

8.

9. $a = 13\ 1/3$ $b = 10$
    $c = 17\ 7/9$ $d = 42\ 7/9$

10. (a) No. If so, the two triangles
        would be similar. However, the
        sides are not proportional.
    (b) Yes. The triangles are similar
        by the SAS similarity property.
        Hence, by the corresponding
        angles property, the lines are
        parallel.

11. (a) bases 1:2, heights 1:2, areas
        1:4
    (b) bases 3:4, heights 3:4, areas
        9:16
    (c) lengths 1:3, widths 1:3, areas
        1:9
    (d) The ratio of the areas is equal
        to the square of the ratios of
        the linear dimensions.

12. Yes. We can use either the AA or
    SAS similarity properties of
    triangles.

13. (a) Apply the alternate interior
        angles theorem and AA
        similarity property.
    (b) $a = 14$, $b = 60$

14.
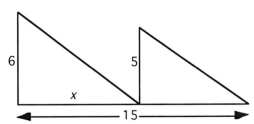

$6/x = 5/(15-x)$, thus Tom's
shadow is 90/11 ft and Carol's is
75/11 ft.

15. 25.86 ft

16. 6.53 feet

17. Assuming ACBD is a rectangle, we
    have $DC^2 = 50^2 + 70^2$, so DC » 86.
    But, AB = DC, so AB ≈ 86 ft.

18. AB = BC and XY = YZ so
    AB/BC = XY/YZ (equal 1) or
    AB/XY = BC/YZ (interchanging

means of the proportion). Since
$\angle B \cong \angle Y$ and AB/XY = BC/YZ,
$\triangle ABC \sim \triangle XYZ$ by the SAS
similarity property. (Could also
prove using AA similarity
property.)

19. (a)
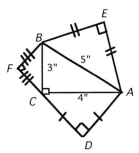

Area($\triangle$ACD) = 4 in^2
Area($\triangle$BFC) = 2.25 in^2
Area($\triangle$AEB) = 6.25 in^2
Therefore, Area($\triangle$ACD) +
Area($\triangle$BFC) = Area($\triangle$AEB).

(b)
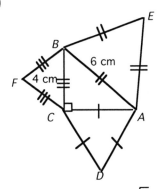

Area($\triangle$ACD) = $5\sqrt{3}$ in^2
Area($\triangle$BFC) = $4\sqrt{3}$ in^2
Area($\triangle$AEB) = $9\sqrt{3}$ in^2
Therefore, Area($\triangle$ACD) +
Area($\triangle$BFC) = Area($\triangle$AEB).

(c)
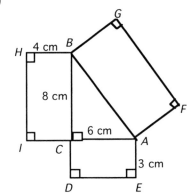

Area of ACDE = 18 cm^2
Area of BHIC = 32 cm^2
Area of AFGB = 50 cm^2
Therefore, Area(ACDE) +
Area(BHIC) = Area(AFGB).

(d)

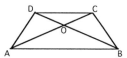

Area of ACDE = 6 in^2
Area of BHIC = 9.375 in^2
Area of AFGB = 15.375 in^2
Therefore, Area(ACDE) +
Area(BHIC) = Area(AFGB).

20.   AB = 5/3, AE = 7/4, DE = 21/4

21.   Lines $\overleftrightarrow{A'B'}$, $\overleftrightarrow{B'C'}$, $\overleftrightarrow{A'C'}$ form
      transversals. These can be used
      with pairs of parallel sides and
      corresponding angles to show that
      $\angle A \cong \angle A'$, $\angle B \cong \angle B'$, and
      $\angle C \cong \angle C'$. Thus the triangles are
      similar by AAA similarity.

22.   (a) 4.5   (b) 6.75

      (c) 10.125   (d) $3^n\left(\dfrac{1}{2^{n-1}}\right)$

23.   (a) 3/4   (b) 9/16

      (c) 27/64   (d) $\left(\dfrac{3}{4}\right)^{n-1}$

24.

When the two diagonals of an
isosceles trapezoid are drawn,
there are actually 8 triangles
formed. However, Kim is probably
looking at the 4 non-overlapping
triangles. $\triangle DOC \sim \triangle BOA$ by AA,

and $\triangle AOD \cong \triangle BOC$ by AAS (after
proving $\triangle DAC \cong \triangle CBD$).

25.   At noon the shadows may be too
      short (or nonexistent) for accurate
      measurement.

**Problems related to the NCTM
Standards and Curriculum Focal Points**

1.   Problem: At the same time Alana
      (who is 5 feet tall) cast a 7.5 foot
      shadow, a tree nearby cast a 24
      foot shadow. How tall is the tree?

      Answer: $\dfrac{5}{7.5} = \dfrac{x}{24}$; $x = 16$ feet.

2.   Since similar triangles have
      proportional sides, if two of the
      lengths on one triangle are known
      and one of the corresponding
      lengths on a second triangle is
      known then a proportion can be
      created to find the other
      corresponding length on the
      second triangle.

3.   A deductive argument was used
      for Exercise 6a of Set A. Since two
      angles of one triangle were
      congruent to two angles of the
      second triangle, it could be
      deduced that the triangles had to
      be similar by the AA similarity
      property. Answer may vary.

Section 14.3

1.   Follow the steps of the *1. Copy a
      Line Segment* construction.

2.   Follow the steps of the *2. Copy an
      Angle* construction.

3.   Follow the steps of the *3. Construct
      a Perpendicular Bisector*
      construction.

4.   Follow the steps of the *4. Bisect an
      Angle* construction.

5.   Follow the steps of the *5.
      Construct a Perpendicular Line
      through a Point on a Line*
      construction.

6. Follow the steps of the *6. Construct a Perpendicular Line through a Point not on a Line* construction.

7. Follow the steps of the *7. Construct a Line Parallel to a give Line through a Point not on the Line* construction.

8. (a) Follow the steps of the *5. Construct a Perpendicular Line through a Point on a Line* construction.
   (b) Follow the steps of the *6. Construct a Perpendicular Line through a Point not on a Line* construction.
   (c) Follow the steps of the *7. Construct a Line Parallel to a give Line through a Point not on the Line* construction.
   (d) Follow the steps of the *7. Construct a Line Parallel to a give Line through a Point not on the Line* construction.

10. (a) Follow the steps of the *5. Construct a Perpendicular Line through a Point on a Line* construction.
    (b) Follow the steps of the *7. Construct a Line Parallel to a give Line through a Point not on the Line* construction.
    (c) They are perpendicular to each other.

11. Construct the midpoint of each side using the *3. Construct a Perpendicular Bisector* construction. Connect these midpoints with the corresponding vertices on the opposite side of the triangle.

12. For each vertex of the triangle and it's opposite side, follow the steps of the *6. Construct a Perpendicular Line through a Point not on a Line* construction.

13. (a) Use constructions 2 and 1 to copy angles and side.
    (b) Make copy of ∠D, copy length AB along both sides of the

angle, and connect endpoints of two segments.

14. (b) By construction, $\overline{RS} \cong \overline{DE}$, $\overline{RT} \cong \overline{DF}$, and $\overline{ST} \cong \overline{EF}$. Thus, $\triangle RST \cong \triangle DEF$ by SSS congruence property.

15. $\triangle ADC \cong \triangle BDC$ by ASA so $\overline{AD} \cong \overline{BD}$.

16. (a) RQ = 2a, $\angle B \cong \angle Q$, $\angle C \cong \angle R$.
    (b) $\triangle ADC \sim \triangle PQR$ because all 3 corresponding pairs of angles are congruent and all 3 pairs of corresponding sides are proportional.
    (c) SAS similarity

17. They do in an equilateral triangle. In every isosceles triangle the perpendicular bisector of the base and the altitude to the base coincide.

18. This occurs when the triangle is isosceles and not equilateral.

19. (a) Construct right triangle with legs 3 and 1
    (b) Construct right triangle with legs 2 and 1 and hypotenuse $\sqrt{5}$, then construct right triangle with legs $\sqrt{5}$ and 1 .
    (c) Construct isosceles right triangle with legs $\sqrt{6}$ [see part (b)].
    (d) Construct right triangle with hypotenuse 4 and leg 1. The other leg will be $\sqrt{15}$.

20. $\triangle ABC \sim \triangle AQP$ by AA similarity and $\triangle ACD \sim \triangle APR$ by AA similarity. Therefore, ABCD ~ AQPR, since corresponding angles are congruent and corresponding sides are proportional

21. $\overline{AC} \cong \overline{BC}$ (equidistant), $\overline{AD} \cong \overline{BD}$ (midpoint) , $\overline{CD} \cong \overline{CD}$ (common side), $\triangle ACD \cong \triangle BCD$ (SSS), $\angle ADC \cong \angle BDC$

(corresponding parts of congruent triangles), ∠ADC and ∠BDC are right angles (congruent and supplementary), $\overleftrightarrow{CD}$ is perpendicular bisector of $\overline{AB}$.

22. The line should be the perpendicular bisector of the segment $\overline{AB}$.

23. In an isosceles triangle, the altitude, median, and angle bisector from the *vertex* angle all lie on the same line. In Gwennette's case, she is looking at the altitude, median and angle bisector from one of the two *base* angles, and the theorem does not hold there (unless the triangle is equilateral).

Problems related to the NCTM Standards and Curriculum Focal Points

1. By doing the construction of the perpendicular bisector one may come to realize the property that all of the points on the perpendicular are equidistant from the endpoints of the segment. Answers may vary.

2. Each of the new construction in this section is accompanied with a justification of why the construction works. These justifications are deductive arguments.

Section 14.4

1. Construct perpendicular bisectors (Construction 3).

2.

3 (a) Inside
   (b) On the hypotenuse
   (c) Outside
   (d) Yes

4. (a) Inside   (b) Yes

5. Construct a circle with the center on one endpoint of the given segment and the radius point on the other endpoint. Construct another circle reversing the roles of the endpoints. Where the two circles intersect is the third point of the triangle.
   This is similar to the compass and straightedge construction except the circles are replaced with compass arcs.

6. (a) Dodecagon
   (b) 24-gon, 48-gon.

7. (a) Decagon
   (b) 20-gon
   (c) 40-gon, 80-gon

4. (a) Add together a right angle and 45°.
   (b) Subtract 60° from 135° angle.
   (c) Take central angle of regular pentagon.
   (d) Bisect 72° and add that 36° to 72° to get 108°.

9. 3, 4, 5, 6, 8, 10, 12, 15, 16, 17, 20, 24, 30, 32, 34, 40, 48, 51, 60, 64, 68, 80, 85, 96 (24 polygons).

10. 3, 5, 6, 7, 9, 10, 12, 13, 14, 15

11. (a) Use the same procedure except mark off four congruent segments on $\overline{AC}$.
    (b) Use construction 3 to find midpoint M of $\overline{AB}$. Then repeat construction 3 to bisect $\overline{AM}$ and $\overline{MB}$.

12.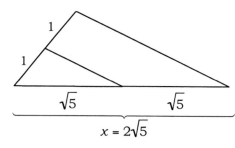

$$\frac{\sqrt{5}}{1} = \frac{x}{2}$$

13. (a) Construct triangle with sides 1 and 2.

    (c) $(\sqrt{5} - 1)/2$

14. Let P be equidistant from A and B. Then $AP = BP$. Let m be the line through the mid point M and P, then $AM = BM$ and $PM = PM$ so $\triangle APM \cong \triangle BPM$ by SSS. Thus $\angle AMP \cong \angle BMP$ so $m\angle AMP = 90°$ which means that m is the perpendicular bisector of $\overline{AB}$. Therefore P is on the perpendicular bisector of $\overline{AB}$.

15. (c) It is the midpoint of the hypotenuse.

16. Yes

17. (c) $M_1M_3 = M_2M_4$ and $\overline{M_1M_3} \perp \overline{M_2M_4}$ (Aubel's theorem).

18. (a) About 26°   (b) $\dfrac{360°}{7}$

    (c) First double the angle to get on which measures $\dfrac{360°}{7}$. Then draw a circle so that $\dfrac{360°}{7}$ is a central angle whose sides intersect the circle at A and B. Set radius of compass to AB and mark off arcs around the circle. Connect points to get the regular heptagon.

19. Draw $\overline{AB} \perp \overline{XY}$ and $\overline{AC} \perp \overline{YZ}$.
    $\overline{AB} \cong \overline{AC}$, since A is equidistant from YX and YZ.
    $\overline{AY} \cong \overline{AY}$. Thus, $\triangle ABY \cong \triangle ACY$ by HL for right triangles.
    $\angle AYB \cong \angle AYC$, since they are corresponding parts of congruent triangles and therefore $\overrightarrow{YA}$ bisects $\angle XYZ$.

20. (a) QR
    (b) QS

    (c) Yes; $\angle RAQ \cong \angle SAQ$ (angle bisector), $\angle ARQ \cong \angle ASQ$ (both right angles), $\angle RQA \cong \angle SQA$ (third pair of angles of triangles are congruent if other 2 pairs are), $\overline{AQ} \cong \overline{AQ}$ so $\triangle ARQ \cong \triangle ASQ$ by the ASA congruence property.

    (d) $\overline{QR} \cong \overline{QS}$ because they are corresponding sides of congruent triangles.

    (e) Refer to procedure of construction 9. Since Q is on line l, the bisector of $\angle CAB$, Q is equidistant from $\overline{AC}$ and $\overline{AB}$. Also Q is on line m, so Q is equidistant from $\overline{AC}$ and $\overline{BC}$. Hence, Q is equidistant from $\overline{AB}$, $\overline{BC}$, and $\overline{AC}$, the sides of $\triangle ABC$. Thus, Q is the incenter of $\triangle ABC$.

21. An equilateral triangle has three 60° angles. If 6 equilateral triangles are gathered around a common vertex, the sum of the angles would be 360°. Furthermore, since all of Craig's triangles are congruent, the "radial" sides will match in length, the angles of the hexagon formed will be 120° (60°+ 60°), and the sides of the hexagon will all be equal in length. So Craig's method will work.

22. Since 5 = 4 + 1, if Joan constructs two perpendicular line segments of lengths 1 and 2 and connects their endpoints to form a hypotenuse, the Pythagorean theorem will show the length of the hypotenuse is $\sqrt{5}$.

Problems related to the NCTM Standards and Curriculum Focal Points

1. One possible answer is that a unique circle can be constructed in the inside of any triangle that touches each side exactly once. Another possible answer is that a

unique circle can be constructed through the three vertices of any triangle and the center of that circle is equidistant from these vertices. Answers may vary.

2. Each of the new constructions in this section is accompanied by a justification, which is an explanation of why the construction works.

Section 14.5

1. (a) For example, $\overline{AB} \cong \overline{AD}$, $\overline{BC} \cong \overline{DC}$.
   (b) $\overline{AC} \cong \overline{AC}$ (congruent to itself)
   (c) SSS
   (d) Corresponding parts of congruent triangles are congruent.
   (e) By definition of angle bisector.

2. (a) $\angle 2 \cong \angle 4$, $\angle 1 \cong \angle 3$
   (b) Yes; base angles of isosceles triangle
   (c) Yes; $\angle 1 \cong \angle 2 \cong \angle 3 \cong \angle 4$ from parts (a) and (b).

3. $\angle P \cong \angle Q$ since they are opposite the congruent sides $\overline{QR}$ and $\overline{PR}$. Further, $\angle Q \cong \angle R$ since they are opposite the congruent sides $\overline{PR}$ and $\overline{PQ}$. Thus, $\angle P \cong \angle Q \cong \angle R$.

4. m ($\angle A$) + m ($\angle D$) = 180° (interior angles on same side of transversal are supplementary), m ($\angle D$) = m ($\angle C$) (base angles congruent), so m ($\angle A$) + m ($\angle C$) = 180° (substitution). Thus, $\angle A$ and $\angle C$ are supplementary. Similarly, $\angle B$ and $\angle D$ are supplementary

5. WXYZ is a rectangle. Since opposite sides of a parallelogram are congruent, $\overline{DE} \cong \overline{FG}$ and $\overline{EF} \cong \overline{DG}$. Since $\overline{DE} \cong \overline{EF}$ is given, $\overline{FG} \cong \overline{DE} \cong \overline{EF} \cong \overline{DG}$ and all 4 sides are congruent.

6. Since $\angle W$ and $\angle Z$ are supplementary (90° + 90° = 180°), $\overline{WX} \parallel \overline{ZY}$ (since interior angles on same side of transversal are supplementary). Similarly, $\angle W$ and $\angle X$ are supplementary and $\overline{WZ} \parallel \overline{XY}$. Therefore, WXYZ is a parallelogram since both pairs of opposite sides are parallel.

7. Since HIJK is a rectangle, it has 4 right angles. We need to show that it has four congruent sides. Since HIJK is a parallelogram, opposite sides are congruent; thus $\overline{HI} \cong \overline{JK}$ and $\overline{HK} \cong \overline{IJ}$. Combined with the given information $\overline{JK} \cong \overline{HI} \cong \overline{IJ} \cong \overline{HK}$. Therefore, HIJK is a square.

8. Construct $\overline{AB}$ with the length of the side. At A and B construct perpendiculars $\overline{AS}$ and $\overline{BT}$. With compass set the length of the diagonal mark an arc centered at A and intersecting $\overline{BT}$ (call intersection point C). Similarly, with the same compass setting, mark an arc centered at B intersecting $\overline{AS}$ (call intersection point D). ABCD is the desired rectangle.

9. Construct $\overline{AB}$ with length d, then construct perpendicular bisector of $\overline{AB}$. Bisect the original segment of length d and mark off the other vertices C and D on the perpendicular diagonal using one half the length of d as the compass setting. Thus, ACBD is the desired square.

10. (a) A quadrilateral with diagonals that bisect each other is a parallelogram, and a parallelogram with perpendicular diagonals is a rhombus (shown in earlier problems).

(b) Construct $\overline{AB}$ with length a, then construct perpendicular bisector of $\overline{AB}$ Bisect the original segment of length b and mark off other vertices C and D on perpendicular diagonal using one half the length of b as the compass setting.

11. $\angle D \cong \angle F$ and $\angle R \cong \angle T$ (base angles of isosceles triangle are congruent). Since $\angle D \cong \angle R$, it follows that $\angle D \cong \angle R$. Hence, $\triangle DEF \sim \triangle RST$ by AA similarity property.

12. AD/CD = CD/DB (CD is geometric mean) and $\angle ADC \cong \angle CDB$ (both are right angles) so $\triangle ADC \cong \triangle CDB$ (SAS similarity property). $\angle A \cong \angle DCB$ since they are corresponding angles of similar triangles. However, m ($\angle ACD$) + m($\angle A$) = 90° (acute angles of right triangles are complementary) so m ($\angle ACD$) + m ($\angle DCB$)= 90° and $\angle ACB$ is a right angle. Thus, $\triangle ABC$ is a right triangle.

13. (a) 36° (central angle of decagon), 72°, 72° (base angles of isosceles triangle)
    (b) 72°, 36°
    (c) 36°, isosceles (since base angles are congruent)
    (d) x, $1 - x$,
    (e) AC = AB = 1, BC = x, m ($\angle A$) = 36°, m($\angle B$) = m($\angle C$) = 72° BD = BC = x,, CD = $1 - x$, m($\angle B$) = 36°, m($\angle C$) = m($\angle D$) = 72° Yes (by the AA similarity property)
    (f) BD, CD, x, $1 - x$
    (g) $1 - x = x^2$ or $x = \dfrac{1 \pm \sqrt{5}}{2}$
    (h) Yes, we can construct the length $\sqrt{5}$ then subtract length 1, and bisect it.

14. If AC = A'C', then $\triangle ABC \cong \triangle A'B'C'$ by SAS. If not, let AC = A'D'. Then, $\triangle ABC \cong \triangle A'B'D'$ by SAS. Therefore, $\angle B \cong \angle A'B'D'$. But, from the given information, $\angle B \cong \angle B'$. Thus, $\angle B \cong \angle A'B'D'$, which is a contradiction.

15. $\triangle BAD \sim \triangle B'A'C'$ by SAS. Thus the sides of $\triangle BAD$ are proportional respectively to the sides of $\triangle B'A'C'$ which, by the given, are proportional respectively to the sides of $\triangle BAC$. Since $\triangle BAD$ and $\triangle BAC$ share the side $\overline{AB}$, the two triangles must be congruent by the SSS congruence property. Therefore, $\angle BAC \cong \angle BAD \cong \angle B'A'C'$. Thus, $\triangle BAC \sim \triangle B'A'C'$ by SAS similarity property.

16. If it is has been *proved* that a rhombus has two pairs of parallel sides, then it can be concluded that a rhombus is a parallelogram. If Caesar is only saying that the rhombus and the parallelogram share a property, then he might believe that a rhombus is a parallelogram *and* a parallelogram is a rhombus. This is not true. A teacher needs to consider the various Van Hiele levels, which might represent Caesar's perspective.

17. The property that Victoria is trying to prove could be stated as follows: In an isosceles triangle, the angle bisector of the vertex angle divides the opposite side into two congruent segments. What we have been "given" is an isosceles triangle and the angle bisector of the vertex angle. So Victoria can infer that since she has an isosceles triangle, PK = KC. She can infer that since KI is an angle bisector, $\angle PKI \cong \angle CKI$. She cannot assume that PI=IC, because that is what she is trying to prove. She cannot assume that angles $\angle PIK$ and $\angle KIC$ are right angles, because it has not been

"given." However, she can prove that ΔPIK ≅ ΔCIK by SAS. Therefore, PI = IC.

Problems related to the NCTM Standards and Curriculum Focal Points

1. In order to prove properties of quadrilaterals it is common to first prove that a pair of triangles are congruent and then use the other congruent corresponding parts. Example 14.11 does this by proving ΔABC ≅ ΔDCB and then using the corresponding parts of the congruent triangles $\overline{AC} \cong \overline{DB}$. These corresponding parts are also the diagonals of the rectangle. Answers may vary.

2. A conjecture is something that a person believes to be true but has yet to prove that it is true. A conjecture usually results from observing a pattern and using inductive reasoning to come up with an educated guess.

Chapter Review

Problems for Writing/Discussion

1. No. Notice that in one triangle the marked side is opposite the angle with two arcs and in the other triangle the marked side is opposite the angle with one arc. These are not corresponding sides. They could be congruent if the marked angles with one arc were congruent to the angles with two arcs. However, we cannot make that assumption.

2. False. The ratios of the corresponding sides of two cubes will be the same. However, this is not the case with rectangular prisms. For example, if one such prism was a cube and the other one not a cube, you could not set up a correspondence between sides that would be the same.

3. All cubes are similar, so all their measures will be proportional, but the proportion will be affected by the dimension being considered. If the cubes' sides are 3 and 5, then all linear measures, such as height, length of diagonal, perimeter of the base, etc. will have the same proportion, 3:5. Areas will have the ratio $3^2:5^2$, that is, 9:25; this includes areas of matching faces, lateral surface area, total surface area. Volume will have the ratio $3^3:5^3$, that is, 27:125.

4. The best way to investigate this problem would be to look at an obtuse triangle, a right triangle, and an acute triangle. The circumcenter and orthocenter are not necessarily inside the triangle, but the incenter and centroid are inside the triangle.

5. You can start with any side, although starting with the longest side may ensure the triangle doesn't go off the paper!

6. If you draw a long, narrow rectangle that does not look like a square, students may be able to see that the angles are not bisected.

If the rectangle is a square, however, then you can prove that the diagonals bisect the angles.

7. Rectangles have all their angles congruent to each other. You would need to know that the length and width of one rectangle were congruent to the length and width of the other. For a parallelogram, once you know one angle, the other three angles are determined (Why?). So if you know the lengths of two consecutive sides and any angle of one parallelogram are congruent

to the corresponding parts of another parallelogram, the two parallelograms would be congruent.

8. Dwight is thinking that x represents a side of the larger triangle, whereas it is only a part of a side. The equation $\dfrac{6}{10} = \dfrac{8}{8+x}$ would be the correct proportion to solve.

9. If the linear measures are in ratio 5:8, then their volumes would be in ratio of the cubes, 125:512, which is about 1 to 4. Mass is in the same ratio as volume. As a four-legged animal gets larger, it gets much heavier, and so its legs need to be much stronger to carry the weight.

10. By determining x in the drawing below, it would be possible to find the volumes of the large cone and the small cone and subtract them to find the volume of the truncated cone. $x = 24$ (Why?). The volume of the truncated cone would be

$(1/3)\pi 9^2 36 - (1/3)\pi 6^2 24$
$= (1/3)\pi 2052 \approx 2148.8$ cu. units.

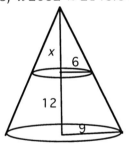

Chapter 15

Section 15.1

1. (a) $\sqrt{73}$ (b) 7

2. (a) $2\sqrt{5} + 4\sqrt{5} = 6\sqrt{5}$; yes
    (b) $\sqrt{212} + \sqrt{13.25} = \sqrt{331.25}$; yes

3. (a) (1, 7)   (b) (-9, 3)
    (c) (7, 5)   (d) (2, -5)

4. (a) -5/7   (b) no slope

5. (a) Yes   (b) Yes

6. (a) Rises to the right
    (b) Vertical
    (c) Horizontal
    (d) Rises to the left

7. Not collinear

8. (a) No   (b) Yes
    (c) No   (d) No

9. (a) Top, bottom are horizontal,
    $\dfrac{2-(-2)}{4-1} = \dfrac{4}{3}, \dfrac{2-(-2)}{6-3} = \dfrac{4}{3}$,
    parallelogram
    (b) $\dfrac{10-(-5)}{-5-10} = -1, \dfrac{5-(-10)}{-10-5} = -1$,
    parallel; $\dfrac{10-5}{-5-(-10)} = 1$,
    $\dfrac{-5-(-10)}{10-5} = 1$, parallelogram

10. (a) Slope of $\overline{AB}= 1/6$, slope of $\overline{PQ}= -6$; $-6(1/6) = -1$.
    (b) Slope of $\overline{AB}= 1$, slope of $\overline{PQ}= -1$; $1(-1) = -1$.

11. (a) and (b) are right triangles.

12. All.

13. (a) False for both.
    (b) True for both.
    (c) False for both.

14. (a) 3   (b) 2

15. (a) Scalene obtuse
    (b) Scalene acute

16. (a) GH = 8, HI = $\sqrt{32}$. Since $GH^2 = HI^2 + GI^2$, ΔGHI is a right triangle.
    (b) LM = $2\sqrt{5}$, MN = $\sqrt{5}$, LN = 5. Since $LM^2 + MN^2 = LN^2$, ΔLMN is a right triangle.

17.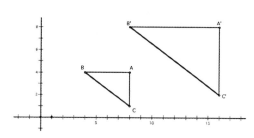

    (a) Double   (b) Same

18. Trapezoid with right angles at A and B.

19. (a) (7,-9), (-3,15), or (13, -1)
    (b) Area = 56 square units in each case.

20. (a)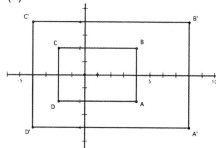

    (b) B'(12,6), C'(-6,6), D(-6,-6)
    (c) perimeter of A'B'C'D' = 3(perimeter of ABCD)
    (d) area of A'B'C'D' = 9(area of ABCD)
    (e) A'(2,-1), B'(2,1), C'(-1,1), D'(-1,-1)
    Perimeter of A'B'C'D' = (1/2)(perimeter of ABCD)
    area of A'B'C'D' = (1/4)(area of ABCD)

(d) True for (ii) only.

21. (a) 792 ft
    (b) 28,512 ft (This is higher than any mountain in North America!
    (c) Percent grade is the absolute value of the slope times 100.

22. Slope of $l = \dfrac{b}{a}$, slope of $m = -\dfrac{y}{b}$
    Hence $(b/a)(-y/b) = -1$, so $a = y$.
    Also, $OQ^2 + OP^2 = b^2 + y^2) + (a^2 + b^2) = 2a^2 + 2b^2$, and $QP^2 = (a + b)^2 + (b - y)^2 = (a^2 + 2ab + b^2) + (b^2 - 2yb + b^2) = 2a^2 + 2b^2$
    $= OQ^2 + OP^2$. Thus, ΔOPQ is a right triangle, so $l \perp m$.

23. (a) All but Rio and Sydney.
    (b) Nome
    (c) No. All points in the contiguous United States are east of the 180° meridian.
    (d) 52° S
    (e) 106° E
    (f) 34° N 29° W

24. (a) (a, y, z)
    (b) $\sqrt{(y - b)^2 + (z - c)^2}$
    (c) $QR = |x - a|$
    (d) $PQ = \sqrt{QR^2 + PR^2}$
    $= \sqrt{(x - a)^2 + (y - b)^2 + (z - c)^2}$

25. Shirdena and Edmund both started out correctly. However, when Edmund got to -15 ÷ -3, he needed to remember that a negative divided by a negative gives a positive answer, 3. So both students should have gotten the same answer.

Problems related to the NCTM Standards and Curriculum Focal Points

1. The lengths and slopes of the sides could be determined by using the coordinates. These values could them be used to decide if certain sides are congruent or parallel or if certain angles are right angles.

2. In general terms the slope is the steepness of a line. More specifically, it shows how much the y values increase for each increase in the x values. For example, if income were graphed as a function of hours worked, the slope would be the hourly wage and would show how much the income increases for each hour of work. Answers may vary.

3. Find the slopes and lengths of all four sides. If all sides were the same length and if adjacent sides were perpendicular, the quadrilateral would be a square.

Section 15.2

1. (a) $(-2)7.5 = -15$ and $6(-3) + 3$
       $= -15$
   (b) $4(4) + 2 = 18$ and $3(6) = 18$

2. There are three points given in each answer, however, there are infinitely many correct possibilities in each case.
   (a) $(4,0), (5,1), (6,2)$
   (b) $(3,0), (0,-2), (6,2)$
   (c) $(3,0), (3,1), (3,-5)$
   (d) $(0,0), (4,-1), (2,-1/2)$

3. (a) -3,2   (b) 3/2,-5
   (c) 5/2,-3   (d) 2/7, -8/7

4. (a) $y = 1/4$, slope = 0, y-intercept = 1/4
   (b) $y = (3/4)x - 3$, y-intercept = -3

5. (a) $y = -2x + 5$
   (b) $y = -(7/3)x - 2$
   (c) $y = -(-3)x - 1/4$

6. $(-2, 1), (-2, 0)$
   All such points must have x-coordinate -2.

7.   (a)   14.   (a) (2, 2)   (b) (4, 8)
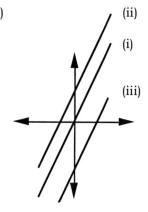   (c) No solution
                                                            (d) $\{(x, y) \mid 3y = 5x + 1\}$

                                                     15.   (a) (3,2)   (b) (3,-4)
                                                            (c) No solution   (d) (31/2, 3/2)

                                                     16.   (a) (1,4)   (b) (1/2, 5/4)

                                                     17.   (a) (5,0)   (b) (1,4)
                                                            (c) (3,1)

      (b) They are parallel.   18.   (a) No solution
      (c) They are the set of all lines in   (b) Unique solution
           the plane parallel to the line   (c) Infinitely many solutions
           $y = cx$. Each has slope c and
           y-intercept d, for a particular   19.   (a) $(-3 + 1)^2 + (7 - 2)^2 = 4 + 25 =$
           value of d.   29

                                                            (b) $(\sqrt{15})^2 + (-3 + 5)^2 = 5 + 4 = 9$
8.   (a) $y = -3x - 5$ (b) $x = -2$
      (c) $y = -x + 5$ 20.   (a) (2,-5), $r = 8$

9.   (a) $(y - 1) = 4(x + 5)$ (b) (-3,4), $r = 2\sqrt{5}$
      (b) $(y - 6) = (-2/5)(x - 2)$
                                                     21.   (a) $(x + 1)^2 + (y + 2)^2 = 5$
10.   (a) $y = -x - 1$ (b) $(x - 2)^2 + (y + 4)^2 = 41$
      (b) $y = (-3/5)x - 19/5$ (c) $(x - 1)^2 + (y - 4)^2 = 8$

11.   (a) $y = (1/2)x + 6$ 22.   (a) 0   (b) No solutions
      (b) $y = (-3/2)x + 9$
      (c) $y = 2x - 5$ 23. $y = -3x + 5$
      (d) $y = (-2/3)x - 22/3$
                                                     24. $y = 1/2x, y = -1/2x + 3$
12.   (a) (i) $y - 2 = -1/2(x + 5)$ or
                  $y - 1 = -1/2(x + 3)$ 25. $y = (-2/5)x + 29/10$
           (ii) $y = -1/2x - 1/2$
      (b) (i) $y - 7 = 0$ 26.   (a) $5.60; $13.10
           (ii) $y = 7$ (b) $y = 0.5x + 0.6$

13.   (a)   (b)   27.   (a) $y = 0.65x + 350$
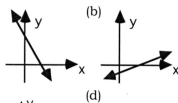   (b) $y = x$
                                                            (c) 1,000 items

      (c)   (d)   28.   (a)
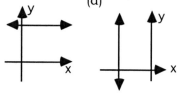   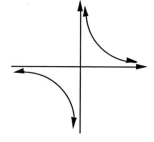

(b) If $x = 0$, there is no solution for
y, and vice versa.

(c) When $x > 0$ and near 0, y is
very large. When $x < 0$ and
near 0, y is very small.

29. (a)

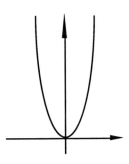

(b)

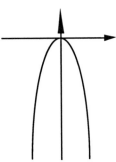

The graph in (b) is the
reflection image of the graph in
(a), in the y-axis.

30. (a)

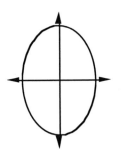

(b)

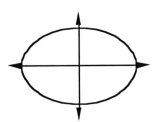

The graph in (b) is a 90°
rotation image of the graph in
(a), around the origin.

31. $(x - 4/3)^2 + (y + 4/3)^2 = 425/9$

32. Many students think that when
they know x, their problems are
over. However, geometrically, we
are looking for the intersection of
two lines. If the lines intersect in
one point, we must find both
coordinates, x *and* y.

33. No. The center is in the interior of
the circle, not one of the points of
the circle itself.

**Problems related to the NCTM
Standards and Curriculum Focal Points**

1. Solving an equation means finding the
values of the variable that when
plugged in would make the equation
true.

2. The y-intercept is the value of y where
the graph of the line crosses the y
axis. It is also the value of y when $x =$
0.

Section 15.3

1. (a) (-1,5)   (b) (1,4)

2. (a) $(-1, -3\sqrt{3})$
(b) (-4,6) and (2,6)

3. $(a + b, c)$

4. (a) $(a + b, c)$
(b) $b^2 + c^2 = a^2$ since MP = MN = a

5. (a) (-5,0), (5,0), (5,8), (-5,8)
(b) (-5,-4), (5,-4), (5,4), (-5,4)

6. AB = 1 - (-4) = 5,
BC = $\sqrt{(4-1)^2 + (3+1)^2}$ = 5,
CD = 4 - (-1) = 5,
DA = $\sqrt{(-1+4)^2 + (3+1)^2}$ = 5. Since
AB = BC = CD = DA, ABCD is a
rhombus.

7. AB = BC = CD = AD = $\sqrt{17}$ and

$\overline{AB} \perp \overline{BC}$ since the slope of $\overline{AB}$ = -1/4 and the slope of $\overline{BC}$ = 4.

8. The midpoint of $\overline{EG}$ is (-3/2, -5/2) and the midpoint of $\overline{FH}$ is (-3/2, -5/2). Since the diagonals meet at the midpoint of both, the diagonals are bisected.

9. (a) $y = -2x + 15$
   (b) $y = x - 12$
   (c) $x = 9$
   (d) (9, -3); yes it lies on $x = 9$.
   (e) $\sqrt{90}$ for all three distances
   (f) circumcenter

10. The midpoint is $M(\dfrac{b}{2}, \dfrac{a}{2})$.

$AM = \sqrt{\left(\dfrac{b}{2}\right)^2 + \left(\dfrac{a}{2}\right)^2}$

$= \dfrac{1}{2}\sqrt{b^2 + a^2}$

$MB = \sqrt{\left(\dfrac{b}{2}\right)^2 + \left(\dfrac{a}{2}\right)^2}$

$= \dfrac{1}{2}\sqrt{b^2 + a^2}$

$MC = \sqrt{\left(\dfrac{b}{2}\right)^2 + \left(\dfrac{a}{2}\right)^2}$

$= \dfrac{1}{2}\sqrt{b^2 + a^2}$

Thus, AM = MB = MC.

11. (a) $3\sqrt{53}$; $2\sqrt{53}$; 2/3
    (b) $3\sqrt{29}$; $2\sqrt{29}$; 2/3
    (c) $6\sqrt{5}$; $4\sqrt{5}$; 2/3
    (d) On any median, 2/3 of the distance from the vertex point.

12. $b^2 + c^2 = a^2$;

Slope of $\overline{AC}$ = $\dfrac{c}{b+a}$.

Slope of $\overline{BD}$ = $\dfrac{c}{ba}$;

$\left(\dfrac{c}{b+a}\right)\left(\dfrac{c}{b-a}\right) = \dfrac{c^2}{b^2 a^2} =$

$\dfrac{a^2 b^2}{b^2 a^2} = -1$. So $\overline{AC} \perp \overline{BD}$.

13. (a) Slope of $\overline{QG}$ = slope of $\overline{QM_2}$ = $2b/(2a - c)$ so that Q, G, and M_2 are collinear.
    (b) Slope of $\overline{RG}$ = slope of $\overline{RM_1}$ = $b/(a - 2c)$ so that R, G, and M_1 are collinear.

14. (a) $QG = \sqrt{\left(a - \dfrac{a+c}{3}\right)^2 + \left(b - \dfrac{b}{3}\right)^2}$

$= \dfrac{\sqrt{(2a - c)^2 + (2b)^2}}{3}$

$GM_2 = \sqrt{\left(\dfrac{a+c}{3} - \dfrac{c}{2}\right)^2 + \left(\dfrac{b}{3}\right)^2}$

$= \dfrac{\sqrt{(2a - c)^2 + (2b)^2}}{6}$

$= \dfrac{1}{2}QG$

Hence $QG:GM_2$ = 2:1

(b) $RG = \sqrt{\left(c - \dfrac{a+c}{3}\right)^2 + \left(-\dfrac{b}{3}\right)^2}$

$= \dfrac{\sqrt{(2c - a)^2 + b^2}}{3}$

$GM_1 =$

$\sqrt{\left(\dfrac{a+c}{3} - \dfrac{a}{2}\right)^2 + \left(\dfrac{b}{3} - \dfrac{b}{2}\right)^2}$

$= \dfrac{\sqrt{(2c - a)^2 + b^2}}{6} = \dfrac{1}{2}RG$

Hence $RG:GM_1$ = 2:1

15. (a) $(a/2, \sqrt{3}\,a/2)$
    (b) $x = a/2$, $x = a/2$, $x = a/2$, yes
    (c) Yes, $y = (\sqrt{3}/3)x$
    (d) Yes, $y = -(\sqrt{3}/3)x + (\sqrt{3}/3)a$
    (e) In an equilateral triangle, the median and altitude to a side

is contained in the perpendicular bisector of that side.

16. (a) Let A = (0, 0), B = (*m, n*), C = (*p, q*), D = (*r, s*). Then M = (*p*/2, *q*/2) and N = ((*m + r*)/2, (*n + s*)/2). Also,

$$AB^2 = m^2 + n^2,$$
$$BC^2 = (m\text{-}p)^2 + (n\text{-}q)^2,$$
$$CD^2 = (p\text{-}r)^2 + (q\text{-}s)^2,$$
$$DA^2 = r^2 + s^2, \quad \text{etc.}$$

(b) If ABCD is a parallelogram, then N = M. Thus, the sum of the squares of the sides of a parallelogram equals the sum of the squares of the diagonals.

17. Solution: Top--13, 2, 10, 3; Middle--5, 6, 9, 8; Bottom--4, 11, 1, 12 such that one side face has 13, 5, 4, 6 around it.

18. 24 3-point questions and 7 4-point questions.

19. Gold--16 g.; Silver--13 g.; Copper--15 g.

20. 66 and 82

21. 20

22. Yes, a 5 × 12 mat or a 6 × 8 mat.

23. It can be *proved* that the diagonals of a rhombus bisect each other and are perpendicular to each other. Thus, *if* Shelley has this information from previous work, her placement and labeling is correct.

Problems related to the NCTM Standards and Curriculum Focal Points

1. First, a general parallelogram with variable coordinates would be drawn on a set of axes. Using the coordinates of opposite vertices, the equations of the diagonals can be determined. These equations are used to find the point of intersection of the two diagonals. Finally, the distances from the intersection point to each of the vertices will show that the diagonals bisect each other.

2. In problem #1, the distance formula was used to determine if the point of intersection of the two diagonals was the same distance from opposite vertices. Answers may vary.

3. 1) Diagonals of a parallelogram bisect each other. 2) Diagonals of a rhombus are perpendicular to each other (Set B #12). 3) The perpendicular bisector of the three sides of a triangle are concurrent (Set B #9). Answers may vary.

Chapter Review

Problems for Writing/Discussion

1. His method of finding the coordinates of a midpoint on the number line is correct. However, he misapplied it in this case. If he had taken the numbers he found, 4 and 1.5, and added them to the smaller of the *x*'s and the smaller of the *y*'s respectively, he would have found the correct coordinates, namely (7, 5.5).

2. If you take any two points on a horizontal line, their *y*-coordinates will be equal. Thus, when you compute the slope of the line, find that the numerator is zero; hence the slope is 0. If you take any two points on a vertical line, their *x*-coordinates will be equal. Thus, when you compute the slope of the line, find that the denominator is zero. Since a fraction with a zero denominator is undefined, we say that the vertical line has no slope.

3. Lines such as $y = (3/2)x$ and

$y = (2/3)x$ are interesting in that they are reflections of each other in the line $y = x$.

has two pairs of parallel sides, hence a parallelogram.

4. Lines such as $y = 4x + 5$ and $y = -4x + 5$ are reflection images of each other in the line $y = 5$.

5. The equation $y = 3$ indicates that every y-coordinate on the line is 3. The set of points whose y-coordinates are 3 is a horizontal line. The equation $x = 5$ indicates every x-coordinate on that line is 5. The set of all points whose x-coordinates are 5 is a vertical line.

6. The numbers on the coordinate axes are not properly spaced.

7. The bear must be white because the explorer must be at the North Pole.

8. If Warren divides the second equation by 2, he gets $2x + 5y = 7.5$. The first equation is $2x + 5y = 7$. The slope of both lines is -2/5. If Warren notices that the coefficients of the x and y are in the same ratio, he will know that the lines are parallel. If the 15 in the original second equation were changed to a 14, the two equations would be equivalent and the two lines would be coincident.

9. One way is to find the lengths of the sides and determine if they could make a true statement when substituted into the equation $x^2 + y^2 = z^2$. Another way is to look at the slope of each segment and see if any two sides are perpendicular to each other.

10. No. To prove her conjecture, she would have to find the coordinates of the midpoint of each side. Then she would calculate the slope of each of the four sides of the inner quadrilateral hoping to find two pairs of equal slopes. If so, she

Chapter 16

Section 16.1

1. (a)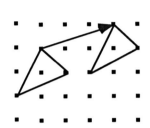

   (b)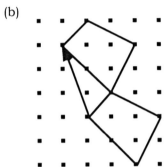

2.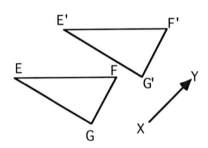

3. (a) A'(1, 2), B'(4, 3),
   C'(6, 1), D'(2, -2)
   (b) $(x + 3, \ y - 1)$

4. Construct image of A, image of B,
   image of C and connect.

5. (a) 180°   (b) -20°

6. (a)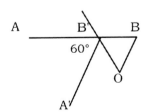

(b)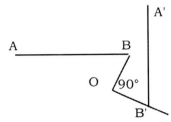

(c)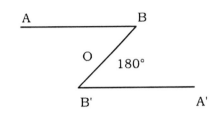

7.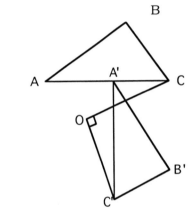

8. (a)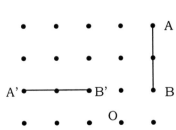

(b)

9. (a)

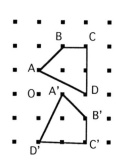

(b)

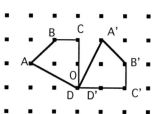

(c)

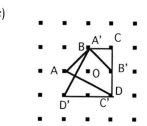

10. A'(3, -1) B'(6, -3) C'(1, -4)

11. (a) (5, -1)   (b) (3, 1)
    (c) (-4, 2)   (d) (-1, 3)
    (e) (-2, -5)   (f) $(y, -x)$

12. (a) (3 -2)   (b) (1, 3)
    (c) (-4, 5)

13. (a) $(y, -x)$ (b) $(-x, -y)$

14. Construct a perpendicular at O
    such that AO = A'O as shown
    below. Repeat for points B and C
    to find B' and C' respectively.

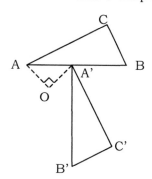

15. (a)

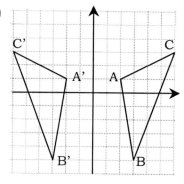

(b) A'(-2, 1), B'(-3, -5), C'(-6, 3)
(c) $(-a, b)$

16.

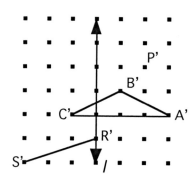

17. (b) (-2, 1) (-3, -5), (-6, 3)
    (c) $(-a, b)$

18. (a) Drop perpendiculars from A
    and B to line l. Then find A'
    and B' so AX = XA' and BY =
    YB'.

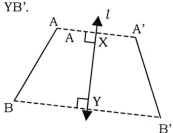

(b) Repeat the construction in
    part (a) on points A, B, and C.
    Then connect A', B', and C'.

19. (a)

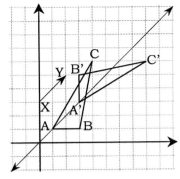

(b) (3, 3), (3, 5), (8, 6)
(c) (y + 2, x + 2)

20. Construct lines, through A and B, parallel to $\overrightarrow{XY}$ and mark off the translation. Then construct perpendiculars to l through A' and B' to find reflection of the translated image.

21. (a) and (c). The original image ABCDE is traversed clockwise as are the images for (a) and (c).

22. (a)

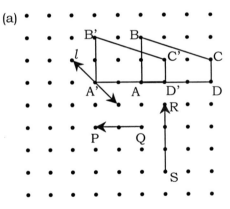

(b)

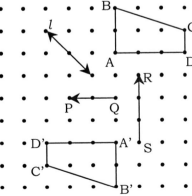

(c)

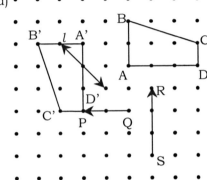

(d)

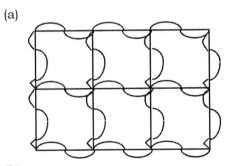

23. (a) Rotation (90°, 180°, 270°), Reflection (4 lines)
(b) Rotation (90°, 180°, 270°),
(c) Rotation 180°, Reflection (2 lines)
(d) None

24. (a)

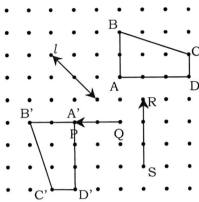

(b)

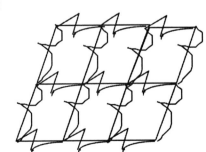

25. (a)

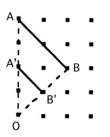

(b)

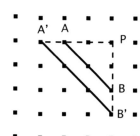

(c)

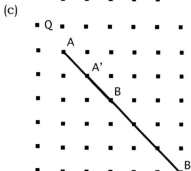

26. (a) $S_{P,1/2}$ Note: The scale has been changed so that the figure can fit this column.

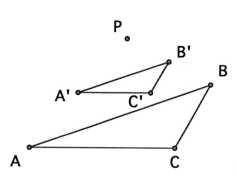

(b) $S_{P,3}$
Note: The scale has been changed so that the figure can fit this column.

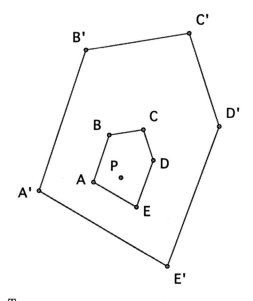

27. (a) T_{XY}

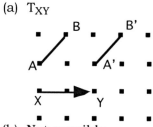

(b) Not possible
(c) Not possible
(d) M l followed by T_{XY}

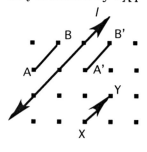

28. (a) Not possible
(b) $R_{O,-90°}$

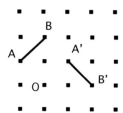

(c) Not possible

(d) M$_l$ followed by T$_{XY}$

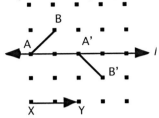

29. (a) None

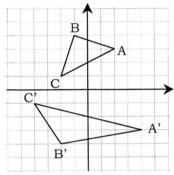

(b) Rotation

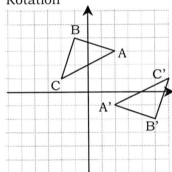

(c) Glide reflection

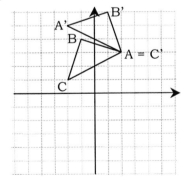

30. (a)

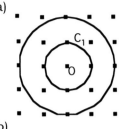

(b)

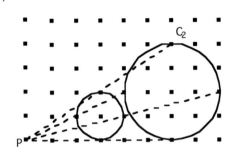

31. No, the location of the line of reflection does not affect the size and shape of the image. It only effects the location of the image

32. Yes. Although one can think of this as one slide or two slides, mathematicians tend to minimalize and call it one. In this case the slide is $4\sqrt{2}$ units on a line 45° south of east

33. This would only be true under very special circumstances. If the figure being rotated has line symmetry, and the line of symmetry is perpendicular to the reflection line at the center of rotation, then the image after a 180° rotation would be the same as the image after a flip over the reflection line.

Problems related to the NCTM Standards and Curriculum Focal Points

1. Translations, rotations, reflections, and glide reflections all preserve size so the image is congruent to the original figure.

2. By starting with polygons that tessellation, an irregular side created in one part of the polygon can be translated or rotated to another part

of the polygon so that the resulting image will still tessellate (see Figure 16.19).

3. Slide, turns, and scaling (size transformations) all maintain the orientation of a figure. Flips change the orientation of the figure.

Section 16.2

1. (a) A = (-3, 1), B = (1, 2.5)
   (b) A' = (1, 6), B' = (5, 7.5)
   (c) AB = $\sqrt{(31)^2 + (12.5)^2}$ = $\sqrt{18.25}$. A'B' = $\sqrt{18.25}$, as well.

2. (a) $\sqrt{(c-a)^2 + (d-b)^2}$
   (b) A' = $(a + p,\ b + q)$, B' = $(c + p,\ d + q)$
   (c) $\sqrt{(c-a)^2 + (d-b)^2}$
   (d) Yes

3. (a) A'(-1, -2), B'(3, 0), C'(0, 5)
   (b) Yes, by SSS; AB = A'B' = $2\sqrt{2}$ AC = A'C' = $\sqrt{50}$, BC = B'C' = $\sqrt{34}$
   (c) Yes, since ΔABC ≅ ΔA'B'C', the corresponding angles are congruent.

4. A' = (2, -3), B' = (3, 1); AB = $\sqrt{1^2 + 4^2}$ = 17, A'B' = $\sqrt{(-1)^2 + (-4)^2}$ = 17, so AB = A'B'.

5. (a) A = (4, 2) and B = (-1, -3)
   (b) A' = (4, -2) and B' = (-1, 3)
   (c) AB = $\sqrt{(4+1)^2 + (2+3)^2}$
       = $5\sqrt{2}$,

       A'B' = $\sqrt{(4+1)^2 + (-2-3)^2}$
       = $5\sqrt{2}$

6. (a) $(-a, b)$
   (b) AB = $\sqrt{(a-c)^2 + (b-d)^2}$; A' = $(-a, b)$, B' = $(-c, d)$

and A'B' = $\sqrt{(-a+c)^2 + (b-d)^2}$
= $\sqrt{(a-c)^2 + (b-d)^2}$

7. (a) A' (2, -2), B'(3, 1), C'(-1, 4)
   (b) Yes, by SSS; AB = A'B' = $\sqrt{10}$, AC = A'C' = $3\sqrt{5}$, BC = B'C' = 5
   (c) Yes, since ΔABC ≅ ΔA'B'C', the corresponding angles are congruent.

8. (a) (-2, 1), (2, 3)
   (b) (-2 + p, -1), (2 + p, -3)
   (c) AB = $\sqrt{(-2-2)^2 + (1-3)^2}$ = $2\sqrt{5}$
       A'B' =
       $\sqrt{[(-2+p)-(2+p)]^2 + (-1+3)^2}$ =
       $2\sqrt{5}$

9. (a) Reflection (b) Glide refection
   (c) Rotation

10. (a) Rotation   (b) Glide reflection

11. (a)

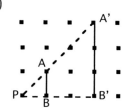

   (b) PA' = $3\sqrt{2}$, PA = $\sqrt{2}$, so PA' = 3PA
   (c) PB' = 3PB = 1, so PB' = 3PB
   (d) 1, 3; A'B' = 3AB (same scale factor)

12. (a) P is at lower right corner of lattice, $k = 2$
    (b) $h = 1/2$
    (c) They are reciprocals

13. (a) $T_{C_1C_2}$ followed by $S_{C_1,3/2}$ would map A_1 to A_2.
    (b) Yes; the transformation $T_{C_1C_2}$ followed by $S_{C_1, r_2/r_1}$ maps one circle (center C_1, radius r_1) to a second circle (center C_2, radius r_2)

14. (a) For example, $S_{B,5/2}$ followed by a rotation through -90°.
    (b) For example, $S_{B,2/3}$ followed by a glide reflection.
    (c) For example, $S_{B,2}$ followed by a glide reflection.

15. Since translations map lines to parallel lines, $p \parallel p'$ and $q \parallel q'$. Thus, since $p \parallel q$, we have that $p' \parallel q'$.

16. Since rotations preserve distances, AB = A'B', AC = A'C', and BC = B'C'. Since A, B, and C are collinear, AB + BC = AC. Therefore A'B' + B'C' = AB + BC = AC = A'C' and A', B', and C' are collinear.

17. Since rotations preserve distance, $\overline{AB} \cong \overline{A'B'}$, $\overline{BC} \cong \overline{B'C'}$, and $\overline{CA} \cong \overline{C'A'}$. Thus, $\triangle ABC \cong \triangle A'B'C'$. Therefore, $\angle BAC \cong \angle B'A'C'$ since they are corresponding parts of congruent triangles.

18. Since reflections preserve distance, $\overline{BP} \cong \overline{B'P'}$. Also, since l is the perpendicular bisector of $\overline{BB'}$, $\overline{BQ} \cong \overline{B'Q}$. Further, $\overline{PQ} \cong \overline{PQ}$ so $\triangle BPQ \cong \triangle B'PQ$ by the SSS congruence property. Therefore, $\angle BPQ \cong \angle B'PQ$ since they are corresponding angles of congruent triangles.

19. (a) Both are perpendicular to $\overline{AC}$ and therefore parallel.
    (b) $M_l(A) = C$ since l is the perpendicular bisector of $\overline{AC}$. Then, $T_{CB}(C) = B$.

(c)

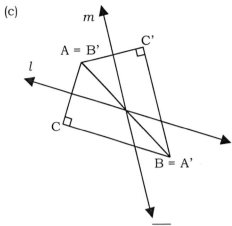

(d) At the midpoint of $\overline{AB}$. No.

20. $p \parallel q$ implies $\angle 1 \cong \angle 2$. Since an isometry preserves angle measure, $\angle 1 \cong \angle 3$ and $\angle 2 \cong \angle 4$. Thus, $\angle 3 \cong \angle 4$ and $p' \parallel q'$, by the corresponding angles property.

21. (a) One; the reflection line is the perpendicular bisector of $\overline{PQ}$.
    (b) Infinitely many; reflect P to S in any line through the midpoint of $\overline{PQ}$, then translate T_{SQ}.

22. Construct ray $\overrightarrow{PB}$ and line through A' parallel to $\overline{AB}$. They intersect at B'. In a like manner, draw ray $\overrightarrow{PC}$ and line through B' parallel to $\overline{BC}$. They intersect at C'. A similar procedure yields D'.

23. Construct line through P' parallel to $\overline{PR}$, and also the line through Q' parallel to $\overline{QR}$. These two lines will intersect at the point R'.

24. 1. X' = X (by definition of reflection)
    2. Vertical angles, corresponding angles of $\triangle AXP$ and $\triangle A'X'P'$, vertical angles
    3. 180°, m($\angle A'X'B'$) = m($\angle A'X'B$) + m($\angle BX'Q$) + m($\angle QX'B'$) = $b + 2a = 180°$, yes
    4. Case (2) of reflection preserves distances: point X is on the reflection line.

5. AB = AX + XB (collinear with X between A and B) = A'X' + X'B' (part 4) = A'B' (collinear with X' between A' and B')

25. Yes it is a rotation around the intersection of the two lines of reflection. The angle of rotation is twice the angle between the intersecting lines

26. Yes, in a size transformation angle measure is preserved, so parallel lines (and perpendicular lines) within a figure will retain their relationship after transformation. The same is not true for similitudes since they are combinations of size transformations and isometries (for example, a rotation).

27. Yes, by the definition of congruence.

Problems related to the NCTM Standards and Curriculum Focal Points

1. Since congruent figures are the same size and shape, one could pick up a figure and move it using slides, flips, and turns to exactly coincide with a second congruent figure.

2. Every size transformation requires a scale factor. Thus, if the scale factor were 3, then every side of the transformed figure will be 3 times as big as the corresponding side of the original figure. Also each point on the transformed figure would be 3 times further away from the center of the transformation as the corresponding point on the original figure.

3. The image of every size transformation or similitude is similar to the original figure. Also, for any two similar shapes there is a similitude that maps one shape onto the other.

Section 16.3

1. All of them

2. $R_{G,120°}$, $R_{G,240°}$, $R_{G,360°}$, M_{AF}, M_{BD}, M_{CE}

3. M_{AI}, M_{BJ}, M_{CF}, M_{DG}, M_{EH}, $R_{O,72°}$, $R_{O,144°}$, $R_{O,216°}$, $R_{O,288°}$; $R_{O,360°}$

4. H_P; $R_{P,360°}$

5. (a) $H_C(H_B(H_A(H_C(H_B(H_A(P)))))) = P$
    (b) $H_C(H_B(H_A(H_C(H_B(H_A(Q)))))) = Q$
    (c) The combinations of six half turns, around the vertices of a triangle in succession, maps each point to itself.

6. Apply $T_{AA'}$ to $\triangle ABC$ first, for example. Let $B^* = T_{AA'}(B)$ and $C^* = T_{AA'}(C)$. Then the rotation with center A' and directed angle $\angle B^*A'B'$ (or $\angle C^*A'C'$) will map $\triangle A^*B^*C^*$ to $\triangle A'B'C'$.

7. $A^* = M_r(A)$, $B^* = M_r(B)$, $C^* = M_r(C)$. Then $M_r(\triangle ABC) = \triangle A^*B^*C^*$ and $S_{O,1/2}(\triangle A^*B^*C^*) = \triangle A'B'C'$

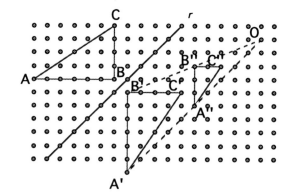

8. (a) $S_{A,2}(P)$ = B, by definition.
    $S_{A,2}(R)$ = C, by definition.
    $S_{A,2}(A)$ = A, by definition.
    Hence, $S_{A,2}(\triangle APR)$ = $\triangle ABC$.
    Other size transformations are possible.

    (b) $\overline{PR} \parallel \overline{BC}$ since the size transformation image of a line is parallel to the line. Hence, $\overline{PR} \parallel \overline{BQ}$. Similarly $\overline{RQ} \parallel \overline{PB}$ so PBQR is a parallelogram.

9. $H_P(\overline{BC}) \parallel \overline{BC}$ and since $H_P(A)$ = C, we must have that $H_P(B)$ is on $\overline{AD}$. Similarly, $H_P(B)$ is on $\overline{CD}$ by considering $H_P(\overline{AB})$. Hence $H_P(B)$ = D. Thus, P is the midpoint of $\overline{BD}$ also.

10. $M_l(A)$ = C and $M_l(C)$ = A by definition of M_l. Also, $M_l(B)$ = B, so $M_l(\overline{AB})$ = $\overline{CB}$. Hence, AB = BC.

11. (a) PA = PA' = PA''. Also, PA' and r form an angle measuring $x°$, while PA'' and s form an angle measuring $y°$. Hence, m($\angle APA'$) = $2x°$ and m($\angle A'PA''$) = $2y°$. Thus, A'' = $R_{P,2(x+y)}(A)$. Since A was arbitrary, and orientation is preserved, M_r followed by M_s is $R_{P,2(x+y)}$.

    (b) Point P, the intersection of r and s, is the center of the rotation. The measure of the angle of the rotation is twice the measure of the angle between r and s.

12. (a)

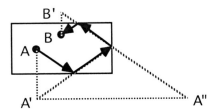

    (b) Argument is similar to the billiard problem in set A.

13. Let P = $\overline{AC} \cap \overline{BD}$ as was shown earlier, $\overline{AC} \perp \overline{BD}$ and $\overline{AC}$ and $\overline{BD}$ are perpendicular bisectors of each other. Hence, $M_{AC}(B)$ = D and $M_{BD}(A)$ = C. Thus, M_{AC} followed by M_{BD} maps ABCD to CDAB, i.e. M_{AC} followed by M_{BD} is equivalent to the half turn H_P. (See also problem 5.) Thus, $\overline{AB} \parallel \overline{CD}$ since a half turn maps a line to a line parallel to it. Similarly, $\overline{AD} \parallel \overline{CB}$.

14. Use $R_{B,90°}$ to map $\triangle ABD$ to $\triangle FBC$. Use $R_{C,-90°}$ to map $\triangle ACE$ to $\triangle KCB$.

15. $\dfrac{\pi - \sqrt{3}}{2}$

16. Yes, because the isosceles triangle has two equal sides, so the triangle together with its reflection will have four equal sides. Therefore, it is a rhombus by definition.

17. The reflection line is the perpendicular bisector of a segment joining a point of a figure to its corresponding point. If you take the upper right vertex and drop a perpendicular from that to the reflection line and extend it an equal length beyond the reflection line, you should arrive at the image of that vertex. But there is not any point of the figure there at all. Also, if this were a reflection, angle measure would be

preserved. However, the angle at top left is obtuse, and the angle at lower left is acute, so obviously one is not the image of the other under a reflection.

Problems related to the NCTM Standards and Curriculum Focal Points

1. Problem 9 of Set B has students use transformations to prove that the diagonals of a parallelogram bisect each other. Problem 12 of Set B has students show that a rhombus is a parallelogram by using transformations. Answers may vary.

2. Problem 6 of Set B requires one to find a combination of isometries that will map one triangle onto another. Answers may vary.

Chapter Review

Problems for Writing/Discussion

1. Join a point of the figure with its corresponding image, measure the length of the segment, and measure the angle the segment makes with the horizontal (or vertical). Then you would be able to describe the translation by means of its direction and distance.

2. Join a point of the figure with its corresponding image. Then find the perpendicular bisector of the segment. That would be the reflecting line.

3. Join a point of the figure with its image. Then find the perpendicular bisector of the segment. Repeat this with another pair of corresponding points. The intersection of the two perpendicular bisectors would be the turn center. To find the amount of the turn, connect a point of the figure and its image to the turn center. Measure the

angle formed by these two line segments. The direction of the turn can be determined once you decide whether to use an angle less than or greater than 180° for the amount of the turn.

4. Join three points of the original figure to their images. Find the midpoints of the three segments and connect them to form the reflection line. (Only two points are necessary to determine the reflecting line; the third point acts as a check.) The translation will be parallel to the reflecting line. Its distance can be found by reflecting the image over the reflecting line and measuring the distance from one point on the new image to its corresponding point on the original image.

5. Join a point of the figure to its image. Repeat this with another pair of points. Extend both segments till they intersect. This point would be the center of the size transformation. Measure the distance from the center of the transformation to some point of the figure. Then measure the distance from the center of the transformation to the corresponding point on the image. The scale factor is the ratio of the second distance to the first.

6. The final image could not be a flip image of the L because it has the same orientation. However, the two flips could be replaced with one rotation, using the point of intersection of the two flip lines as the center of the turn and an angle of 80° (double the angle between the flip lines). The direction would be clockwise because the 40° represents a clockwise rotation from the first line of reflection to the second.

7. No, a slide is only equivalent to two flips. One flip reverses

orientation, whereas a slide preserves orientation.

8. She would have to specify what relationship the lines have to each other (they must be intersecting), how the turn center is related to the lines (it is the intersection of the flip lines), what the angle between the lines would be (half the angle of the turn).

9. Since the glide is really a slide, it could be replaced by two flips. So a glide reflection could be replaced by three flips.

10. Any figure and its image can be made coincident using a maximum of three flips. If two congruent figures are randomly placed on the plane, first determine if they have the same orientation. If they do, then at most two flips are needed. Flip one point of the first figure to its corresponding point on the second figure. Then, using a line through this point as the line of reflection, flip the image of the first figure over the line to the second figure. If the two figures have opposite orientations, either one more flip is required or exactly one flip may suffice.

Epilogue

1. $\angle ABD \cong \angle CDB$ (alternate interior angle property with $\overline{AB} \parallel \overline{DC}$, $\overline{BD} \cong \overline{DB}$, so $\triangle ABD \cong \triangle CDB$ (by SAS congruence property), $\angle ADB \cong \angle CBD$ (corresponding parts of congruent triangles) so $\overline{AD} \parallel \overline{BC}$ (alternate interior angle property) and $ABCD$ is therefore a parallelogram.

2. (a) $M = \left(\dfrac{a}{2}, \dfrac{b}{2}\right)$ and $N = \left(\dfrac{c+d}{2}, \dfrac{b}{2}\right)$

   Hence, $MN = \dfrac{c+d-a}{2}$,

   $AB = d$, and $DC = c - a$.
   $AB + DC = d + c - a$ or $2\,MN$.

   Thus, $MN = \dfrac{1}{2}(AB + DC)$.

   Slopes of $\overline{AB}$ and $\overline{MN}$ are 0, thus $\overline{MN} \parallel \overline{AB}$.

3. (a) The diagonals, $\overline{AC}$ and $\overline{BD}$, *bisect* each other at point P. Hence, by the definition, $H_P(A) = C$ and $H_P(B) = D$.

   (b) $H_P(C) = A$ and $H_P(D) = B$, as well, so H_P maps the parallelogram onto itself. Notice that $H_P(\overline{AB}) = \overline{CD}$, etc. for the other sides, since an isometry maps a line segment to a line segment. The parallelogram rotates onto itself under a 180° rotation, hence has rotation symmetry.

4. $\overline{BE} \cong \overline{DE}$ and $\overline{AE} \cong \overline{CE} \cong$ (diagonals bisect each other). $\angle BEC \cong \angle DEA$ (vertical angles are congruent), so $\triangle BEC \cong \triangle DEA$ (SAS congruence property). Thus, $\angle BCE \cong \angle DAE$ (corresponding parts of congruent triangles) so $\overline{BC} \parallel \overline{AD}$ (alternate interior angle property). Similarly, $\angle BAE \cong \angle DCE$ and $\triangle BEA \cong \triangle DEC$ (SAS congruence property) so $\angle BAE \cong \angle DCE$ (corresponding parts of

congruent triangles) and $\overline{AB} \parallel \overline{DC}$ (alternate interior angle property). Since both pairs of opposite sides are parallel, $ABCD$ is a parallelogram.

5. Since $ABCD$ is a rhombus, $AB = AD$.

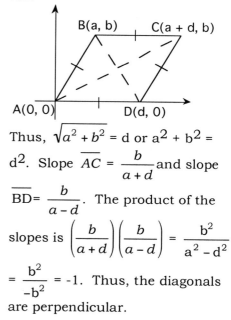

   Thus, $\sqrt{a^2 + b^2} = d$ or $a^2 + b^2 = d^2$. Slope $\overline{AC} = \dfrac{b}{a+d}$ and slope $\overline{BD} = \dfrac{b}{a-d}$. The product of the slopes is $\left(\dfrac{b}{a+d}\right)\left(\dfrac{b}{a-d}\right) = \dfrac{b^2}{a^2 - d^2}$

   $= \dfrac{b^2}{-b^2} = -1$. Thus, the diagonals are perpendicular.

6. $\overline{LP} \cong \overline{NP}$ and $\overline{MP} \cong \overline{OP}$ (diagonals of parallelogram bisect each other) and $\angle LPM \cong \angle NPM \cong \angle NPO \cong \angle LPO$ (diagonals are perpendicular), so $\triangle LPM \cong \triangle NPM \cong \triangle NPO \cong \triangle LPO$ (SAS congruence property).
   Therefore, $\overline{LM} \cong \overline{NM} \cong \overline{NO} \cong \overline{LO}$ (corresponding parts of congruent triangles) and $LMNO$ is a rhombus by definition.

7. Since $ABCD$ is a trapezoid, we have the following coordinates.

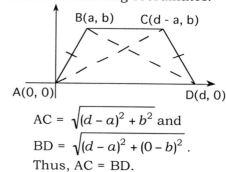

   $AC = \sqrt{(d-a)^2 + b^2}$ and
   $BD = \sqrt{(d-a)^2 + (0-b)^2}$.
   Thus, $AC = BD$.

8.　A parallelogram with perpendicular diagonals is a rhombus and thus has four congruent sides. Therefore, HIJK is a square.

Section T1 - Part B

1. (a) Roses are red and the sky is blue.
    (b) Roses are red and the sky is blue or turtles are green.
    (c) If the sky is blue, then roses are red and turtles are green.
    (d) Turtles are not green and turtles are green implies that roses are not red.

2.

p	q	$p \to q$	$\sim(p \wedge q)$	$p \wedge q$	$q \to p$
T	T	T	F	T	T
T	F	F	T	F	T
F	T	T	T	F	F
F	F	T	T	F	T

3. (a) T   (b) F   (c) T   (d) T

4. $p \to q$ and $p \vee q$ have the same truth table.

5. (a) Hypotheses:
    All football players are introverts and Tony is a football player
    Conclusion:
    Tony is an introvert.
    (b) Hypotheses:
    Bob is taller than Jim and Jim is taller than Sue.
    Conclusion:
    Bob is taller than Sue.
    (c) Hypotheses:
    All penguins are elegant swimmers and no elegant swimmers fly.
    Conclusion:
    Penguins don't fly.

6. (c) and (e)

7. (a) Necessary
    (b) Sufficient
    (c) Sufficient

8. (a) T   (b) T
    (c) Unknown   (d) T
    (e) F   (f) Unknown
    (g) T   (h) T
    (i) Unknown   (j) F
    (k) T   (l) Unknown
    (m) Unknown (n) T   (o) T

9. (a) $[(w \to t) \wedge t] \to w$ Invalid
    (b) $[(s \to l) \wedge \sim s] \to \sim l$ Invalid
    (c) $[(\sim s \to e) \wedge (w \to \sim e)] \to (w \to s)$ Valid
    (d) $[(m \wedge s)(j \to m)] \to j$ Invalid

10. (d), (e), and (f)

Section T2 - Part B

1. (a) 6 and 6
    (b) 6 and 6
    (c) 2 and 2
    (d) 4 and 4
    (e) Multiplication distributes over addition and subtraction in clock arithmetic.

2. (a) 1 and 1   (b) 0 and 0
    (c) 0 and 0
    (d) The exponent rule $a^m b^m = (ab)^m$ holds in clock arithmetic.

3. 1, 4, 5, 2, 3, 6

4. (a) 4   (b) 1   (c) 4   (d) 4
    (e) 3   (f) 2   (g) 0   (h) 0

5. (a) -17, -12, -7, -2, 3, 8, 13, 18
    (b) -17, -10, -3, 4, 11, 18
    (c) 2, 4, 8
    (d) 2, 3, . . . , 20

6. $3 \times 4 = 0$

7. (a) 0, 2, 4, 6
    (b) 0, 2, 4, 5, 6, 8
    (c) 0, 2, 3, 4, 6, 8, 9, 10
    For the 36-clock, 0, 2, 3, 4, 6, 8, 9, 10, 12, 14, 15, 16, 18, 20, 21, 22, 24, 26, 27, 28, 30, 32, 33, 34.

8. (a) 7   (b) 4   (c) 11 (d) 9
    In clock n, $n - 1$ is its own inverse.

9. a is the square root of b if $a^2 = b$.
    (a) 2   (b) 1, 3, 5, 7
    (c) 3   (d) 7
    Numbers may have zero or many square roots depending on the clock number.

10. Let 1 be positive. Then, if the sum of two positives is positive, 1 + 1 = 2, 2 + 1 = 3, 3 + 1 = 4, and 4 + 1 = 0 are all positive . Thus all numbers in the 5-clock are positive.

11. Multiplication is closed because addition is closed and multiplication can be viewed as repeated addition.

12. If $a \equiv b$ mod m, then $m \mid (a - b)$. But then $m \mid (a - b)c$, or $m \mid (ac - bc)$. Thus, $ac \equiv bc$ mod m.

13. $2 \times 3 \equiv 4 \times 3$ mod 6, but 2 is not congruent to 4 mod 6.

14. $7^2 \equiv 1$ mod 8. So $(7^2)^{50} \equiv 1^{50}$ mod 8, or $7^{100} \equiv 1$ mod 8. Therefore, $7^{101} \equiv 7$ mod 8, so the remainder when 7^{101} is divided by 8 is 7.

Introduction to Graph Theory (on the Web)

1. (a) A = F = 2, B = C = 3, D = E = 1
    (b) B = C = E = F = 3, A = D = 2
    (c) A = B = E = F = G = H = 3, D = C = 4

2. (i) (a) A: B, F; B: A, C, F; C: B,D,E.
         (b) A: B,F; B: A, E, F; C: D,E,F.
         (c) A: B,D,F; B: A,C,G; C: B,D,H
    (ii) The degree of a vertex is the same as the number of vertices it is adjacent to.

3.
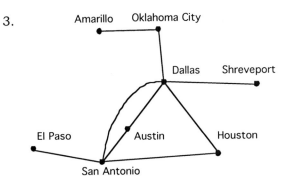

4. (a) Connected since there is a path from any vertex to any other vertex.
    (b) Not connected. For example, U does not have a path to X.
    (c) Connected since there is a path from any vertex to any other vertex.

5. (i) and (v) are equivalent; (ii) and (iii)are equivalent.

6. (a) (i) Yes, exactly two odd vertices
        (ii) Euler Path by Euler's Traversable Graph Theorem.
    (b) (i) No, four odd vertices.
        (ii) None
    (c) (i) Yes, all even vertices.
        (ii) Euler Circuit by Euler's Traversable Graph Theorem.
    (d) (I) Yes, exactly two odd vertices.
        (ii) Euler Path by Euler's Traversable Graph Theorem.

7. (a) Hamiltonian Path LMNOPQ
    (b) None, since the graph is not connected.
    (c) Hamiltonian Circuit ACDEBA

8. (a)
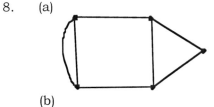
    (b)
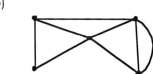

9. Since R + V = E +2, we have V = E + 2 – R, or V = 13 + 2 – 8 = 7.

10. (a) Hexagonal prism
    (b) Hexagonal pyramid
    (c) Pentagonal pyramid

11. Add 2 edges. For example HJ and LM. An Euler Circuit is NJINLMLKJHIKNHMN

12 (a)

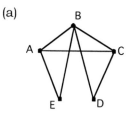

or

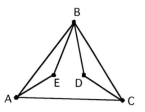

(b)

or

13. (a)

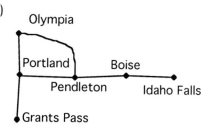

(b)

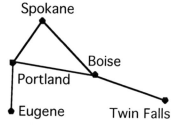

(c)

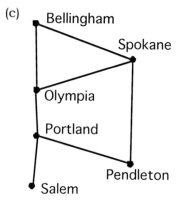

14. (a) 1a: 12 1b: 16; 1c: 26; 4a: 14; 4b: 16; 4c: 16.
    (b) 1a: 6; 1b: 8; 1c: 13; 4a: 7; 4b: 8; 4c: 8
    (c) The sum of the degrees of the vertices is twice the number of edges.

15.

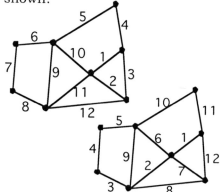

16. (a) 1a: 2; 1b: 2; 1c: 3.
    (b) 1a: BC, DE; 1b: AE, BC; 1c: AF, BF, EH.
    (c) 3; one edge for each pair of odd vertices.

17. Many solutions possible. Two are shown.

Logo Programs

L12.1.   REPEAT 10[FD 20 RT 360/10]

L12.2.   TO REG.POLY :N
        REPEAT :N[FD 20 RT 360/:N]
    END

L12.3.   TO RIGHT.TRI :A :B
     BK :A
     RT 90
     FD :B
     HOME
     END

L13.1.   (a) TO RECTANGLE :A :B
        HT
        REPEAT 2[FD :A RT 90
             FD :B RT 90]
        REPEAT INTEGER
          (:A/10) [FD 10
          RT 90 FD :B BK :B
          LT 90]
        HOME
        RT 90
        REPEAT INTEGER
          (:B/10) [FD 10
          LT 90 FD :A BK :A
          RT 90]
        HOME
        END
     (b) 100
     (c) 28

L14.1.   Let :ANGLE=180.

L14.2.   (a) TO SAS.TRI :SIDE 1 :ANGLE
        :SIDE 2
        BK :SIDE 1
        RT :ANGLE
        FD :SIDE 2
        HOME
        END
     (b) (i) :ANGLE=90
         (ii) :SIDE 1=:SIDE 2
         (iii) : ANGLE > 90 and :
        ANGLE=90
         (iv) :SIDE 1=:SIDE 2
         (v) : ANGLE=90 and :
        SIDE 1 ≠ :SIDE 2
         (vi) :SIDE 1=:SIDE 2 and
             :ANGLE=60

L14.3.   TO MAGNIFY.TRI :SIDE 1
        :ANGLE :SIDE 2 :K
        SAS.TRI :SIDE 1 :ANGLE
        :SIDE 2
        BK :K∗:SIDE 1
        RT :ANGLE
        FD :K∗:SIDE 2
        HOME
        END

L15.1.   TO TRI.COORDS :X1 :X2 :Y1 :Y2
        AXES
        SETXY :X1 :Y1
        SETXY :X2 :Y2
        HOME
        END

L15.2.   TO TRI.COORDS.MDPTS :X1 :X2
        :Y1 :Y2
        TRI.COORDS :X1 :X2 :Y1 :Y2
        PU
        SETXY (:X1)/2 (:Y1)/2
        PD
        SETXY (:X2)/2 (:Y2)/2
        PU
        HOME
        PD
        END

L15.3.   AXES
        SETXY 20 90
        SET X Y 100 30
        HOME
        SETXY 60 60
        PU
        SETXY 20 90
        PD
        SETXY 50 15
        PU
        SETXY 100 30
        PD
        SETXY 10 45
        PU
        HOME
        PD

L15.4.   TO MEDIANS :X1 :Y1 :X2 :Y2
        SETXY :X1 :Y1
        SETXY :X2 :Y2
        HOME
        SETXY (:X1+:X2)/2
        (:Y1+:Y2)/2
        PU

```
        SETXY (:X1)/2 (:Y1)/2                      HOME
        PD                                         TRANS :X1 :Y1 :X2 :Y2 :X3
        SETXY :X2 :Y2                                  :Y3 :M
        PU                                         TRI.PLOT (-:X4) :Y4 (-:X5)
        SETXY :X1 :Y1              :Y5             (-:X6) :Y6
        PD                                         END
        SETXY (:X2)/2 (:Y2)/2
        HOME
        END


L16.1.  TO X.REF :X1 :Y1 :X2 :Y2 :X3 :Y3
        SET X 100
        SET X (-100 )
        HOME
        TRI.PLOT :X1 :Y1 :X2 :Y2 :X3
            :Y3
        TRI.PLOT :X1 (-:Y1) :X2
            (-:Y2) :X3 (-:Y3)
        END


L16.2.  TO TRANS :X1 :Y1 :X2 :Y2 :X3
            :Y3 :N : M
        TRI.PLOT :X1 :Y1 :X2 :Y2 :X3
            :Y3
        MAKE "X4 :X1+N
        MAKE "Y4 :Y1+M
        MAKE "X5 :X2+N
        MAKE "Y5 :Y2+M
        MAKE "X6 :X3+N
        MAKE "Y6 :Y3+M
        TRI.PLOT :X4 :Y4 :X5 :Y5 :X6
            :Y6
        END


L16.3.  TO ROTATE.90 :X1 :Y1 :X2 :Y2
            :X3 :Y3
        TRI.PLOT :X1 :Y1 :X2 :Y2 :X3
            :Y3
        TRI.PLOT(-:Y1):X1(-:Y2):X2
        (-:Y3) :X3
        END


L16.4.    (a)  TO GLIDE.REF.X :X1 :Y1 :X2
                  :Y2 :X3 :Y3 :N
               TRANS :X1 :Y1 :X2 :Y2
                  :X3 :Y3 :N
               X.REF :X4 :Y4 :X5 :Y5 :X6
                  :Y6
               END
          (b) TO GLIDE.REF.Y :X1 :Y1 :X2
                  :Y2 :X3:Y3 :M
               SETY 100
               SETY (-100)
```

Answers To Even Numbered Problems In The PROBLEM SOLVING STUDY GUIDE

1. Guess and Test

1-B.   13 and 78

1-2.   53 and 32

1-4

2. Use a Variable

2-B.
$$n + 10$$
$$n \qquad n + 2$$
$$n + 8 \qquad n + 4 \qquad n + 6$$

2-2.   Bruce was 52 years old in 1988.
He was born in 1936 = 44 × 44.
1988 - 1936 = 52.

2-4.   11 cows and 2 turkeys.
$4c + 2t = c + t + 35$
$3c + t = 35$

3. Draw a Picture

3-B.   30 seconds
2.5 seconds per floor
middle floor is 17
12 × 2.5 = 30

3-2.   The fence will cost $2280.
120 posts and 120 sections

3-4.   Jason will be halfway to his office
at 6:56 A.M.

4. Look for a Pattern

4-B   (a) H 29 30 31
(b) R 69 70 71
(c) M 49 50 51
(d) P 61 26 63
(e) V 85 86 87

4-2.   18 girls and 12 boys
18 × 18 + 12 × 12 = 468

4-4.   99,225
99,225 = 315 × 315 = 9 × 11,025

5. Make a List

5-B   The total number of coins cannot
be 18.
10 coins :10 quarters
13 coins : 5 dimes and 8 quarters
16 coins : 10 dimes and 6
quarters
19 coins : 15 dimes and 4
quarters
22 coins : 20 dimes and 2
quarters
25 coins: 25 dimes

5-2.   36 ways; 3 pennies: 1 way,
4 pennies: 3 ways,
. . . , 10 pennies : 36 ways

5-4.   Box Z: 9 marbles (X:18   Y:9)

6. Solve a Simpler Problem

6-B   There are 864 dots on the 864
chips.

6-2.   Largest 4-digit cube is 21^3 = 9261.
9261 - 45 = 9216
Possible answers: 4 36 64
4 9 256   9 16 64

6-4.   (a) 9,801 = 99^2
(b) 27,000 = 30^3
(c) 178 = 89 × 2

7. Draw a Diagram

7-B   Nine are red, not compact, and
have 4 doors.

7-2.   18 ways Ted, Amy, Bart

126	162	216	261	612
621	135	153	315	351
513	531	234	243	324
342	423	432		

7-4.   120 youth T-shirts, 80 adult

8.   Use Direct Reasoning

8-B   Ask either computer this question: What will the other computer answer if I ask it to tell   me which box contains $100?"

8-2.   There are 89 ways to get to the top step.
1 step stairway : 1 way
2 step stairway : 2 ways
3 step stairway : 3 ways
4 step stairway : 5 ways
. . . 10 step stairway : 89 ways

8-4.   The thousands digit is 8.
hundreds : 6
tens : 2
ones : 4

9.   Use Indirect Reasoning

9-B   Suppose that there is a triangle on the back side of card A. Then the statement on card A is true. This means that the statement on card B is also true. But this conclusion contradicts the fact that one statement is true and the other is false. Hence, the triangle must be on the back side of card B.

9-2.   (a) 1   (b) 2   (c) 6

9-4.   My vacation was 18 days, 13 with rain and 5 with no rain.

10.   Use Properties of Numbers

10-B   7,840

10-2. There are 3 × 28 = 84 different triangles.

10-4. Possible solutions:
Games/ 1 peg
Games/ 3 pegs
Games/ 4 pegs

5	14	1
6	11	3
7	8	5
8	5	7
9	2	9

11.   Solve an Equivalent Problem

11-B   There are 28 possible two-girl committees.

11-2. Eight dogs
Cans/dogs/days:
5/4/1   40/32/1   40/8/4

11-4. Suppose the chip under cup Z is not red. This means that Linda would have been able to guess the color of the chip under cup Y. Hence, the chip under cup Z must be red.

12.   Work Backward

12-B   Karen stated with $36.

12-2. There are 92 girls.

12-4. 7/8
1/2 × 5/6 = 5/12
2/3 - 5/12 = 1/4
2 × 1/4 = 1/2
3/8 + 1/2 = 7/8

13.   Use Cases

13-B   Cody cannot place his cards as described in the problem. When the total in any two piles is even, the total in the other three piles must be odd and vice versa.

13-2. 7 children: 3 boys and 4 girls.

13-4. Go second and then always make exactly the same move as your opponent.

14.   Solve an Equation

14-B   Jeff's number is 8.
$100n + 100 = 900$
If you decrease the final result by 100 and then divide by 100, the answer will be the original number selected.

14-2.   16 red-odd chips, 75 blue-even chips

14-4.   40 members
$18x = 24(x - 10)$ yields $x = 40$

15.   Look for a Formula

15-B $(1/2)^{30}$
$1 - 1/2 = 1/2$
$1 - 1/2 - 1/4 = 1/4$
$1 - 1/2 - 1/4 - 1/8 = 1/8 \ldots$

15-2.   16,800
$(1/3)n + (1/5)n + (1/6)n + (1/4)n + 42 = n$ implies $n = 840$
$0.05\, e = 840$
$e = 16{,}800$

15-4.   The snail will be 4 cm from the top.
$23/24 \times 96 = 92$
$96 - 92 = 4$

16.   Do a Simulation

16-B   Answers will vary.

16-2.   Both cases have a probability of 3/8 that exactly two of the children will be girls.

16-4.   There were 240 chickens.
$x - 0.3x + 0.2x = 216$
$x = 240$

17.   Use a Model

17-B   A model will show that figure I cannot be separated as shown.

17-2.   The total value cannot be $3.
(a) 6 nickels + 4 dimes = $3.40
(b) 3 nickels + 7 dimes = $5.35

(d) 7 nickels + 6 dimes = $6.05

17-4.   One possible solution:
0 1 2 3 4 5   1 1 1 7 7 7

18.   Use Dimensional Analysis

18-B   About 10.24 kilometers per liter

18-2.   1,200,000,301
The nth term is $9n - 2$. Hence, two more than any number in the sequence must be divisible by 9.

18-4.   20 20 0 0
20 12 8 0 → 20 0 8 12 →
18 0 8 14 → 18 8 0 14 →
18 8 8 6   → 20 8 6 6

19.   Identify Subgoals

19-B   8400 ways = 6 × 20 × 70

19-2.   3 to 2
$7j + 3c = 81$
$j = (81 - 3c)/7$
Hence $c = 6$ and $j = 9$.
$j : c = 9 : 6 = 3 : 2$

19-4.   A tennis court, 36' by 78', has a perimeter of 228 feet.

20.   Use Coordinates

20-B   Isosceles triangle: Two sides are 5 units long.
Right triangle: Two sides have slopes 4/3 and -3/4.
($4/3 \times -3/4 = -1$)
The area of the triangle is 12.5 square units ($1/2 \times 5 \times 5$).

20-2.   11 A. M. on Friday.
LCM(15, 28, 40) = 840 minutes = 14 hours

20-4.   If x and y are the lengths, cut the longer rope at a distance $(x + y)/3$ from one end.

21. Use Symmetry

21-B.

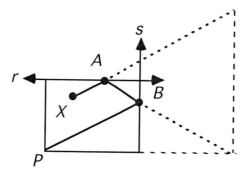

21-2. 20,000
6/150 = 4%, estimate 4% tagged
4% p = 800
p = 20,000

21-4. 2,950 π square feet

Printed in the United States
152624LV00001B/13/A